1998

ARRIVA

Bus Handbook

Body codes used in the Bus Handbook series:

Type:
A	Articulated vehicle
B	Single-deck bus
C	Coach - High-back seating
D	Low floor double-deck bus (4-metre)
DP	Express - high-back seating in a bus body
H	Full-height double-deck
L	Low-height double-deck
M	Minibus
O	Open-top bus
P	Partial or convertible open-top

Seating capacity is then shown. For double-decks the upper deck first,

Door position:-
C	Centre entrance/exit
D	Dual doorway
F	Front entrance/exit
R	Rear entrance/exit (no distinction between doored and open)
T	Three or more access points

Equipment:-
L	Lift for wheelchair
T	Toilet

e.g. - H32/28F is a high-bridge bus with thirty-two seats upstairs, twenty-eight down and a front entrance/exit.
B43D is a bus with two doorways.

Re-registrations:-
Where a vehicle has gained new index marks the details are listed at the end of each fleet showing the current mark, followed in sequence by those previously carried starting with the original mark.

Other books in the series:
The Scottish Bus Handbook
The Ireland & Islands Bus Handbook
The North East Bus Handbook
The Yorkshire Bus Handbook
The Lancashire, Cumbria and Manchester Bus Handbook
The Merseyside and Chechire Bus Handbook
The North and West Midlands Bus Handbook
The East Midlands Bus Handbook
The South Midlands Bus handbook
The North and West Wales Bus Handbook
The South Wales Bus Handbook
The Chilterns and West Anglia Bus Handbook
The East Anglian Bus Handbook
The South West Bus Handbook
The South Central Bus Handbook
The South East Bus Handbook

Annual books are produced for the major groups:
The 1998 Stagecoach Bus Handbook
The 1998 FirstBus Bus Handbook
The 1998 Cowie Bus Handbook

Associated series:
The Hong Kong Bus Handbook
The Model Bus Handbook
The Toy & Model Bus Handbook - Volume 1 - Early Diecasts
The Fire Brigade Handbook (fleet list of each local authority fire brigade)
The Fire Brigade Handbook - Special Appliances Volume 1
The Fire Brigade Handbook - Special Appliances Volume 2

Contents

1998 Cowie Group Bus Handbook

The 1998 Cowie Group Bus Handbook is a special edition of the Bus Handbook series which contains the various fleets of Arriva plc at the time the group embarked on a major change on name and image. The Bus Handbook series is published by British Bus Publishing, an independent publisher of quality books for the industry and bus enthusiasts. Further information on these may be obtained from the address below.

Although this book has been produced with the encouragement of, and in co-operation with, Cowie Group plc management, it is not an official Cowie Group fleet list and the vehicles included are subject to variation, particularly as the vehicle investment programme continues. Some vehicles listed are no longer in regular use on services but are retained for special purposes also out of use vehicles awaiting disposal are not all listed. The services operated and the allocation of vehicles to subsidiary companies are subject to variation at any time, although accurate at the time of going to print. Livery details given aim to show standard fleet colours and significant variations. Minor variations or local identity and marketing schemes are not all included and in some cases older liveries being phased out are not shown. The contents are correct to November 1997 when the group named changed to Arriva Group plc and reflect operations as the new image was launched. This will be the final appearance for many of the long-established fleet names as considerable re-structuring of the group will be ongoing through 1998.

To keep the fleet information up to date we recommend the Ian Allan publication Buses, published monthly, or for more detailed information, the PSV Circle monthly news sheets.

Edited by David Donati and Bill Potter

Acknowledgements:
We are grateful to Keith Grimes, Colin Lloyd, John Rimmington, Steve Sanderson, Tony Wilson, the PSV Circle and the management and officials of Arriva Group plc, and their operating companies, for their kind assistance and co-operation in the compilation of this book.

The front cover photo is by Bill Potter
The rear cover photographs are by Tony Wilson

ISBN 1 897990 71 5
Published by British Bus Publishing Ltd
The Vyne, 16 St Margarets Drive, Wellington,
Telford, Shropshire, TF1 3PH
© British Bus Publishing Ltd, November 1997

The Cowie Group plc

In August 1996 the Cowie Group completed the acquisition of British Bus plc and at a stroke became the second largest bus operating group in the United Kingdom, the move led to the reclassification of the enlarged group from being a motor trader to the Transport classification.

This introduction will chart the evolution of the elements of the grouping under their different historical strands which in itself will shed some light on the different trading names and types of vehicles to be found in the fleet. Full historical details will for the most case be found elsewhere in other published material reference to which is recommended for the serious student of the history of the British bus industry.

For the future the group has just announced a bold rebranding of all its business interests under the new trading identity of 'Arriva, further information on this can be found on this development on an insert sheet in this volume. The group livery and identity will replace the existing versions progressively over the next 12 to 18 months and therefore this volume is a timely record of the present and will stand comparison with the next planned edition of this booklet which will reveal the progress with rebranding.

Now to some background.

The Cowie name - early years

Like other large transport names Cowie started from humble beginnings. In 1931 the Cowie family started a motorcycle repair business in Sunderland. In 1934 the first sales outlet opened on what is at present the location of the Group Head Offices. By 1942 the effects of the war saw the business coming to a halt.

After the war in 1948 the business reopened and benefits from the boom in personal mobility offered by the motorcycle, a second motorcycle shop was opened in Newcastle in 1952. Further expansion occurred in 1955 with a second branch in Newcastle, and new branches in Durham and Stockton-on-Tees.

A move into the Scottish market was taken with the acquisition of the J R Alexander motorcycle dealerships in Edinburgh and Glasgow in 1960. However there were signs that the market was moving against the motorcycle and in favour of the motor car which was becoming a more mass market item in availability and price.

In 1962 Cowie acquired its first car dealership in Sunderland, and such was the pace of change that by 1963 Motor Car sales constituted

80% of sales. On the back of this change a public company - T Cowie Ltd was formed in 1965, the same year saw two more car dealerships acquired, one in Redcar and a second in Sunderland.

In 1967 there was investment in new car showrooms for the Ford franchise in Sunderland, there has been a long association with Ford over the years. In 1971 this was strengthened with the acquisition of Ford Blackburn and another Ford dealership in Middlesbrough. By 1971 as a measure of the development of the trading interests the group turnover reached £8m per annum.

Growing on the motor business

In 1972 a new business was set up in the form of Cowie Contract Hire, this and its antecedents have grown to be large element of the present group.

The first exposure to the bus and coach industry came in 1980. In that year Cowie took over The George Ewer Group which had various motor interests including Eastern Tractors. It also included the long established Grey Green Coach operation with its involvement in historic operations such as East Anglian Express, the Eastlander Pool, and joint services to Scotland with SBG. Private Hire coaching also played a large part in the business, operating bases at Stamford Hill and Dagenham in London and also Ipswich in East Anglia were assets bought with the business.

In 1984 Cowie acquired the Hanger Group which brought Ford dealerships in Nottingham and Birmingham, and significantly, Interleasing contract hire. The pace of expansion continued in 1987 when seven main dealerships were acquired from the Heron Group. On the leasing side of the business Marley Leasing was acquired. Further growth in this area of the business came in 1991 when RoyScot Drive and Ringway Leasing were acquired adding to the prominence of this activity.

1992 was the year that Cowie very nearly took another step into the bus and coach market narrowly failing to purchase Henlys which by that time had ownership of Plaxtons. Consolation came with the addition of a Ford dealership in Swindon, a Peugeot dealership in Middlesbrough, and a Toyota dealership in Wakefield. In 1993 the Keep Trust Group was acquired, the dealership network being boosted by 70%.

Another notable event in 1993 was the retirement of Sir Tom Cowie, the Chairmanship of the business being taken up by the present Chairman Sir James McKinnon in 1994.

Explosion into Buses!

The privatisation of the newly created subsidiaries of London Buses offered the opportunity to reinforce the favourable experience of Grey Green in the London bus market. Leaside was acquired in 1994 and was renamed Cowie Leaside. Later in 1995 the previously troubled South London company was purchased becoming Cowie South London. These two acquisitions made Cowie the largest single operator in the London Buses area when taken with the existing Grey Green business.

In 1994 the FMM contract hire and fleet management business was acquired continuing the growth in that sector.

1996 was the year that pushed Cowie in to the number two slot in the UK bus industry. County Bus was purchased from the National Express Group adding to the South East presence. The acquisition of British Bus added a whole raft of bus companies across the country and very nearly brought all the disparate elements of the former London Country company under one ownership and this included Green Line Travel.

The final acquisition of 1996 brought another previously divided company back under common ownership being North East Bus. United Auto became a bedfellow of Northumbria which was split off from it in 1986.

There was a Monopolies and Mergers Commission inquiry into the acquisition of British Bus with particular focus on the situation in London and the South East however the report did not require any disinvestment, and the market for London Buses tenders remains highly competitive.

Grey Green

A most distinguished name in coaching has transformed itself into a major operator of London bus routes. The involvement in the East Anglian Express Pool transformed itself in the mid 1980s into National Express operation before withdrawal from this sector, along with the former Eastlander pool.

Great opportunities were perceived in the 1980s in commuter coaching after the deregulation of coach services under the 1980 Act and there was subsequent absorption and expansion. An area again sold on to National Express was the operation of International Services. Early day success in London Bus tendering brought Grey Green operation into to the very heart of the City, notably on route 24. Bus operation is now very much the key to the business and is reflected in the fleet composition which now has only 20 coaches.

County Bus and Coach

This company is quite recent having come into being at the beginning of 1989 to carry on the eastern operations of the former London Country North East, which in itself was one of the four parts into which London Country was divided. Operations were carried out at Harlow, Hertford and Grays. Ownership had progressed through the AJS group in 1988, the South of England Travel group in 1989, the Lynton Travel group in 1990. The company was then purchased by the West Midlands Travel holding company, and then joined the National Express Group when WMT merged into NEG. A retraction into core business led NEG to sell County to Cowie in 1996. A significant acquisition in 1989 was the bus interests of a well known operator Sampsons of Hoddesdon together with their base at Hoddesdon, this allowed the Hertford operation to be relocated. Under a recent restructuring of responsibilities County Bus has taken over the controlling supervision of Southend Transport and Colchester Transport from London and Country.

The growth of British Bus plc

British Bus is the other major component of what was the Cowie Groups bus interests. it is at present still a division of the group but further restructuring associated with the adoption of the Arriva identity could change this.

Drawlane Ltd

The privatisation of the National Bus Company followed the 1985 Transport Act with the National Bus Company becoming a vendor unit selling its subsidiaries to pre qualified and interested parties. Endless Holdings Ltd was one of those interested parties being a group of companies based in the cleaning and building service sector with a head office on Endless Street in Salisbury. The prime mover in Endless was Ray McEnhill. Endless set up a subsidiary called Drawlane Ltd to bid for NBC companies as they were made ready for sale.

The first company bought by Drawlane was Shamrock and Rambler in July 1987. This was the major part of the coaching activities of Hants and Dorset and was based at a modern depot in Bournemouth. The business was heavily dependant on National Express contracts, although an NBC style minibus operation was set up to compete in the Bournemouth area with Yellow Buses. As Shamrock and Rambler did not have an ongoing existence it is necessary to record here that the bus operations were reduced in scale, though difficulties with the National Express contracts led to notice being given to Shamrock and Rambler which sealed its fate. National Express set up a local joint venture company called Dorset Travel Services Ltd to take over the workings of Shamrock and Rambler with other vehicles and based as a tenant of Yellow Buses at Mallard Road, who eventually purchased Dorset Travel Services. The Shamrock and Rambler vehicles were dispersed as required around the then Drawlane Group and Shamrock and Rambler was wound up.

Drawlane was then preferred bidder for three more companies: Southern National, North Devon, and London Country (South West). Each purchaser was limited to three NBC companies in the first instance. However there was concern that Drawlane might be related to another bidder called Allied Bus which had been selected as preferred bidder for another three companies: Lincolnshire Road Car, East Midland Motor Services and Midland Red North. The concern was sufficient for the preferred bidder status to be withdrawn from both and offers reinvited.

Drawlane was successful in acquiring Midland Red (North) in January 1988 and at the time of purchase had 248 vehicles and 491 employees, for more detail see below. The following month London Country (South West) Ltd was purchased with 415 vehicles and 1250 employees, though here the garages were purchased separately by Speyhawk Properties who then leased them to the bus company with varying securities of tenure, reflecting the premium value of property in London and the South East. Finally in March 1988 Drawlane acquired the 'new' North Western Road Car Company Ltd with 340 vehicles and 870 staff.

Drawlane had also bought East Lancashire Coachbuilders from the industrial conglomerate John Brown. East Lancs were based in Blackburn and had a strong customer base in the local authority sector.

Further expansion for Drawlane would now come from acquiring bus operations from other sources. ATL (Western) Ltd had purchased Crosville Motor Services from NBC in March 1988 and in early 1989 was ready to sell. Drawlane purchased the company adding a further 470 vehicles. A quick overview of the future of Crosville would be appropriate here as it disappears before the present day. In an exercise to realise value from the company the South Cheshire operations at Crewe and Etruria were transferred to Midland Red North. The Runcorn and Warrington depots were transferred to North Western, and the Macclesfield and Congleton depots were merged into Bee Line Buzz of which more later. The remaining operations at Rock Ferry and Chester were sold to PMT Ltd along with the trading name of 'Crosville' which PMT, now part of FirstBus, still uses. The original Crosville Motor Services Company was renamed North British Bus Ltd and still exists but does not trade as a bus company, and the registered office is that of North Western at Aintree.

Midland Fox was bought from its management team in September 1989, and a minority share holding in the company from Stevensons of Uttoxeter. Bee Line Buzz operations in Manchester had been started up by BET venturing back into bus operation in the UK after selling its companies in 1968. A similar operation was started in Preston. Both were sold to Ribble's management buyout team, who in turn sold Ribble to the Stagecoach Group.As part of an exchange of assets with Stagecoach in the Manchester area, Drawlane bought Bee Line Buzz from Stagecoach along with Hulme Hall Road depot in Manchester and added into the company the former Crosville operations at Macclesfield and Congleton. Bee Line had an independent existence within the group until 1993 when its operations were merged into North Western, with Macclesfield depot going to Midland Red North.

Drawlane in Transition

In 1991 Drawlane became a partner in a consortium with several banks setting up a company called Speedtheme Ltd, which offered to buy National Express Holdings from its management team. National Express Holdings as well as the main National Express business owned Crosville Wales Ltd and its Liverpool subsidiary Amberline Ltd, Express Travel in Perth, and Carlton PSV the Neoplan coach dealer in Rotherham.

Speedtheme Ltd did not want Crosville Wales and Amberline/Express Travel and these were immediately sold to a company set up by two of the main shareholders of Drawlane, Ray McEnhill and Adam Mills, called Catchdeluxe Ltd. Whilst not part of Drawlane these two companies were under common management.

Ray McEnhill became the Chairman and Chief Executive of National Express Group and as this group prepared for its floatation on the Stock Exchange Ray McEnhill and Adam Mills severed their involvement with Drawlane. The London and Country business called Speedlink Airport Services was sold by Drawlane to National Express at this time, though it retained the Green Line Travel Company.

There was in effect a management buyout of Drawlane in the autumn of 1992 to coincide with the successful floatation of National Express and shortly thereafter Drawlane was renamed British Bus plc. (The British Bus Ltd company had been a by then dormant subsidiary of National Express Holdings, originally set up by NBC to market the Britexpress card overseas). Shortly before this Crosville Wales had become part of the Drawlane Group as had Express Travel, as the combined businesses of Amberline and Express Travel had become.

British Bus grows

There were throughout this period various smaller acquisitions by the group companies but these are dealt with in the short histories of these companies that follow. More significant acquisitions in 1993 were Southend Transport and Colchester Transport both former municipal operations. Southend had found itself fighting a bus war with Thamesway, the Badgerline subsidiary and weakened by this extended competition found itself offered for sale by its owners. A similar story applied at Colchester where Eastern National had put the municipal under pressure. After acquisition the two companies were put under common management and the supervision of London and Country, a programme of rationalisation put both back onto a firm footing, though down sized.

1993 also saw North Western acquire Liverline of Liverpool, by then a 51 vehicle company, which it was to run as a separate subsidiary until 1997. North Western had also by this time absorbed the bus operations of Amberline. There was also a sale of Tellings Golden Miller back to its original owners, Tellings had been taken over by Midland Fox and come into the group, at the time of its sale it had bases both in Surrey and Cardiff. In the latter location Tellings had become the joint operator of the Trawscambria service with Crosville Cymru! That role has by 1997 passed to Rhondda Bus in which British Bus had a share holding for a while.

At the end of 1993 British Bus became the preferred bidder for the purchase of GM Buses North, however the position was overturned by the vendors and new bids invited. The outcome of this exercise was a winning bid from a employee based team which was eventually completed in the spring of 1994.

Further expansion was to be funded by expanding the capital base of the group through investment by two merchant banks who took a share of the increased equity in a new parent company British Bus Group, though operational control remained with British Bus plc.

During 1994 ownership of both East Lancs and Express Travel were transferred out of the group, though they were still associated companies. East Lancs in particular was still a preferred supplier to the group for bus bodies. The National Greenway programme was coming to an end at this point, the programme saw the stripping down and re-engineering of Leyland National shells with new Gardner or Volvo engines and gearbox and new body panels mounted on the shell framework. The stripping down and mechanical overhaul work was carried out at London and Country's Reigate garage, though later some of this work was carried out by Blackburn Transport closer to East Lancs. East Lancs then did the body work with customer options as to the front design. Notable numbers were carried out for both Group companies and others. Large orders for new Dennis Darts were by then possible and made inroads into the Leyland National fleets.

Luton, Derby and Clydeside

In July 1994 British Bus acquired Luton and District Transport from its employees, by this time it also included the former London Country Bus North West and the Stevenage operations of Sovereign Bus. This meant that a sizeable part of the former London Country company was now in common ownership. Luton and District had also assisted other employee buyouts such as Derby City Transport where as a result it had a 25% share holding, and Clydeside 2000 plc, where there was a 19% share holding. A third company, Lincoln City Transport had not met with success and the employees had agreed to a sale to Yorkshire Traction owned Lincolnshire Road Car Ltd before the British Bus take-over. In both companies the shareholders voted to accept offers from British Bus for the balance of the shares and they became fully owned members of the British Bus group.

At the same time there were discussions about the acquisition of Stevensons of Uttoxeter. Stevensons had grown dramatically after deregulation and operated well away from its traditional area, a strong expansion in the West Midlands was initially successful. however West Midlands Travel responded to the competition and through its Your Bus acquisition started up operations in Burton on Trent which was by then the heartland of Stevensons. A long struggle looked in prospect and a sale to British Bus was agreed. There was a scaling down of operations in the West Midlands and surplus vehicles were distributed around the group. After this process was complete the geographically separated Macclesfield depot of Midland Red North was transferred to Stevensons control in January 1995.

Proudmutual and Caldaire Holdings

The summer of 1994 was a busy time as the Proudmutual group was acquired. Proudmutual had been the management buyout vehicle for the management team of Northumbria Motor Services to buy their business from NBC, it also had acquired some smaller businesses in the North East including Moor-Dale. Proudmutual had also bought Kentish Bus, the former London Country South East from NBC in March 1988. There was considerable success in the London Transport tendering process and further LT work was added when the LT contracts of Maidstone Boroline were purchased in February 1992. The

Proudmutual acquisition thus gave British Bus a very strong position in LT tendering when the activities of London and Country and the LDT group were taken into account. It also brought another part of the former London and Country into common ownership.

The privatisation of the London Transport Bus companies brought no success for British Bus, but as we have seen earlier the Cowie Group was successful in acquiring two of the subsidiaries.

In March of 1995 the Caldaire group was acquired. Caldaire was the buyout vehicle with which the management of West Riding Group had purchased their business from NBC in January 1987, in the December of that year they also bought United Auto from NBC. However a demerger later on saw the United business being separated off again into North East Bus. The long established independent South Yorkshire Road Transport was acquired and formed one of the trading identities of the Caldaire Group, the others being, West Riding, Yorkshire Woollen, and Selby and District. After acquisition the group of companies was renamed Yorkshire Bus Group by British Bus.

In April 1995 what turned out to be the last major acquisition by British Bus was made. Maidstone and District had been one of the earliest of NBC sales in late 1986, it purchased New Enterprise of Tonbridge in 1988, and the remaining vehicles and the premises of Maidstone Boroline in 1992. The head office of the company was moved to Maidstone and the company was put under common management with Kentish Bus and Londonlinks as the Invictaway Group under British Bus ownership.

Floatation or Trade Sale?

Throughout 1995 preparations for floatation had been underway with the appointment of advisors however in the summer of 1995 these plans were thrown off course by reports of alleged irregularities involving support from the Bank of Boston for British Bus at an earlier point in the groups history. The timing of these allegations made postponing of the floatation a necessary move. The alternative route for shareholders and the investing banks to realise their investment was a trade sale of the group. There were discussions with various interested parties.

The group was in the meantime looking to expand its interests into other modes of transport as the opportunities in the bus industry were becoming scarce due to the growth of the major players. The subsequent sales of the two former GM Buses companies by their employee owners and that of Strathclyde Buses were opportunities for growth, but British Bus was not successful.

British Bus had become a partner in the Eurotrans consortium which had been selected as the preferred bidder for the South Leeds Supertram Project which was being promoted by West Yorkshire PTE. This was a PFI project where bidders were fighting for the concession to Design, Build, Operate, and Maintain the tramway for a period of thirty years. The consortium included big construction companies such as Taylor Woodrow, Morrison Construction, and Christiani and Neilsen, the tram supplier was Vevey Technologies of Switzerland. The intention is that Yorkshire Bus Group would set up a tram operating subsidiary to operate the tramway for the concession life on behalf of Eurotrans. Other similar activities included involvement in a bidding consortium for the Croydon Tramlink project, and the Manchester Metrolink Concession again as Eurotrans.

British Bus was also active in the Franchising of the Train Operating Companies by OPRAF though none of these bids were successful, however the exposure to the process paid off in arranging through ticketing deals with the successful bidders later on.

In June 1996 the Cowie Group made an offer to acquire British Bus, though not East Lancs or Express Travel which had been owned outside the group for some time. There was an Monopolies and Mergers Commission investigation into the take-over in view of the concentration of operation in London and the South East in the combined business. However in due course this investigation made no recommendation about disinvestment recognising the considerable presence of the other groups in the area. The acquisition by Cowie was completed in August 1996

Developments since 1996

The enlarged Cowie group became the second largest bus operating group in the UK, ahead of Stagecoach and behind First Bus. The position was consolidated by the acquisition of North East Bus also in August 1996. This was the United Auto, and Teeside Motor Services which after the separation from the Caldaire group had been sold to West Midlands Travel. West Midlands Travel itself had then merged with the National Express Group and it was from this source that North East Bus had been bought as had County Bus earlier.

The Hughes-DAF bus and coach dealership, acquired earlier in Cowies growth became responsible for the ordering of new vehicles and an immediate influx of ex-stock vehicles helped the fleet replacement programme of some fleets.

In 1996 British Bus formed a consortium with Cegelec-AEG and Adtranz to bid for the Merseyside Rapid Transit project being promoted by Merseytravel the PTE serving Merseyside. Adtranz withdrew when the technology selection favoured an electronically guided trolleybus rather than a tramway solution. The consortium, Transform, was selected in 1997 as the development partner with Merseytravel to develop the project and to obtain the Transport and Works Act Powers and to obtain both the Private Sector and Public Sector funding for the project. Here too the intention is that the local subsidiary North Western will operate the system on behalf of the consortium for the proposed twenty year concession period. The vehicles proposed are a virtually 100% low floor articulated trolley bus with a clean diesel generator set allowing full performance away from the overhead cables, the final drive will be electric hub motors and the external styling will be more tram like than bus. they will be the most sophisticated buses in the UK on entering service at the turn of the century.

Unibus

1997 also saw the acquisition of the first overseas subsidiary in Denmark. Unibus with its Head Office in Hvidovre in the southern suburbs of Copenhagen is a operator of around 150 vehicles, employing some 400 drivers. Founded in 1985 Unibus has grown by winning tendered bus operation for the Transport Authority for Copenhagen- HT. Unibus was the biggest coach operator in Copenhagen until in 1995 the coaching business was sold to Lyngby Turistfart. However Unibus has kept in touch with the incoming tourist market by starting Copenhagen Pride a double deck open top hop on hop off circular tour familiar to us in the UK. Unibus vehicles are painted in the HT livery of yellow and depending upon which contracts they are operating carry the company fleet name on the cove panels or on the side. Other European acquisitions are expected to follow.

The former British Bus headquarters at Salisbury which dated back to Drawlane days was wound down and closed at the end of 1996, with the group administration being moved to Sunderland. The present Head Office of British Bus Division of the group is to be found at Leicester sharing the Head Office of Midland Fox in the Pickerings premises which also now accommodates a depot of Midland Fox.

There follows now a brief history of each of the trading companies in the group except those which have been covered in the narrative above. This will cover the smaller acquisitions and developments which the reader will find reflected in the fleet lists which follow.

Clydeside Buses Ltd

Clydeside Buses and its predecessors, has been serving its core area of Renfrewshire and Inverclyde since 1928. Prior to 1985 the operation had formed the northern section of Western Scottish part of the Scottish Bus Group (SBG). In preparation for the deregulation of local bus services Clydeside Scottish assumed the responsibility for the Glasgow, Renfrewshire and Inverclyde operations of Western Scottish in 1985. Over the next 6 years there were a complex series of reorganisations between Clydeside and Western, until in 1991 Clydeside became the last SBG subsidiary to be privatised when it was purchased by its employees with assistance from Luton and District Transport Group, emerging as Clydeside 2000 plc.

After 1986 there were numerous competitors in the core area and trading proved extremely difficult. When the LDT group sold to British Bus there was an offer put to the shareholders of Clydeside which was accepted and Clydeside joined British Bus. There was immediate effort to update the fleet against a background of tightening up of enforcement generally in the area. Some of the competitive battles had led to the Traffic Commissioner taking steps to control the number of departures and waiting times in certain town centres.

The development of services has seen Flagship Routes introduced to raise quality levels. Additionally opportunity has been taken to acquire various smaller operators in the area. Ashton Coaches of Greenock, and a significant share in Dart Buses of Paisley. operations from the Greenock base were restyled as GMS-Greenock Motor Services with a separate livery. Also in 1997 McGills Bus Service Ltd of Barrhead was acquired by the group and at present has been kept as a separate entity from Clydeside Buses. Most recently Clydeside has acquired Bridge Coaches of Paisley being fully absorbed into Clydeside.

Crosville Cymru

Crosville Wales Ltd was until August 1986 the Welsh and Shropshire operations of Crosville Motor Services Ltd based in Chester. In 1986 it was resolved that the Crosville company was too large to be offered for privatisation as a whole. Therefore the then dormant Devon General Omnibus and Touring Company Ltd was revived by NBC in order to take over the assets and business of Crosville in Wales to be renamed Crosville Wales. The management team of Crosville Wales purchased the company from NBC in December 1987.

In January 1989 the company was bought by National Express Holdings Ltd, in July of that year it purchased a subsidiary company called Amberline based at Speke in Liverpool and added a bus operation to the mainly National Express coach contracts operated.

In July 1991 the National Express group was purchased by a consortium of banks led by Drawlane as explained above. Ultimately this led to Crosville Wales becoming a full member of the Drawlane

Group shortly before its transformation into British Bus plc. In January 1992 the Oswestry depot and its outstation at Abermule had been sold to Midland Red North.

Crosville Wales has taken advantage of second hand vehicles from other group companies and other operators, its fleets of Leyland Lynxes and National 2s being so acquired, whilst at the same time buying further new Mercedes minibuses. New full size vehicles have also started to appear.

In 1995 some of the services, but no vehicles, of Alpine Travel were acquired leading to an operation of certain services as Alpine Bus in a red and white livery. This has now been superseded by a Shoreline livery of Blue, white and yellow.

Kentish Bus

Though shown as a separate fleet Kentish Bus is a part of the Invictaway group of companies in the current structure. Its size will be reduced by the forthcoming transfer of operations at Battersea, the Routemasters, to South London. The operations at Cambridge Heath will transfer to Leaside.

Kentish Bus started its existence as London Country South East on the division of London Country Bus Services in 1986. It had its Head Office at Northfleet and in April 1987 was relaunched as Kentish Bus and Coach Ltd with a new livery.

In March 1988 Kentish Bus was sold to Proudmutual on privatisation. There was considerable expansion into the LT tender market with new buses being added many with North East originating registration indexes. In February 1992 there was further expansion in this area when Kentish acquired the LT tendered work of the troubled Maidstone Boroline operation, some 57 vehicles, many of which are still current.

After the acquisition of the Proudmutual group by British Bus in 1994 Kentish Bus and Londonlinks were jointly managed from Northfleet, however on the acquisition of Maidstone and District the management was relocated to Maidstone, Armstrong Road under the Invictaway grouping. The balance of the operation continues to be controlled from Maidstone after the reallocation of the two London depots to South London and Leaside.

Kentish Bus was notable in the 1990s for winning the best bus route competition organised by the London Transport Passengers Committee.

London and Country

London and Country Ltd was formerly London Country South West Ltd, one of the four parts that London Country Bus Services Ltd was divided into in advance of the privatisation of NBC. The former head office of LCBS at Reigate became that of L &C. The company was bought by Drawlane as outlined above in February 1988, though the properties were to be leased having been sold separately. The company was relaunched with a new livery and trading name in April 1989.

London and Country was successful in winning LT tenders and this led to the addition of new vehicles and the high profile opening of an impressive new garage at Beddington Farm in Croydon.

In 1990 the Woking, Guildford, and Cranleigh operations of the former Alder Valley were purchased, and whilst kept as a separate company- Guildford and West Surrey, were put under the same management as L & C. Also in 1990 a separate company was established called Horsham Buses for operations in the Horsham area.

Spare capacity at the Reigate garage allowed the development of the National Greenway concept in conjunction with East Lancs and many vehicles were dealt with at Reigate. Briefly L & C had two subsidiaries in Dorset, Stanbridge and Crichel and Oakfield Travel, both of these were later sold to Damory Coaches. Another subsidiary until recently sold to its management was Linkline Coaches of Harlesden in London which specialised in coaching and corporate work.

1993 saw the acquisition of Southend Transport and Colchester Transport with many L & C influences, but these have now been transferred to the supervision of County Bus which is closer.

The Croydon based operations and other LT tender operations at Walworth had been transferred into a new company called Londonlinks. This was in 1995 put under common management as Kentish Bus and Maidstone and District as part of the Invictaway Group, however the latest reallocation of responsibilities in the enlarged group has seen Londonlinks return to L & C control.

A final consequence of the property sales was the vacation of Reigate garage and its replacement by a facility at Merstham, this left the Head Office remote from operation and in 1997 this as closed and the functions moved to other premises including Crawley garage.

Maidstone and District

This is the original Maidstone and District Motor Services Ltd founded in 1911, though in NBC days it did share common management with East Kent from 1972 to 1983. In 1983 the Hastings and Rye area services were hived off as Hastings and District.

Maidstone and District was one of the first NBC companies to be privatised being bought by its management team in November 1986. In 1988 New Enterprise of Tonbridge was purchased and, until recently, kept as a separate entity. In June 1992 the remaining operations of Maidstone Boroline and the premises at Armstrong Road were purchased.

In April 1995 the company was sold to British Bus, that November the hitherto Head Office at Chatham was closed and control moved to the former Maidstone Boroline premises at Maidstone under the Invictaway banner.

Under British Bus/Cowie control the group acquired a number of additional operators including Mercury Passenger Services of Hoo, Wealden Beeline of Five Oak Green, and the Grey Green (Medway) bus operations. In May of 1997 the Green Line operations at Northfleet and Gravesend were sold to the Pullman Group. In the first part of 1997 103 new vehicles were introduced into Kentish Bus and Maidstone and District, an investment of £8.3m.

Midland Red North and Stevensons

Midland Red North Ltd was founded in 1981 when the Midland Red company was divided into four operating parts by NBC. The company traded with local network names for a considerable time such as Chaserider, these were based upon the networks generated from the Market Analysis Project later carried out across NBC.

The company was sold to Drawlane in January 1988 after a false start. In 1989 it took over the Crewe and Etruria depots of fellow Drawlane subsidiary Crosville Motor Services Ltd. In 1992 Midland Red North purchased the Oswestry and Abermule operations of Crosville Wales Ltd then an associated company. In 1993 with the dispersion of the Bee Line Buzz Company the Macclesfield depot of that company which had traded as C-Line was taken over, having been part of Crosville for some time in earlier years.

Stevensons of Uttoxeter commenced services in that part of Staffordshire in 1926, and continued as a small but successful family owned business. During the 1980s, and particularly after deregulation, significant growth occurred. In 1985 a controlling interest was acquired in the East Staffordshire Borough Councils bus operations in Burton-on-Trent. in 1987 the Swadlincote depot of Midland Fox was purchased from NBC.

Growth in the West Midlands and the acquisition of a number of small companies including Crystal Coaches in Burslem and Viking Tours and Travel saw the company become a major independent operator in the early 1990s.

In April 1994, however, West Midlands Travel through its Your Bus subsidiary decided to retaliate in the Burton area against the significant level of operation Stevensons then had in the West Midlands area, this led to the sale of the company to British Bus in August 1994. There followed a significant scaling down of Stevensons operations in the West Midlands.

Macclesfield depot was transferred into Stevensons in January 1995 from Midland Red North. From April 1995, Midland Red and Stevensons have been jointly managed and the closure of the Stevensons Head Office at Spath with the provision of central administration services from the Cannock head office became effective in 1996. A common livery was established between the two fleets though the Stevensons fleet name was retained on vehicles allocated to Stevensons depots. Viking coaches retained a separate two shades of grey livery.

Midland Fox

Midland Red East Ltd was formed in 1981 to take over the Leicestershire operations of Midland Red. In 1984 the company name was changed to Midland Fox Ltd, and there was a major relaunch of the company with a new livery and fox logo. there was also the launch of a new minibus network in Leicester under the Fox Cub brand.

In 1987 the company was bought from NBC by its management with the help of the directors of Stevensons of Uttoxeter who also separately bought the Swadlincote depot.

Several smaller operators were taken over, these have included Wreake Valley of Thurmaston, Fairtax of Melton Mowbray, Astill & Jordan of Ratby, Shelton Orsborn of Wollaston, Blands of Stamford, and Loughborough Coach and Bus.

In 1989 Midland Fox was acquired by Drawlane.

In 1990 Midland Fox acquired Tellings Golden Miller in Byfleet which in turn acquired the Coach Travel Centre in Cardiff amongst others. Tellings bus operations eventually became part of London and Country, whilst Tellings was sold back to its management in 1994 before expansion into bus operation in Cardiff.

In 1994 Pickerings Transport was purchased by British Bus. Pickerings built lorry bodies at their extensive site at Thurmaston and also offered body repair and painting services which saw many group vehicles appearing there.

In September 1994 Midland Fox launched a new taxi service in Leicester marketed as Fox Cabs. 1996 saw a launch of high quality services under the Urban Fox brand in a striking new blue livery.

Derby City Transport Ltd was the long established municipally owned bus company. In August 1989 it was sold to its employees who were assisted by Luton and District Transport. Luton and District took a 25% share holding in the business. There was a competitive interlude in Derby where Midland Red North started operations, but this ended with Derby buying out the competition in February 1990. Derby also assisted in the employee purchase of Lincoln City Transport taking a share of that company, this was realised when Lincoln was sold to the Yorkshire Traction group.

In 1990 "75"Taxis started as a division of Derby City Transport building up a fleet of London style taxis.

In 1994 after the acquisition of Luton and District by British Bus, the shareholders in Derby decided to accept an offer from British Bus for the rest of the share capital of the company. After a period of autonomy the business was relaunched under the City Rider brand name and a yellow red and blue livery. In January 1996 Derby City Transport was incorporated into the Midland Fox group.

In September 1996 the Head Office of Midland Fox moved to the Pickerings of Thurmaston premises along with a depot facility. It was later joined by the British Bus head office.

Northumbria Motor Services Ltd

In 1986 the operations of United Auto were split into two parts in preparation for privatisation. The dormant Southern National Omnibus Company Ltd was renamed Northumbria and took over operations in September 1986 with a new head office in Jesmond.

In October 1987 Northumbria was acquired form NBC by its management using Proudmutual as a holding company, that holding company also acquired Kentish Bus in March 1988. Other acquisitions included Moor-Dale Coaches, and Hunters.

In 1994 the Proudmutual group was acquired by British Bus, at the same time Moor-Dale Coaches was sold back to former directors.

North Western Road Car Company Ltd

Ribble Motor Services was another NBC company that was to be divided in preparation for privatisation. The dormant Mexborough and Swinton Traction Company was renamed as above to take over the Merseyside, West Lancashire, and Wigan operations of Ribble in September 1986. The head office of the new company was at Bootle in Liverpool.

The company was acquired by Drawlane in March 1988. In 1989 the Runcorn and Warrington depots of Crosville were acquired. Expansion saw North Western open a depot in Altrincham, though eventually rationalisation saw the operations assumed by the Bee Line Buzz Company during its independent existence as a Drawlane subsidiary.

In 1993 Bee Line was put under the same management as North Western, also in 1993 Liverline of Bootle was acquired with 51 vehicles. Both have been maintained as separate identities. Also acquired in 1993 were the bus operations of Express Travel which were still branded as Amberline, this identity was not maintained.

The head office of the company was moved to Aintree depot, though a subsequent move saw the depot sold and redeveloped leaving the head office building free standing.

1995 was a busy year with two operations in Wigan area acquired, Little White Bus, and Wigan Bus Company. Also acquired in 1995 was Arrowline Travel based in Knutsford, but trading as Star Line, this brought luxury coaches on Airport related work as well as a modern fleet of mini and midi buses. The Star Line operations have since been relocated to Wythenshaw.

Competition in the Warrington area saw a new depot being established at Haydock to supplement existing facilities. The collapse of a Cheshire operator Loftys of Mickle Trafford saw further growth in the mid Cheshire area taking vehicles as far south as Whitchurch.

1997 has seen the acquisition by the group of the residue of South Lancs Transport following that operators withdrawal from Chester, the business being under the supervision of North Western. Quality and low floor initiatives are being developed with both Merseytravel and GMPTE, and as explained earlier there is involvement in the development of the Merseyside Rapid Transit project. Considerable investment has seen many new buses and the introduction of refurbished vehicles including a large batch of Leyland Nationals from West Midlands travel, all in brighter liveries.

The Shires

In 1986 United Counties Omnibus Company Ltd was divided into three parts, the southernmost of these was Luton and District Transport Ltd which took over operations in Aylesbury, Hitchin, and Luton. The new head office of the company was in Luton.

In August 1987 Luton and District became the first employee owned bus operator in the UK when its employees bought it from NBC. In the period from January 1988 to October 1990, LDT expanded the size and the area of its operations by a number of strategic acquisitions. The assets and business of Red Rover Omnibus Ltd, operating bus services from a depot in Aylesbury, were acquired in January 1988. In June 1988 Milton Keynes Coaches was acquired, and in May 1990 two thirds of the bus services operated in the Stevenage area by Sovereign Bus Ltd.

In October 1990 LDT acquired London Country North West Ltd. LCNW operated a vehicle fleet of a similar size to LDT from a head office and depot in Watford and other depots in Hemel Hempstead, High Wycombe, Amersham, and Slough

LDT assisted in the employee buyouts of two other companies and acquired a share holding in both, Derby City Transport in 1989, and Clydeside 2000 plc in 1991.

In July 1994 LDT became part of British Bus. In October 1994 the bus operations of Stuart Palmer Travel based in Dunstable was taken over, followed in May 1995 by Buffalo Travel of Flitwick and Motts Travel of Aylesbury in July 1995.

April 1995 saw the launch of a brand new blue and yellow company livery with local trading names. The legal name was changed to LDT Ltd in May and the corporate operating name became The Shires.

In late 1997 Lucketts Garages (Watford) Ltd was acquired. in addition to local bus services in Watford there are substantial dial-a-ride operations and a commercial workshop.

United, Tees & District, and Teeside Motor Services Ltd

United Automobile Services Ltd was another NBC subsidiary which was to be divided up in preparation for privatisation. Here in 1986 the northern part of the operating area was hived off into a new company called Northumbria. United continued to trade south of the Tyne with its head office in Darlington. the operations in Scarborough and Pickering were transferred into a subsidiary of East Yorkshire Motor Services.

In December 1987 United was bought from NBC by Caldaire Holdings the management buyout vehicle of the West Riding management team. In 1989 the National Express coaching activities of United were sold off to a joint venture company Durham Travel Services, set up by two ex-United managers with National Express.

In 1990 United was split into two parts, the Durham and North Yorkshire section continuing to trade as United, the section in Cleveland trading as Tees and District. At this time the associated businesses of Trimdon Motor Services and Teeside Motor Services were acquired, with the Trimdon business being absorbed into United and the Teeside business continuing.

In the summer of 1992 there was a demerger of the Caldaire Group with the North East operations passing to the Westcourt Group, with Caldaire North East becoming North East Bus.

In 1994 a new head office and engineering works in Morton Road, Darlington allowed the vacation of the Grange Road site for redevelopment. Also in 1994 the Westcourt Group sold to West

Midlands Travel in the November, this led to North East Bus being part of the National Express Group following the merger with that group in 1995.

Eden Bus Services of Bishop Auckland was acquired in October 1995.

National Express Group sold North East Bus to the Cowie Group on the last day of July 1996, later in October the Ripon depot operations were sold to Harrogate and District Travel.

Yorkshire Bus Group

The West Riding Automobile Company and Yorkshire Woollen District Transport were put under common management by NBC. Therefore when privatisation happened in January 1987 the management team bought both companies. Selby and District was a trading title turned into a separate company by the new owners Caldaire Holding company. Whilst Caldaire became involved in the North East the core business in West Yorkshire changed very little with there being steady investment in fleet replacement and upgrade.

There was involvement in the splitting up of National Travel East leaving a residue of operations on National Express contracts, and also competitive operations in Sheffield that led to corresponding competition in Wakefield.

One acquisition was the South Yorkshire Road Transport Company of Pontefract which has been maintained as a separate trading identity.

In March 1995 Caldaire Group was acquired by British Bus.

The single deck fleet is particularly modern with a batch of thirty Dennis Dart SLFs delivered in 1997 for Dewsbury displacing the last of the Leyland National 2s to other group companies. The double deck fleet is composed entirely Olympians and the oldest of these are now being cascaded to other group companies.

Arriva

On the 6th November at an Extraordinary General Meeting of Cowie Group plc the overwhelming majority of shareholders voting approved an immediate change in the name of the Group to Arriva plc.

Cowie's vehicle management operations became Arriva Automotive solutions from 17th November 1997.

Other operations in the Group will be rebranded from January 1998 as Arriva Pasenger Services, Arriva Bus and Coach, and Arriva Motor Retailing.

The bus operations will be rebranded Arriva Passenger Services. A new corporate identity has been created that will apply at all aspects of the business from stationery, to buses, to premises. The buses will be progressively repainted into a new livery of Shimmering Aquamarine with a Light Stone flash at the front of the vehicle. The new Arriva logo form and name will appear on the side of the buses together with a localised subscript in the form 'Serving ...'. Therefore the parent company names will not be carried on the vehicles beyond the legal lettering and operator's discs. There will be specific local branding of services emphasised in lettering along the side of the vehicle where this is required.

Vehicles for imminent delivery are being prepared in the new livery at the manufacurers. As part of the launch, many London-based vehicles were rebranded with vinyls replacing the existing fleet name. Vehicles operating for London Regional Transport will receive a livery complying with the contract conditions for this work with the correct portion of red, but reflecting the new corporate identity. There will also be other vehicles in the rest of the country which are contracted into a specific livery for customers or Local Authorities.

Over the next few months, the local names will be replaced by the new Arriva logo form and name will appear on the side of the buses together with a localised subscript in the form of 'Serving...'. Therefore the parent company names will not be carried on the vehicles beyond the legal lettering and operator's discs. There will be specific local branding of services emphasised in lettering along the side of the vehicle where this is required. One of the liveries to disappear will be the TMS blue and white, seen here with lettering for service 15 on Optare Delta 4006. *Keith Lee*

CLYDESIDE

Clydeside Buses Ltd, The Gatehouse, Porterfield Road, Renfrew, PA4 8JB

1	LAZ5847	Renault-Dodge S46	Northern Counties	B22F	1987	Ex North Western (Bee Line), 1996
11	E338WYS	Renault-Dodge S56	Alexander AM	B25F	1987	Ex Western Scottish, 1991
12	E325WYS	Renault-Dodge S56	Alexander AM	B25F	1987	Ex Western Scottish, 1991
13	E323WYS	Renault-Dodge S56	Alexander AM	B25F	1987	Ex Western Scottish, 1991
14	E330WYS	Renault-Dodge S56	Alexander AM	B25F	1987	Ex Western Scottish, 1991
15	E337WYS	Renault-Dodge S56	Alexander AM	B25F	1987	Ex Western Scottish, 1991
16	E350WYS	Renault-Dodge S56	Alexander AM	B25F	1987	Ex Western Scottish, 1991
18	G195NWY	Renault-Dodge S56	Reeve Burgess Beaver	B23F	1990	Ex Rider (York), 1992
21	G902MNS	Mercedes-Benz 811D	Reeve Burgess Beaver	B33F	1989	Ex Stevensons, 1995
22	G32OHS	Mercedes-Benz 811D	Alexander AM	B33F	1989	Ex Westside, Gourock, 1996
140	MIL9320	Leyland Tiger TRCTL11/3R	Van Hool Alizée	C50FT	1984	Ex Pullman, Crofty, 1996
170	4225FM	Leyland Tiger TRCLXC/2RH	Plaxton Paramount 3200 E	C49FT	1984	Ex Western Scottish, 1991
172	WLT924	Leyland Tiger TRCLXC/2RH	Plaxton Paramount 3200 E	C49FT	1984	Ex Western Scottish, 1991
173	407CLT	Leyland Tiger TRCLXC/2RH	Plaxton Paramount 3200 E	C49FT	1984	Ex Western Scottish, 1991
175	WLT956	Leyland Tiger TRCLXC/2RH	Plaxton Paramount 3200 E	C49FT	1984	Ex Western Scottish, 1991

201-208

	Optare MetroRider		Optare		B29F	1996	

201	N201NHS	203	N203NHS	205	N205NHS	207	N207NHS	208	N208NHS
202	N202NHS	204	N204NHS	206	N206NHS				

209-216

	Optare MetroRider MR09		Optare		B23F	1991	Ex Yorkshire Bus (WR), 1997

209	H706UNW	211	H713UNW	213	H702UNW	215	H701UNW	216	H710UNW
210	H712UNW	212	H704UNW	214	H703UNW				

217-227

	Optare MetroRider		Optare		B29F	1996

217	P217SGB	219	P219SGB	221	P221SGB	224	P224SGB	226	P226SGB
218	P218SGB	220	P220SGB	223	P223SGB	225	P225SGB	227	P227SGB

228	M883DDS	Mercedes-Benz 811D	WS Wessex II	B33F	1994	Ex Ashton Group, Greenock, 1997
229	M95EGE	Mercedes-Benz 709D	WS Wessex II	B33F	1995	Ex Ashton Group, Greenock, 1997
230	M799EUS	Mercedes-Benz 811D	WS Wessex II	B33F	1995	Ex Ashton Group, Greenock, 1997
231	D168VRP	Mercedes-Benz L608D	Alexander AM	B20F	1986	Ex Crosville Cymru, 1996
232	D202SKD	Mercedes-Benz L608D	Reeve Burgess	DP19F	1986	Ex Midland, 1995
234	D204SKD	Mercedes-Benz L608D	Reeve Burgess	DP19F	1986	Ex Midland, 1995
235	D205SKD	Mercedes-Benz L608D	Reeve Burgess	DP19F	1986	Ex Midland, 1995

One method of competing with smaller operators is the establishment of separate operational units. Clydeside's F&L Transport unit is one such operation. The vehicles wear a lemon livery and operate from Johnstone depot. Among the seven vehicles so employed is 22, G32OHS, itself acquired from another independent in 1996.
Clydeside Buses

Greenock and Paisley have seen much competition for several years and many smaller minibus operators have come and gone culminating with the Ashton group selling their operations to Clydeside in 1997. Around sixty vehicles, most less than three years old, came with the business. Such was the reputation of the GMS (Greenock Motor Services) operation that Clydeside changed all their vehicles at Greenock to GMS branding. Mercedes-Benz 287, N228MUS, with Marshall bodywork, demonstrates the livery. *Clydeside Buses*

236	D25KKP	Mercedes-Benz L608D	Rootes	B20F	1986	Ex Maidstone & District, 1997	
237	C707JMB	Mercedes-Benz L608D	Reeve Burgess	B20F	1986	Ex Midland, 1995	
238	C708JMB	Mercedes-Benz L608D	Reeve Burgess	B20F	1986	Ex Midland, 1995	

239-243		Mercedes-Benz 811D	WS Wessex II	B33F	1995	Ex Ashton Group, Greenock, 1997	
239	M278FNS	**240**	M277FNS	**241**	M276FNS	**242**	M422GUS	**243**	N991KUS

239	M278FNS	240	M277FNS	241	M276FNS	242	M422GUS	243	N991KUS

244	N253PGD	Mercedes-Benz 811D	UVG CitiStar	B33F	1996		
245	N808PDS	Mercedes-Benz 811D	Marshall C16	B33F	1996	Ex Ashton Group, Greenock, 1997	
246	N806PDS	Mercedes-Benz 811D	Marshall C16	B33F	1996	Ex Ashton Group, Greenock, 1997	
247	F760VNH	Mercedes-Benz 609D	Wadham Stringer Wessex	C21F	1989	Ex Cowan and Hamilton, Johnstone, 1995	
248	H901GNC	Mercedes-Benz 609D	Made-to-Measure	C24F	1991	Ex Inverclyde, Port Glasgow, 1993	
249	N807PDS	Mercedes-Benz 811D	Marshall C16	B33F	1996	Ex Ashton Group, Greenock, 1997	
250	J218HDS	Mercedes-Benz 709D	Carlyle	B29F	1992	Ex Ashton Group, Greenock, 1997	
251	L51LSG	Mercedes-Benz 709D	Plaxton Beaver	B25F	1993		
252	L52LSG	Mercedes-Benz 709D	Plaxton Beaver	B25F	1993		
253	L53LSG	Mercedes-Benz 709D	Plaxton Beaver	B25F	1993		
254	L54LSG	Mercedes-Benz 709D	Plaxton Beaver	B25F	1993		

255-265		Mercedes-Benz 711D	Plaxton Beaver	B25F	1994		
255	L860LFS	**258**	L863LFS	**260**	L865LFS	**262**	L867LFS	**264**	L869LFS
256	L861LFS	**259**	L864LFS	**261**	L866LFS	**263**	L868LFS	**265**	L870LFS
257	L862LFS								

266	N809PDS	Mercedes-Benz 811D	Marshall C16	B33F	1996	Ex Ashton Group, Greenock, 1997	
267	N81PUS	Mercedes-Benz 811D	Marshall C16	B33F	1996	Ex Ashton Group, Greenock, 1997	
268	N82PUS	Mercedes-Benz 811D	Marshall C16	B33F	1996	Ex Ashton Group, Greenock, 1997	
269	N26KYS	Mercedes-Benz 811D	Plaxton Beaver	B33F	1995	Ex Ashton Group, Greenock, 1997	
270	N27KYS	Mercedes-Benz 811D	Plaxton Beaver	B33F	1995	Ex Ashton Group, Greenock, 1997	
271	P932YSB	Mercedes-Benz 811D	Mellor	B33F	1997	Ex Ashton Group, Greenock, 1997	
272	P936YSB	Mercedes-Benz 811D	Mellor	B33F	1997	Ex Ashton Group, Greenock, 1997	

Clydeside's large fleet of Renault-Dodge minibuses is now almost history. Filling the need for larger capacity and second-generation comfort, two batches of Optare MetroRiders entered service during 1996 followed by a pre-owned batch from the Yorkshire Bus Group. Representing the first new batch is 208, N208MHS. *Philip Stephenson*

273	P937YSB	Mercedes-Benz 811D	Mellor	B33F	1997	Ex Ashton Group, Greenock, 1997
274	P491TGA	Mercedes-Benz 711D	UVG CitiStar	B29F	1996	Ex Ashton Group, Greenock, 1997
275	P490TGA	Mercedes-Benz 711D	UVG CitiStar	B29F	1996	Ex Ashton Group, Greenock, 1997
276	P492TGA	Mercedes-Benz 711D	UVG CitiStar	B29F	1996	Ex Ashton Group, Greenock, 1997
277	P527UGA	Mercedes-Benz 711D	Marshall C19	B29F	1996	Ex Ashton Group, Greenock, 1997
278	P526UGA	Mercedes-Benz 711D	Marshall C19	B29F	1996	Ex Ashton Group, Greenock, 1997

279-283

		Mercedes-Benz 709D	TBP	B29F	1995	Ex Ashton Group, Greenock, 1997

279	M791EUS	280	M792EUS	281	M793EUS	282	M794EUS	283	M423GUS

284	N752LUS	Mercedes-Benz 709D	UVG CitiStar	B29F	1996	Ex Ashton Group, Greenock, 1997
285	N753LUS	Mercedes-Benz 709D	UVG CitiStar	B29F	1996	Ex Ashton Group, Greenock, 1997

286-296

		Mercedes-Benz 709D	Marshall C19	B29F	1996	Ex Ashton Group, Greenock, 1997

286	N754LUS	289	N256PGD	291	N258PGD	293	N802PDS	295	N804PDS
287	N228MUS	290	N257PGD	292	N801PDS	294	N803PDS	296	N805PDS
288	N254PGD								

297	P930YSB	Mercedes-Benz 709D	Plaxton Beaver	B29F	1997	Ex Ashton Group, Greenock, 1997
298	P931YSB	Mercedes-Benz 709D	Plaxton Beaver	B29F	1997	Ex Ashton Group, Greenock, 1997
299	P529UGA	Mercedes-Benz 709D	Plaxton Beaver	B29F	1997	Ex Ashton Group, Greenock, 1997
300	P528UGA	Mercedes-Benz 709D	Plaxton Beaver	B29F	1997	Ex Ashton Group, Greenock, 1997
301	L263VSU	Mercedes-Benz 709D	Dormobile Routemaker	B29F	1994	Ex Ashton Group, Greenock, 1997
302	M880DDS	Mercedes-Benz 709D	WS Wessex II	B29F	1994	Ex Ashton Group, Greenock, 1997
303	M878DDS	Mercedes-Benz 709D	WS Wessex II	B29F	1994	Ex Ashton Group, Greenock, 1997
304	N941MGG	Mercedes-Benz 709D	Marshall C19	B29F	1995	Ex Ashton Group, Greenock, 1997
305	N942MGG	Mercedes-Benz 709D	Marshall C19	B29F	1995	Ex Ashton Group, Greenock, 1997
306	L970VGE	Mercedes-Benz 709D	WS Wessex II	B29F	1994	Ex Ashton Group, Greenock, 1997
307	H183CNS	Mercedes-Benz 609D	Made-to-Measure	B26F	1991	Ex Ashton Group, Greenock, 1997
308	H185CNS	Mercedes-Benz 609D	Made-to-Measure	B26F	1991	Ex Ashton Group, Greenock, 1997
309	H675AGD	Mercedes-Benz 609D	Rapier	C24F	1991	Ex Ashton Group, Greenock, 1997

Clydeside's need in the mid 1990s to rapidly update its fleet saw many vehicles arriving from dealer stock. These included the first Scania low-floor saloons acquired although later East Lancashire-bodied vehicles were a company order. This later batch carry the European style body which carry a Scania-inspired front-end married to the Blackburn constructed body. Seen here is 512, M112RMS. The rapid development of low-floor saloons in recent years has meant that there is a wealth of variety in body styling to fascinate the enthusiast for years to come. *Philip Stephenson*

324-355

Renault-Dodge S56 — Alexander AM — B25F — 1987 — Ex Western Scottish, 1991

324	E324WYS	335	E335WYS	343	E343WYS	348	E348WYS	353	E353WYS
331	E331WYS	339	E339WYS	344	E344WYS	349	E349WYS	354	E354WYS
332	E332WYS	342	E342WYS	345	E345WYS	351	E351WYS	355	E355WYS
334	E334WYS								

359	E813JSX	Renault-Dodge S56	Alexander AM	B25F	1987	Ex Fife Scottish, 1992

361-369

Renault-Dodge S56 — Reeve Burgess Beaver — B23F — 1990 — Ex Rider (York), 1992

361	G421MWY	363	G193NWY	366	G196NWY	367	G197NWY	369	G199NWY
362	G192NWY	364	G194NWY						

401	M65FDS	Dennis Dart 9.8SDL3054	Plaxton Pointer	B41F	1995
402	M67FDS	Dennis Dart 9.8SDL3054	Plaxton Pointer	B41F	1995

441-447

Volvo B6-9.9M — Alexander Dash — B40F — 1993

441	M841DDS	443	M843DDS	445	M845DDS	446	M846DDS	447	M847DDS
442	M842DDS	444	M844DDS						

501	L588JSG	Scania L113CRL	Northern Counties Paladin	B51F	1994	Ex Scania demonstrator, 1995
502	M102RMS	Scania L113CRL	Northern Counties Paladin	B51F	1995	
503	M103RMS	Scania L113CRL	Northern Counties Paladin	B51F	1995	
504	M104RMS	Scania L113CRL	Alexander Strider	B51F	1995	
505	M105RMS	Scania L113CRL	Alexander Strider	B51F	1995	
506	M106RMS	Scania L113CRL	Alexander Strider	B51F	1995	
507	M107RMS	Scania L113CRL	Alexander Strider	B51F	1995	

508-513

Scania N113CRL — East Lancashire European — B45F* — 1995 — *509 is B51F

508	M108RMS	509	M109RMS	510	M110RMS	512	M112RMS	513	M113RMS

Opposite:- In 1997 Cowie acquired the operation of McGills of Barrhead which is now attached to the Clydeside operation. Seen here is M440, N440GHG, one of four Northern Counties-bodied Dennis Darts acquired with the business. Since 1996 Clydeside have taken some forty of their own Dennis Darts with bodywork by both Plaxton and Alexander. One of the former is 816, P816GMS seen in Union Street, Glasgow, shortly after delivery. *Gerald Mead/Murdoch Currie*

The early 1980s saw a move by some NBC subsidiaries to expand commuter services on certain corridors and it was felt that better quality seating was essential to attract car users on board. Thus many standard double-deck buses received high-backed moquette covered seats for this purpose. NBC requested Eastern Coachworks to prepare a specific vehicle and the result entered service on many routes into London. Well-travelled C214UPD is now 893 in the Clydeside fleet. *Terry Wightman*

514-521

				Scania L113CRL			East Lancashire European	B51F	1995	
514	M114RMS	516	M116RMS	518	M118RMS	520	M120RMS	521	M121RMS	
515	M115RMS	517	M117RMS	519	M119RMS					

525	L25LSX	Scania N113CRL	East Lancashire European	B51F	1993	Ex Scania demonstrator, 1995

635-659

				Leyland Leopard PSU3D/4R		Alexander AY		B53F	1978	Ex Western Scottish, 1991
635	TSJ35S	638	TSJ38S	652	TSJ52S	654	TSJ54S	659	TSJ59S	
636	TSJ36S	647	TSJ47S							

691-767

				Leyland Leopard PSU3E/4R		Alexander AY		B53F	1979-80 Ex Western Scottish, 1991	
691	BSJ891T	712	BSJ912T	722	BSJ922T	756	GCS56V	766	WDS234V	
699	BSJ899T	716	BSJ916T	723	BSJ923T	759	GCS59V	767	GCS67V	
702	BSJ902T	721	BSJ921T	725	BSJ925T					

769	TSU642W	Leyland Leopard PSU3G/4R	Alexander AYS	B53F	1981	Ex East Midland, 1993
794	YCS91T	Leyland Leopard PSU3E/4R	Alexander AY	B53F	1978	Ex Western Scottish, 1991

801-805

				Dennis Dart SLF		Plaxton Pointer		B35F	1996	
801	P801RWU	802	P802RWU	803	P803RWU	804	P804RWU	805	P805RWU	

806-815

				Dennis Dart SLF		Alexander ALX200		B40F	1997	
806	P806DBS	808	P808DBS	810	P810DBS	812	P812DBS	814	P814DBS	
807	P807DBS	809	P809DBS	811	P811DBS	813	P813DBS	815	P815DBS	

The Leyland Leopard/Alexander combination, once the workhorse of the Scottish Bus Group has lasted remarkably well as a result of Alexander's extensive use of aluminium in the construction. However, the last two years have seen many withdrawn though 759, GCS59V, is one that remains. It was recently photographed in Paisley. *Gerald Mead*

816-840   Dennis Dart SLF   Plaxton Pointer   B40F   1997

816	P816GMS	821	P821GMS	826	P826KES	831	P831KES	836	P836KES
817	P817GMS	822	P822GMS	827	P827KES	832	P832KES	837	P837KES
818	P818GMS	823	P823GMS	828	P828KES	833	P833KES	838	P838KES
819	P819GMS	824	P824GMS	829	P829KES	834	P834KES	839	P839KES
820	P820GMS	825	P825KES	830	P830KES	835	P835KES	840	P840KES

890	C450BKM	Leyland Olympian ONTL11/2R	Eastern Coach Works	CH45/28F	1985	Ex Northumbria, 1996
891	C451BKM	Leyland Olympian ONTL11/2R	Eastern Coach Works	CH45/28F	1985	Ex Northumbria, 1996
892	C452GKE	Leyland Olympian ONTL11/2RHSp	Eastern Coach Works	CH45/28F	1986	Ex Yorkshire (Selby & District), 1997
893	C214UPD	Leyland Olympian ONTL11/2RSp	Eastern Coach Works	CH45/28F	1985	Ex Northumbria, 1996
894	C454GKE	Leyland Olympian ONTL11/2RHSp	Eastern Coach Works	H45/28F	1986	Ex Northumbria, 1996
895	HSB948Y	Leyland Olympian ONTL11/2R	Eastern Coach Works	H45/28F	1983	Ex Maidstone & District, 1996
896	C453GKE	Leyland Olympian ONTL11/2RHSp	Eastern Coach Works	H45/28F	1986	Ex Yorkshire (Selby & District), 1997
898	GKE442Y	Leyland Olympian ONTL11/2R	Eastern Coach Works	H45/28F	1983	Ex Maidstone & District, 1996
899	C449BKM	Leyland Olympian ONTL11/2R(Cummins) ECW		CH45/28F	1985	Ex Northumbria, 1996
900	TPD106X	Leyland Olympian ONTL11/1R	Roe	H43/29F	1982	Ex Kentish Bus, 1997
901	TPD130X	Leyland Olympian ONTL11/1R	Roe	H43/29F	1982	Ex Kentish Bus, 1997
902	A147FPG	Leyland Olympian ONTL11/1R	Roe	H43/29F	1984	Ex Kentish Bus, 1997
903	TPD116X	Leyland Olympian ONTL11/1R	Roe	H43/29F	1982	Ex Kentish Bus, 1997
905	WSU475	Leyland Olympian ONTL11/2R	Eastern Coach Works	H45/26F	1985	Ex Maidstone & District, 1996
906	HSB949Y	Leyland Olympian ONTL11/2R	Eastern Coach Works	CH45/28F	1983	Ex Maidstone & District, 1996
907	WSU476	Leyland Olympian ONTL11/2R	Eastern Coach Works	H45/26F	1985	Ex Maidstone & District, 1996
1001	N750LUS	Mercedes-Benz OH1416	Wright Urbanranger	B47F	1995	

McGills

	GVD47	Guy Arab III	Duple	H31/26R	1950	Ex Hutchison, Overtown, 1952
M50	XRR50S	Leyland Fleetline FE30AGR	Northern Counties	H43/29F	1978	Ex City Rider (Derby), 1996
M58	G58RGG	Renault-Dodge S56	Reeve Burgess Beaver	B23F	1990	Ex Rider (York), 1992
M60	WYV60T	Leyland Titan TNLXB2RR	Park Royal	H44/26F	1979	Ex Londonlinks, 1996
M88	CUL88V	Leyland Titan TNLXB2RR	Park Royal	H44/31F	1979	Ex Londonlinks, 1997

M91	K91RGA	Mercedes-Benz 709D	Dormobile Routemaker	B25F	1993	Ex Rowe, Muirkirk, 1995
M92	K92RGA	Mercedes-Benz 709D	Dormobile Routemaker	B25F	1993	Ex Rowe, Muirkirk, 1995
M94	CUL94V	Leyland Titan TNLXB2RR	Park Royal	H44/26F	1980	Ex Londonlinks, 1996
M109	KKG109W	Leyland National 2 NL116AL11/1R		B52F	1981	Ex Edmunds, Rassau, 1986
M112	AAK112T	Leyland National 10351B/1R		B44F	1979	Ex Somerbus, Paulton, 1989
M143	CUL143V	Leyland Titan TNLXB2RR	Park Royal	H44/26F	1980	Ex Londonlinks, 1996
M152	CUL152V	Leyland Titan TNLXB2RR	Park Royal	H44/26F	1980	Ex Londonlinks, 1996
M154	LMS154W	Leyland Fleetline FE30AGR	Alexander AD	H44/31F	1980	Ex Western Scottish, 1991
M171	GGE171T	Leyland National 10351A/1R		B41F	1979	Ex Strathclyde's Transport, 1986
M199	WDS199V	Leyland National 2 NL116L11/1R		B49F	1980	Ex Midland Fox, 1994
M206	BHS206X	Leyland National 2 NL116AL11/1R		B52F	1981	
M207	BHS207X	Leyland National 2 NL116AL11/1R		B52F	1981	
M220	WDS220V	Leyland Fleetline FE30AGR	Alexander AD	H44/31F	1980	Ex Western Scottish, 1991
M263	C263FGG	Leyland National 2 NL116HLXCT/1R		B52F	1986	
M264	C264FGG	Leyland National 2 NL116HLXCT/1R		B52F	1986	
M388	UGE388W	Leyland National 2 NL116AL11/1R		B52F	1981	
M389	UGE389W	Leyland National 2 NL116AL11/1R		B52F	1981	
M408	KYV408X	Leyland Titan TNLXB2RR	Leyland	H44/26F	1982	Ex Londonlinks, 1996
M439	N439GHG	Dennis Dart 9SDL	Northern Counties Paladin	B39F	1995	
M440	N440GHG	Dennis Dart 9SDL	Northern Counties Paladin	B39F	1995	
M473	N473MUS	Dennis Dart 9SDL	Northern Counties Paladin	B39F	1995	
M474	N474MUS	Dennis Dart 9SDL	Northern Counties Paladin	B39F	1995	
M536	KRS536V	Leyland National 2 NL106L11/1R		B44F	1980	Ex Northern Scottish, 1991
M596	XYS596S	Leyland National 11351A/1R		B52F	1978	
M705	L705AGA	Mercedes-Benz 709D	WS Wessex II	B29F	1994	
M724	B724AGD	Leyland National 2 NL116TL11/1R		B52F	1984	
M725	B725AGD	Leyland National 2 NL116HLXCT/1R		B52F	1985	
M945	K945SGG	Mercedes-Benz 709D	Dormobile Routemaker	B29F	1993	
M946	K946SGG	Dennis Dart 9SDL3011	Plaxton Pointer	B35F	1993	
M947	K947SGG	Dennis Dart 9SDL3011	Plaxton Pointer	B35F	1993	

Ancilliary vehicles:

451	PUS226P	Leyland Leopard PSU3E/4R	Alexander AYS	B53F	1976	
452	WHN594M	Bristol LH6L	Eastern Coach Works	B43F	1974	Ex Northumbria, 1996
	MGR659P	Bristol LH6L	Eastern Coach Works	B43F	1975	Ex Northumbria, 1997
591	WDS199V	Leyland National 2 NL116L11/1R		B49F	1980	Ex Midland Fox, 1994
	D439NNA	Renault-Dodge S46	Northern Counties	B22F	1987	Ex North Western (Bee Line), 1997

Previous Registrations:

407CLT	A173UGB	PUS226	MHS27P
4225FM	A170UGB	WDS199V	BVP822V, VLT204
G58RGG	G673NUA	WDS212V	GTO46V
HSB874Y	GKE445Y, YSU867	WDS216V	GTO308V
HSB948Y	GKE443Y, YSU865	WDS220V	HSD83V
HSB949Y	GKE444Y, YSU866	WDS234V	GCS66V
KRS536V	GSO2V	WLT924	A176UGB
L588JSG	94D28205	WLT956	A177UGB
LAZ5847	D418NNA	WSU475	B446WKE
MIL9320	A383ROU, JEP417, KIB1767, A661AHB	WSU476	B447WKE

Named vehicles:
228 Coastline Cruiser; 229 Coastline Classic; 279 *Coastline Cutter*; 281 *Coastline Connect*; 283 *Coastline Coaster*

Allocations and liveries:

Livery : White, red and yellow; white, green and gold (GMS); lemon ♣ (F&L); white and red ♦(Clyde Coaster); red and grey (McGills).

Greenock (Pottery Street, Inchgreen) - GMS

Tiger	140	173						
Mercedes-Benz	228	229	230	232	234	235	236	237
	239	240	241	242	243	244	245	246
	249	266	267	268	269	270	271	272
	273	274	275	276	277	278	279	280
	281	282	283	284	285	286	287	288
	289	290	291	292	293	294	295	296
	297	298	299	300	301	302	303	304
	305	306	307	308	309			
Dart	804♦	805♦						

Inchinnan (Greenock Road) - Clydeside

MetroRider	201	202	203	204	205	206	207	208
	217	218	219	220	221	223	224	225
	226	227						
Mercedes-Benz	231	247	248	250	251	252	253	254
	255	256	257	258	259	260	261	262
	263	264	265					
Renault-Dodge	324	325	331	332	334	335	339	344
	353	354	355	359				
Volvo B6	446	447						
Scania	501	502	503	504	505	506	507	508
	509	510	512	513	514	515	516	517
	518	519	520	521	525			
Leopard	635	636	638	652	654	659	712	721
	722	723	766	767	769			
Dart	830	833	834	835	836	837	838	839
	840							
Olympian	900	901	902					

Johnstone (Cochranemill Road) - Clydeside - F&L

Tiger	170	172	175					
MetroRider	209	210	211	212	213	214	215	216
Renault-Dodge	1	11♣	12♣	13♣	14♣	15♣	16♣	18♣
	21♣	22♣	342	345	348	349	350	351
	361	362	363	364	366	367	369	
Volvo B6	441	442	443	444	445			
Leopard	647	691	699	702	716	725	756	759
	794							
Dart	401	402	801	802	803	806	807	808
	809	810	811	812	813	814	815	816
	817	818	819	820	821	822	823	824
	825	826	827	828	829	831	832	
Olympian	890	891	892	893	894	895	896	898
	899	903	905	906	907			

Paisley (Muriel Street, Barrhead) - McGills

Renault-Dodge	M58							
Mercedes-Benz	M91	M92	M705	M945	238			
National	M109	M112	M171	M199	M206	M207	M263	M264
	M388	M389	M536	M596	M724	M725	M733	
Dart	M439	M440	M473	M474	M946	M947		
Fleetline	M50	M154	M220					
Titan	M60	M88	M94	M143	M152	M408		

Routemaster enthusiasts will remember the large fleet of this type operated by Clydeside who transferred the familiar marks to their then large coach fleet. Recently the number of coaches has reduced leaving three former RM marks on rare Gardner-engined Leyland Tigers which were new to Western Scottish. Seen here is 172, WLT924.
Gerald Mead

COLCHESTER

Colchester Borough Transport Ltd, Magdalen Street
Colchester, Essex, CO1 2LD

9	BVP809V	Leyland National 2 NL116L11/1R		B49F	1980	Ex Southend, 1997
10	BVP810V	Leyland National 2 NL116L11/1R		B49F	1980	Ex Southend, 1996
19	EON829V	Leyland National 2 NL116L11/1R		B49F	1980	Ex Midland Fox, 1994
21	BVP821V	Leyland National 2 NL116L11/1R		B49F	1980	Ex Midland Fox, 1994
26	EON826V	Leyland National 2 NL116L11/1R		B49F	1980	Ex Southend, 1997
41	C41HHJ	Leyland Olympian ONLXCT/1RH	Eastern Coach Works	H47/31F	1985	
43	D43RWC	Leyland Olympian ONLXCT/1RH	Eastern Coach Works	H47/31F	1985	
45	F245MTW	Leyland Olympian ONCL10/1RZ	Leyland	DPH43/29F	1988	
46	F246MTW	Leyland Olympian ONCL10/1RZ	Leyland	DPH43/29F	1988	Ex Southend, 1996
47	H47MJN	Leyland Olympian ON2R50C13Z4	Leyland	DPH43/29F	1991	Ex Southend, 1996
48	H48MJN	Leyland Olympian ON2R50C13Z4	Leyland	H47/31F	1991	
49	H49MJN	Leyland Olympian ON2R50C13Z4	Leyland	H47/31F	1991	

55-61

Volvo B10M-61   East Lancashire(1992)   B49F   1984-85 Ex County, 1997

55	A855UYM	57	B857XYR	59	B859XYR	60	B860XYR	61	B861XYR
56	A856UYM	58	B858XRY						

67-90

Leyland Atlantean AN68A/1R   Eastern Coach Works   H43/31F   1977-80 69 Ex Midland, 1994

67	TPU67R	74	TPU74R	78	YNO78S	83	MEV83V	87	MEV87V
68	TPU68R	75	TPU75R	80	YNO80S	84	MEV84V	88	RVW88W
69	TPU69R	76	TPU86R	81	YNO81S	85	MEV85V	89	RVW89W
71	TPU71R	77	YNO77S	82	YNO82S	86	MEV86V	90	RVW90W

95	JHK495N	Leyland Atlantean AN68/1R	Eastern Coach Works	O43/31F	1975	
100	A250SVW	Leyland Tiger TRCTL11/3RP	Duple Caribbean	C57F	1984	Ex Southend, 1995
103	OHE274X	Leyland Tiger TRCTL11/3R	Duple Dominant IV	C53F	1982	Ex West Riding, 1987
104	OHE280X	Leyland Tiger TRCTL11/3R	Duple Dominant IV	C53F	1982	Ex West Riding, 1987
123	H123WFM	Mercedes-Benz 814D	North West Coach Sales	C24F	1991	Ex London & Country (GWS), 1996
M301	BYX301V	MCW Metrobus DR101/12	MCW	H43/28D	1980	Ex Leaside, 1997
M336	EYE336V	MCW Metrobus DR101/12	MCW	H43/28D	1980	Ex Leaside, 1997
347	NIW6507	Leyland 1151/1R/2402(6HLXB)	East Lancs Greenway(1993)	B49F	1974	Ex London & Country, 1996
348	NIW6508	Leyland 11351/1R(6HLXB)	East Lancs Greenway(1993)	B49F	1974	Ex London & Country, 1996
349	NIW6509	Leyland 11351A/1R(6HLXB)	East Lancs Greenway(1993)	B49F	1977	Ex London & Country, 1996
350	NIW6510	Leyland NL116AL11/2R(6HLXB)	East Lancs Greenway(1993)	B49F	1982	Ex London & Country, 1996
351	NIW6511	Leyland 11351/1R(6HLXB)	East Lancs Greenway(1993)	B49F	1978	Ex London & Country, 1996
352	NIW6512	Leyland NL116AL11/2R(6HLXB)	East Lancs Greenway(1993)	B49F	1982	Ex London & Country, 1996
354	JIL2194	Leyland 11351A/1R(6HLXB)	East Lancs Greenway(1994)	B49F	1977	Ex London & Country, 1996
355	JIL2195	Leyland 11351/1R(6HLXB)	East Lancs Greenway(1994)	B49F	1975	Ex London & Country, 1996

Previous Registrations:

JIL2194	CBV779S	NIW6508	GUA821N	NIW6511	LPR938P
JIL2195	JOX477P	NIW6509	TEL491R	NIW6512	FCA6X
NIW6507	NEL863M	NIW6510	FCA8X		

Allocation & liveries:-

Livery: Cream and crimson

Colchester (Magdalen Street)

Coach	100	103	104					
Mercedes-Benz	123			Metrobus		M301	M336	
National	9	10	19	21	26			
Greenway	347	348	349	350	351	352	354	355
Volvo	55	56	57	58	59	60	61	
Atlantean	67	68	69	71	74	75	76	
	77	78	80	81	82	83	84	85
	86	87	88	89	90	95		
Olympian	41	43	45	46	47	48	49	

Many formerly council-owned bus operations still contain elements of individuality even though now independent. Colchester's penchant for Eastern Coachworks-bodied Leyland Atlanteans is still evident as represented by their last example, 90, RVW90W. *Richard Godfrey*

Colchester had a fleet of modern Leyland Lynx at the time British Bus acquired the operation. These were replaced with Leyland National 2s and, latterly, National Greenways. Former London & Country 355 (JIL2195) is seen entering the bus station. *Colin Lloyd*

COUNTY

County Bus & Coach Co Ltd, 15th Floor, Terminus House, Terminus Street, Harlow, Essex, CM20 1YD

AN248	KPJ248W	Leyland Atlantean AN68B/1R	Roe	H43/30F	1980	Ex Luton & District, 1993
BOV594	HDZ8354	Bova FHD12.280	Bova Futura	C49FT	1986	Ex WMT (Central), 1995
BOV595	G545JOG	Bova FHD12.290	Bova Futura	C46FT	1990	Ex WMT (Smiths), 1995
BOV596	JIW3696	Bova FHD12.290	Bova Futura	C47FT	1988	Ex WMT (Smiths), 1995
DI4	P754RWU	DAF DE33WSSB3000	Ikarus Blue Danube	C53F	1997	Ex Cowie Leaside, 1997
DI56	J56GCX	DAF SB220LC550	Ikarus CitiBus	B48F	1992	Ex South London, 1997
DI124	K124TCP	DAF SB220LC550	Ikarus CitiBus	B48F	1992	Ex Cowie South London, 1997
DI926	J926CYL	DAF SB220LC550	Ikarus CitiBus	B48F	1992	Ex Grey Green, 1997
DI927	J927CYL	DAF SB220LC550	Ikarus CitiBus	B48F	1992	Ex Grey Green, 1997
DI928	J928CYL	DAF SB220LC550	Ikarus CitiBus	B48F	1992	Ex Grey Green, 1997
DP1	N551LUA	DAF DE33WSSB3000	Plaxton Première 350	C49FT	1996	Ex Leaside, 1997
DP2	N552LUA	DAF DE33WSSB3000	Plaxton Première 350	C49FT	1996	Ex Leaside, 1997
DP3	P753RWU	DAF DE33WSSB3000	Plaxton Première 350	C53F	1997	Ex Leaside, 1997

DP301-313

Dennis Dart 9SDL3002* — Plaxton Pointer — B35F — 1991 — 309 rebodied 1992
*302-7/13 are 9SDL3011

301	J301WHJ	**304**	J304WHJ	**307**	J307WHJ	**310**	J310WHJ	**312**	J312WHJ
302	J302WHJ	**305**	J305WHJ	**308**	J308WHJ	**311**	J311WHJ	**313**	J313WHJ
303	J303WHJ	**306**	J306WHJ	**309**	J309WHJ				

DP318-323

Dennis Dart 9SDL3011 — Plaxton Pointer — B35F — 1992

318	K318CVX	**320**	K320CVX	**321**	K321CVX	**322**	K322CVX	**323**	K323CVX
319	K319CVX							

DP324-334

Dennis Dart — Plaxton Pointer — B34F — 1996

324	P324HVX	**327**	P327HVX	**329**	P329HVX	**331**	P331HVX	**333**	P833HVX
325	P325HVX	**328**	P328HVX	**330**	P330HVX	**332**	P332HVX	**334**	P334HVX
326	P326HVX							

DP545	K545ORH	Dennis Dart 9SDL3016	Plaxton Pointer	B34F	1992	Ex Cowie Leaside, 1996
DP546	K546ORH	Dennis Dart 9SDL3016	Plaxton Pointer	B34F	1992	Ex Cowie Leaside, 1996
DP951	M951LYR	Dennis Dart 9.8SDL3040	Plaxton Pointer	B40F	1995	Ex Grey Green, 1996

Service revisions on routes between Hertford and Waltham Cross saw the introduction of co-ordinated services between MTL London and County. The latter's contribution is in the shape of some former Grey Green DAF Ikarus CitiBus single-deckers now repainted red and cream. DI 926, J926CYL, departs from Hertford bound for Enfield Town.
Tony Wilson

Four 9-metre Plaxton Pointer Dennis Darts were acquired from Cowie Leaside in 1996 of which two remain. DP545, K545ORH, in the green and cream County livery operates Harlow town services including route 811 as it travels one of the new town's concreted roads. *Colin Lloyd*

DPL405-414

Dennis Dart 9.8SDL3017 Plaxton Pointer B40F 1993

405	K405FHJ	**407**	K407FHJ	**409**	K409FHJ	**411**	K411FHJ	**413**	K413FHJ
406	K406FHJ	**408**	K408FHJ	**410**	K410FHJ	**412**	K412FHJ	**414**	K414FHJ

DW64	J64BJN	Dennis Dart 9SDL3012	Wright Handybus	DP40F	1992	Ex West's, Woodford Green, 1997
DW65	J65BJN	Dennis Dart 9SDL3011	Wright Handybus	B35F	1992	Ex West's, Woodford Green, 1997
DW314	J314XVX	Dennis Dart 9SDL3011	Wright Handybus	B35F	1992	
DW315	J315XVX	Dennis Dart 9SDL3011	Wright Handybus	B35F	1992	
DW316	J316XVX	Dennis Dart 9SDL3011	Wright Handybus	B35F	1992	
DW317	J317XVX	Dennis Dart 9SDL3011	Wright Handybus	B35F	1992	
DW761	K761JVX	Dennis Dart 9SDL3017	Wright Handybus	B40F	1992	Ex West's, Woodford Green, 1997
DW762	K762JVX	Dennis Dart 9SDL3017	Wright Handybus	B40F	1992	Ex West's, Woodford Green, 1997
DWL401	J401XVX	Dennis Dart 9.8SDL3012	Wright Handybus	B40F	1992	
DWL402	J402XVX	Dennis Dart 9.8SDL3012	Wright Handybus	B40F	1992	
DWL403	J403XVX	Dennis Dart 9.8SDL3012	Wright Handybus	B40F	1992	
DWL404	J404XVX	Dennis Dart 9.8SDL3012	Wright Handybus	B40F	1992	
DWL415	L415NHJ	Dennis Dart 9.8SDL3025	Wright Handybus	B40F	1994	
LP5 u	FYT335V	Leyland Leopard PSU3E/4R	Plaxton Supreme IV	C49F	1980	Ex Cowie Leaside, 1996
LP6 u	FYT336V	Leyland Leopard PSU3E/4R	Plaxton Supreme IV	C49F	1980	Ex Cowie Leaside, 1996

LR1-23

Leyland Olympian ONTL11/1R Roe H43/29F 1982

1	TPD101X	**4**	TPD104X	**9**	TPD109X	**11**u	TPD111X	**17**	TPD117X
2	TPD102X	**5**u	TPD105X	**10**	TPD110X	**15**	TPD115X	**23**	TPD123X
3u	TPD103X	**7**	TPD107X					

LX251-258

Leyland Lynx LX2R11C15Z4S Leyland Lynx B49F 1990

251	H251GEV	**253**	H253GEV	**255**	H255GEV	**257**	H257GEV	**258**	H258GEV
252	H252GEV	**254**	H254GEV	**256**	H256GEV				

LX888	E888KYW	Leyland Lynx LX1126LXCTZR1S	Leyland Lynx	B47F	1987	Ex Grey Green, 1996
LX889	E889KYW	Leyland Lynx LX1126LXCTZR1S	Leyland Lynx	B47F	1987	Ex Grey Green, 1996

M1-9

		MCW Metrobus DR101/6		MCW		H43/30F	1979	Ex Cowie Leaside, 1997	
1	GBU1V	4	GBU4V	5	GBU5V	8	GBU8V	9	GBU9V

M170	BYX170V	MCW Metrobus DR101/12	MCW	H43/28D	1979	Ex Leaside, 1997
M175	BYX175V	MCW Metrobus DR101/12	MCW	H43/28D	1979	Ex Leaside, 1997
M366	DTG366V	MCW Metrobus DR102/15	MCW	H46/31F	1980	Ex Grey Green, 1997
M367	DTG367V	MCW Metrobus DR102/15	MCW	H46/31F	1980	Ex Grey Green, 1997
M372	DTG372V	MCW Metrobus DR102/15	MCW	H46/31F	1980	Ex Grey Green, 1997
M537	GYE537W	MCW Metrobus DR101/14	MCW	H43/28D	1981	Ex Leaside, 1997
M573	GYE573W	MCW Metrobus DR101/14	MCW	H43/28D	1981	Ex Leaside, 1997
M625	KYO625X	MCW Metrobus DR101/14	MCW	H43/28D	1981	Ex Leaside, 1997
M649	KYV649X	MCW Metrobus DR101/14	MCW	H43/28D	1981	Ex Leaside, 1997
M782	KYV782X	MCW Metrobus DR101/14	MCW	H43/28D	1982	On extended loan from Leaside
M1248	B248WUL	MCW Metrobus DR101/14	MCW	H43/28D	1984	Ex Leaside, 1997
M1367	C367BUV	MCW Metrobus DR101/14	MCW	H43/28D	1985	Ex Leaside, 1997
M1379	VLT88	MCW Metrobus DR101/14	MCW	H43/28D	1985	Ex Leaside, 1997
M1398	C398BUV	MCW Metrobus DR101/14	MCW	H43/28D	1985	Ex Leaside, 1997
M1437	VLT12	MCW Metrobus DR101/14	MCW	DPH43/24F	1986	Ex Leaside, 1997
MB45	D45OKH	Iveco Daily 49.10	Robin Hood City Nippy	DP19F	1987	Ex East Yorkshire, 1989
MB52	E352NEG	Iveco Daily 49.10	Robin Hood City Nippy	DP19F	1988	Ex Premier Travel, 1989
MB53	E353NEG	Iveco Daily 49.10	Robin Hood City Nippy	DP19F	1988	Ex Premier Travel, 1989
MB54	E354NEG	Iveco Daily 49.10	Robin Hood City Nippy	DP19F	1988	Ex Premier Travel, 1989
MB115	F115JGS	Iveco Daily 49.10	Robin Hood City Nippy	B25F	1988	Ex Sampsons, Hoddesdon, 1988
MB154	F154DKV	Iveco Daily 49.10	Reeve Burgess Beaver	B25F	1988	Ex Iveco demonstrator, 1989
MB706	E296VOM	Iveco Daily 49.10	Carlyle Dailybus 2	B25F	1988	Ex Southend, 1992

MB707-712

		Iveco TurboDaily 59.12		Dormobile Routemaker		B25F	1993		
707	K707FNO	709	K709FNO	710	K710FNO	711	K711FNO	712	K712FNO
708	K708FNO								

MB717-729

		Iveco TurboDaily 59.12		Marshall C31		B25F	1994		
717	L717OVX	720	M720UTW	723	L723PHK	726	M726UTW	728	M728UTW
718	L718OVX	721	M721UTW	724	L724PHK	727	M727UTW	729	M729UTW
719	M719UTW	722	L722OVX	725	M725UTW				

MB730-744

		Iveco TurboDaily 59.12		Marshall C31		B25F	1995		
730	M730AOO	733	M733AOO	736	M736AOO	739	N739AVW	742	N742AVW
731	M731AOO	734	M734AOO	737	M737AOO	740	N740AVW	743	N743ANW
732	M732AOO	735	M735AOO	738	M738AOO	741	N741AVW	744	N744AVW

MB748	E448TYG	Iveco Daily 49.10	Robin Hood City Nippy	DP23F	1988	Ex Keighley & District, 1993
MB795	F795JKX	Iveco Daily 49.10	Reeve Burgess Beaver	B21F	1988	Ex Sovereign, 1992
MB796	F796JKX	Iveco Daily 49.10	Reeve Burgess Beaver	B21F	1988	Ex Sovereign, 1992

MB918-938

		Mercedes-Benz 709D		Reeve Burgess Beaver		B23F	1989-92		
918	G918UPP	926	G926WGS	930	G930WGS	933	J933WHJ	936	J936WHJ
919	G919UPP	927	G927WGS	931	G931WGS	934	J934WHJ	937	J937WHJ
924	G924WGS	928	G928WGS	932	G932WGS	935	J935WHJ	938	J938WHJ
925	G925WGS	929	G929WGS						

MB939	P939HVX	Mercedes-Benz 711D	Plaxton Beaver	DP25F	1997	
MBT713	L713OVX	Iveco TurboDaily 59.12	Marshall C31	B18FL	1994	
MBT714	L714OVX	Iveco TurboDaily 59.12	Marshall C31	B18FL	1994	
MBT715	L715OVX	Iveco TurboDaily 59.12	Marshall C31	B18FL	1994	
MBT716	L716OVX	Iveco TurboDaily 59.12	Marshall C31	B18FL	1994	
MBT801	L801KNO	Peugeot-Talbot Freeway	TBP	B18FL	1993	
MBT802	L802KNO	Peugeot-Talbot Freeway	TBP	B18FL	1993	
MBT803	L803KNO	Peugeot-Talbot Freeway	TBP	B18FL	1993	
MBT804	L804KNO	Peugeot-Talbot Freeway	TBP	B18FL	1993	
MBT805	L805OVX	Peugeot-Talbot Freeway	TBP	B18FL	1993	
MBT865	P865VTJ	LDV Convoy	Whitacre	M8L	1997	
MC540	D40MAG	Iveco Daily 49.10	Robin Hood City Nippy	DP16F	1987	Ex West Yorkshire, 1989
MCW75	JBO75W	MCW Metrobus DR102/20	MCW	H46/31F	1981	Ex Newport, 1994
MCW80	JBO80W	MCW Metrobus DR102/20	MCW	H46/31F	1981	Ex Newport, 1994

Wright Crusader bodywork was introduced to County Bus at the Lea Valley operated Ware depot, when three Dennis Dart SLFs were acquired during 1996. These 10.8metre 41-seaters operate local Hertford route 395 having replaced older Wright Handybus types. Seen here is SLF417, P417HVX.
Richard Godfrey

MD601-612

				Mercedes-Benz 811D		Reeve Burgess Beaver	B28F	1991		
601	J601WHJ	604	J604WHJ	607	J607WHJ	609	J609WHJ	611	J611WHJ
602	J602WHJ	605	J605WHJ	608	J608WHJ	610	J610WHJ	612	J612WHJ
603	J603WHJ	606	J606WHJ						

MD613	L613LVX	Mercedes-Benz 811D	Dormobile Routemaker	B31F	1993	
MD614	L614LVX	Mercedes-Benz 811D	Dormobile Routemaker	B31F	1993	
MR367	F367CHE	MCW MetroRider MF150/110	MCW	B33F	1988	Ex West's, Woodford Green, 1997
MR667	E667YDT	MCW MetroRider MF150/65	MCW	B33F	1988	Ex West's, Woodford Green, 1997
MR711w	F711CWJ	MCW MetroRider MF150/110	MCW	B33F	1988	Ex West's, Woodford Green, 1997
MR712w	F712CWJ	MCW MetroRider MF150/110	MCW	B33F	1988	Ex West's, Woodford Green, 1997
MR713	F713CWJ	MCW MetroRider MF150/110	MCW	B33F	1988	Ex West's, Woodford Green, 1997
MR714	F714CWJ	MCW MetroRider MF150/110	MCW	B33F	1988	Ex West's, Woodford Green, 1997
MR715	F715CWJ	MCW MetroRider MF150/110	MCW	B33F	1988	Ex West's, Woodford Green, 1997
MR718	F718CWJ	MCW MetroRider MF150/110	MCW	B33F	1988	Ex West's, Woodford Green, 1997
MR719	F719CWJ	MCW MetroRider MF150/110	MCW	B33F	1988	Ex West's, Woodford Green, 1997
OD621	G621YMG	DAF SB220LC550	Optare Delta	B47F	1989	Ex West's, Woodford Green, 1997
OD760	K760JVX	DAF SB220LC550	Optare Delta	B49F	1992	Ex West's, Woodford Green, 1997
RMC1464	464CLT	AEC Routemaster R2RH	Park Royal	O32/25RD	1962	Ex Leaside, 1997
RV1	GJG750D	AEC Regent V 2D3RA	Park Royal	H40/32F	1966	Ex Leaside, 1997
SLF165	R165GNW	Dennis Dart SLF	Wright Crusader	B36F	1997	
SLF169	R169GNW	Dennis Dart SLF	Wright Crusader	B36F	1997	
SLF170	R170GNW	Dennis Dart SLF	Wright Crusader	B36F	1997	
SLF266	M266VPU	Dennis Lance SLF	Wright Endeavour	B40F	1994	
SLF267	M267VPU	Dennis Lance SLF	Wright Endeavour	B40F	1994	
SLF268	M268VPU	Dennis Lance SLF	Wright Endeavour	B40F	1994	
SLF269	M269VPU	Dennis Lance SLF	Wright Endeavour	B40F	1994	
SLF416	P416HVX	Dennis Dart SLF	Wright Crusader	B37F	1996	
SLF417	P417HVX	Dennis Dart SLF	Wright Crusader	B37F	1996	
SLF418	P418HVX	Dennis Dart SLF	Wright Crusader	B37F	1996	

SLF419-431

		Dennis Dart SLF	Plaxton Pointer	B42F	1996				
419	P419HVX	422	P422HVX	425	P425HVX	428	P428HVX	430	P430HVX
420	P420HVX	423	P423HVX	426	P426HVX	429	P429HVX	431	P431HVX
421	P421HVX	424	P424HVX	427	P427HVX				

SLF-

	Dennis Dart SLF	Plaxton Pointer	B42F	1997	
R416COO	R420COO	R423COO	R426COO	R429COO
R417COO	R421COO	R424COO	R427COO	R430COO
R418COO	R422COO	R425COO	R428COO	R431COO
R419COO				

STL10	BAZ7384	Leyland Tiger TRCTL11/3RH	Plaxton Paramount 3500 II	C49FT	1985	Ex London & Country, 1992
T69	70CLT	Leyland Titan TNLXB2RRSp	Park Royal	O44/26D	1979	Ex Cowie Leaside, 1997
T83	CUL83V	Leyland Titan TNLXB2RRSp	Park Royal	O44/26D	1979	Ex Cowie Leaside, 1997
T100	CUL100V	Leyland Titan TNLXB2RRSp	Park Royal	O44/26D	1979	Ex Cowie Leaside, 1997
TDB61	F61SMC	Leyland Tiger TRBTL11/2RP	Duple 300	B55F	1988	Ex Sovereign, 1989
TDB62	F62SMC	Leyland Tiger TRBTL11/2RP	Duple 300	B55F	1988	Ex Sovereign, 1989
TDB63	F63SMC	Leyland Tiger TRBTL11/2RP	Duple 300	B55F	1988	Ex Sovereign, 1989
TDL53	C253SPC	Leyland Tiger TRCTL11/3RH	Duple 320	C53F	1986	Ex London & Country, 1993
TDL54	C254SPC	Leyland Tiger TRCTL11/3RH	Duple 320	C53F	1986	Ex London & Country, 1993
TDL55	C255SPC	Leyland Tiger TRCTL11/3RH	Duple 320	C49F	1986	Ex London & Country, 1993
TDL60	C260SPC	Leyland Tiger TRCTL11/3RH	Duple 320	C49F	1986	Ex London & Country, 1993
TDL63	C263SPC	Leyland Tiger TRCTL11/3RH	Duple 320	C49F	1986	Ex London & Country, 1993
TDL65	C265SPC	Leyland Tiger TRCTL11/3RH	Duple 320	C53F	1986	
TP61	B261KPF	Leyland Tiger TRCTL11/2R	Plaxton Paramount 3200 IIE	C49F	1985	Ex Sovereign, 1990
TP70	OIB3520	Leyland Tiger TRCTL11/2R	Plaxton Paramount 3200 IIE	C49F	1985	
TP71	OIB3521	Leyland Tiger TRCTL11/2R	Plaxton Paramount 3200 IIE	C49F	1985	
TP72	OIB3522	Leyland Tiger TRCTL11/2R	Plaxton Paramount 3200 IIE	C49F	1985	
TP75	OIB3523	Leyland Tiger TRCTL11/2R	Plaxton Paramount 3200 IIE	C49F	1985	
TPL1	124CLT	Leyland Tiger TRCTL11/3ARZM	Plaxton Paramount 3200 III	C53F	1989	Ex Cowie Leaside, 1997
TPL2	361CLT	Leyland Tiger TRCTL11/3ARZM	Plaxton Paramount 3200 III	C53F	1989	Ex Cowie Leaside, 1997
TPL8	H643GRO	Leyland Tiger TRCT10/3ARZA	Plaxton Paramount 3200 III	C53F	1991	Ex Cowie Leaside, 1997
TPL518	530MUY	Leyland Tiger TRCTL11/3ARZ(Vo)	Plaxton Paramount 3500 III	C51FT	1988	Ex Alan's Cs, Saffron Walden, 1993
VDL185	185CLT	Volvo B10M-61	Duple 320	C53F	1988	Ex Grey Green, 1997
VDL205	205CLT	Volvo B10M-61	Duple 340	C53F	1988	Ex Grey Green, 1997
VDL891	E891KYW	Volvo B10M-61	Duple 340	C53F	1988	Ex Grey Green, 1996
VP564	E564BNK	Volvo B10M-56	Plaxton Derwent II	B54F	1988	Ex Sampsons, Hoddesdon, 1989
VP565	E565BNK	Volvo B10M-56	Plaxton Derwent II	B54F	1988	Ex Sampsons, Hoddesdon, 1989
VPL1	C874CYX	Volvo B10M-61	Plaxton Paramount 3200 II	C53F	1986	Ex Cowie Leaside, 1997
VPL2	C876CYX	Volvo B10M-61	Plaxton Paramount 3200 II	C53F	1986	Ex Cowie Leaside, 1997
VPL501	L501MOO	Volvo B10M-60	Plaxton Première 350	C49FT	1993	
VPL503	H903AHS	Volvo B10M-60	Plaxton Paramount 3500 III	C53F	1991	Ex Park's, 1994
WS350	H350PNO	Leyland Swift LBM6T/2RS	Wadham Stringer Vanguard	B39F	1991	Ex West's, Woodford Green, 1997

Ancilliary:-

BD357t	OJN357P	Bedford YRQ	Duple Dominant	C32F	1976	Ex Welwyn & Hatfield, 1990
BP504t	DDX741T	Bedford YLQ	Plaxton Supreme III	C45F	1978	Ex Davian, Enfield, 1991
BP507t	SGS497W	Bedford YMT	Plaxton Supreme IV	C53F	1981	Ex Davian, Enfield, 1991
TL30 t	WPH130Y	Leyland Tiger TRCTL11/2R	Eastern Coach Works B51	C49F	1982	Ex Luton & District, 1991

On Order:
15 Mercedes-Benz Vario O814; 16 Dennis Dart SLF/Plaxton Pointer; 9 DAF DE02GGSB220/Plaxton Prestige

Previous Registrations:

70CLT	CUL69V	FYT335V	JVF815V, 185CLT	OIB3520	B270KPF
124CLT	G661WMD	FYT336V	JVF816V, 205CLT	OIB3521	B271KPF
185CLT	E892KYW	G621YMG	G259EHD, A10BUS	OIB3522	B272KPF
205CLT	E893KYW	H350PNO	H550AMT, A19BUS, H20BUS	OIB3523	B275KPF
361CLT	G662WMD	HDZ8354	C904JOF, 245DOC, C566LOG	UJN429Y	WPH120Y
453CLT	From new	J64BJN	J9BUS	UJN634Y	WPH115Y, OIB3510
454CLT	From new	J65BJN	J6BUS	VLT12	C437BUV
530MUY	E118KFV	JIW3696	E908UOH	VLT88	C379BUV
BAZ7384	C210PPE	K760JVX	K5BUS		
BAZ7385	B106KPF	K761JVX	K2BUS		
FBZ2514	WPH129Y	K762JVX	J12BUS		

Opposite:- **Marshall bodywork was supplied to County on the then new Iveco TurboDaily chassis in 1994 with a repeat delivery in 1995. Seating twenty-five MB729, M729UTW, is one of fifteen bus versions to be working on Lea Valley duties from Ware.** *Tony Wilson* **Previously with the Sovereign operation, F62SMC is now currently numbered TDB62 with County. This Duple-bodied Leyland Tiger carries the less-common Duple 300 style of body, the final design of bus built by Duple.** *M H A Flynn*

More new 9-metre Dennis Darts with Plaxton Pointer bodywork were acquired in 1996. Allocated to Grays depot, the vehicles such as DP330, P330HVX, are used on London Transport Buses contract routes, such as the 346, here on the Upminster Park Estate in East London. *Richard Godfrey*

Allocations & Liveries:

Livery: Cream and two-tone green; blue and cream ♣ (Sampsons); two-tone green and red ♠ (Green Line); red ♦ (LRT); maroon, white and blue ⚍ (Leaside Travel); red and cream ✣ (Leaside Travel).

Edmonton (Edmonton Wharf, Lea Valley Trading Estate) - Lea Valley - Leaside Travel

Bedford	BP504♣	BP507♣					
Iveco	MB722	MB723	MBT713♦	MBT714♦	MBT715♦	MBT716♦	
Mercedes-Benz	MB918	MB919	MB927	MB928	MB929	MB930	MB931	MD601
	MD602	MD603	MD604	MD605	MD606	MD607	MD608	MD609
	MD610	MD611	MD612					
Dart	DP301	DP302	DP303	DP304	DP305	DP306	DP307	DP308
	DP309	DP310	DP311	DP312	DP313	DW314	DW315	
Coaches	DI4♣	DP1♣	DP2♣	DP3♣	TPL1♣	TPL2♣	TPL8♣	VPL1
	VPL2							
Metrobus	M6t	M14t	M64	M74	M170 ♣	M175 ♣	M205t	M282t
	M382t	M422t	M426t	M445t	M450t	M469t	M478t	M485t
	M537♣	M573 ♣	M625 ♣	M649 ♣	M1248♣	M1367♣	M1379♣	M1398♣
	M1437♣							

Grays (Europa Park, London Road) - Thameside

Dart	DP323	DP324	DP325	DP326	DP327	DP328	DP329	DP330
	DP331	DP332	DP333	DP334	DW316	DW317	SLF419	SLF420
	SLF421	SLF422	SLF423	SLF424	SLF425	SLF426	SLF427	SLF428
	SLF429	SLF430	SLF431					
Metrobus	M80	M366	M367	M372	M782			
Iveco	MB725	MB726	MB727					
Mercedes-Benz	MB924	MB925	MB926					
(stored at Barking)	LP5	LP6	LR5	LR11				

Harlow (Fourth Avenue) - Townlink

Outstation - Langston Road, Debden.

Tiger	TBD61	TBD62	TBD63	TDL53♠	TDL60♠	TDL63♠	TDL65♠	TL30
Volvo	VP564	VP565						
Iveco	MB707	MB708	MB709	MB710	MB711	MB712	MB717	MB718
	MB719	MB720	MB721	MB730	MB731	MB732	MB733	MB734
	MB735	MB736	MB737	MB738	MB741	MB742	MB743	MB744
Mercedes-Benz	MB932	MB933	MB934	MB935	MB936	MB937	MB938	MD613
	MD614							
MetroRider	MR367	MR667	MR713	MR714	MR715	MR718	MR719	
Purgot-Talbot	MBT801	MBT802	MBT803	MBT804	MBT805			
LDV	MBT865							
Swift	WS350							
Dart	DP318	DP319	DP320	DP322	DP545	DP546		
	DPL406	DPL407	DPL408	DPL409	DPL410	DPL411	DPL412	DPL413
	DPL406	DPL414	DW64	DW65	DW761	DW762		
Lynx	LX251	LX252	LX253	LX254	LX255	LX256	LX257	LX258
	LX888	LX889						
DAF SB220	OD621	OD760						
Lance	SLF266	SLF267	SLF268	SLF269				
Atlantean	AN268							
Olympian	LR1	LR2	LR9	LR17				
(Stored)	MR711	MR712						

Ware (Marsh Lane) - Lea Valley

Outstation - Pindar Road, Hoddesdon

Bova	BOV594♣	BOV595♣	BOV596♣					
DAF SB220	DI56	DI124	DI926	DI927	DI928			
Dart	DP321	DP951	DPL405	DWL401	DWL402	DWL403	DWL404	DWL415
	SLF165	SLF169	SLF170	SLF416	SLF417	SLF418		
Olympian	LR3	LR4	LR7	LR10	LR15	LR23		
Iveco	MB45	MB52	MB53	MB54	MB115	MB154	MB706	MB724
	MB728	MB729	MB739	MB740	MB748	MB795	MB796	MC540
Mercedes-Benz	MB939							
Tiger	STL10 ♣	TP61♠	TP70♠	TP71♠	TP72♠	TP75♠	TDL54♠	TDL55♠
	TPL518♣							
Volvo B10M	VDL185	VDL205	VDL891	VPL501♣	VPL503♣			
Metrobus	M1	M4	M5	M8	M9			

The long route 724 between Stansted and Heathrow Airports winds inexorably through Hertfordshire and the former County of Middlesex. For some time the route has been operated by 1985 Leyland Tiger coaches with a mixture of Plaxton and Duple bodywork. TDL55, C255SPC wearing Green Line livery, will be replaced by new DAF types with Northern Counties bodies.
Philip Stephenson

CROSVILLE CYMRU

Crosville Wales Ltd, Imperial Buildings, Glan-y-Mor Road,
Llandudno Junction LL31 9RH

Single deck vehicles:

SDD24	N24FWU	DAF SB220LC550	Northern Counties Paladin	B49F	1995	Ex West Coast Motors, Campbeltown, 1996
SDD25	N25FWU	DAF SB220LC550	Northern Counties Paladin	B49F	1995	Ex West Coast Motors, Campbeltown, 1996
SLC27	K27EWC	Leyland Lynx LX2R11C15Z4R	Leyland Lynx 2	B49F	1992	Ex Colchester, 1994
SLG28	H28MJN	Leyland Lynx LX2R11G15Z4R	Leyland Lynx	B49F	1991	Ex Colchester, 1994
SLG29	H29MJN	Leyland Lynx LX2R11G15Z4R	Leyland Lynx	B49F	1991	Ex Colchester, 1994
SLC30	H130LPU	Leyland Lynx LX2R11C15Z4R	Leyland Lynx	B49F	1990	Ex Colchester, 1994
SLL31	D31RWC	Leyland Lynx LX112TL11FR1	Leyland Lynx	B49F	1986	Ex Colchester, 1994
SLL32	D32RWC	Leyland Lynx LX112TL11FR1	Leyland Lynx	B49F	1986	Ex Colchester, 1994

SLC33-37

	Leyland Lynx LX112L10ZR1	Leyland Lynx	B49F	1988-89	Ex Colchester, 1994

33	E33EVW	34	E34EVW	35	E35EVW	36	E36EVW	37	E37EVW

SLC38	G38YHJ	Leyland Lynx LX2R11C15Z4R	Leyland Lynx	B49F	1989	Ex Colchester, 1994
SLC39	G39YHJ	Leyland Lynx LX2R11C15Z4R	Leyland Lynx	B49F	1989	Ex Colchester, 1994
SLC40	G40YHJ	Leyland Lynx LX2R11C15Z4R	Leyland Lynx	B49F	1989	Ex Colchester, 1994
SDD47	M847RCP	DAF SB220LC550	Northern Counties Paladin	B49F	1995	Ex Citybus, Southampton, 1996
SDD49	M849RCP	DAF SB220LC550	Northern Counties Paladin	B49F	1995	Ex Citybus, Southampton, 1996
CTL63	C63JTU	Leyland Tiger TRCTL11/3RH	Duple 340	C49FT	1986	Ex Crosville 1986

SLC66-70

	Leyland Lynx LX112L10ZR1R	Leyland Lynx	B49F	1989	Ex Chesterfield, 1995

66	F66FKW	67	F67FKW	68	F68FKW	69	F69FKW	70	F70FKW

SNG76	XUA76X	Leyland National 2 NL116AL11/1R(6HLXB)		B49F	1982	Ex Yorkshire Bus (WR), 1997
CTL83	SIB8583	Leyland Tiger TRCTL11/3R	Plaxton Paramount 3200 E	C51F	1984	Ex Luton & District, 1994
SNG84	VBG84X	Leyland National 2 NL116L11/1R(6HLXB)		B49F	1980	Ex Yorkshire Bus (WR), 1997
SNG91	VBG91X	Leyland National 2 NL116L11/1R(6HLXB)		B49F	1980	Ex Yorkshire Bus (WR), 1996
CTL92	SIB9492	Leyland Tiger TRCTL11/3R	Plaxton Paramount 3200E	C51F	1984	Ex Luton & District, 1994
SNG92	VBG92X	Leyland National 2 NL116L11/1R(6HLXB)		B49F	1980	Ex Yorkshire Bus (YB), 1997
SNG94	VBG94X	Leyland National 2 NL116L11/1R(6HLXB)		B49F	1980	Ex Yorkshire Bus (WR), 1996
SNL206	LRB206W	Leyland National 2 NL116L11/1R		B52F	1980	Ex Yorkshire Bus (YB), 1996

SNG207-215

	Leyland National 2 NL116HLXB/1R		B49F	1982-83	Ex Yorkshire Bus (WR) 213-5(SY), 1996-97

207	EWT207Y	211	EWX211Y	213	EWX213Y	214	EWX214Y	215	EWX215Y
209	EWT209Y	212	EWX212Y						

One of the features of the early days of British Bus was the reallocation of moern vehicles away from their initial operator rather than the cascade principal employed elsewhere. Colchester was the loser when fourteen mixed Leyland Lynx migrated north to Crosville Cymru. Former Colchester Cummins-powered SLC27, K27EWC, arrives in Chester.
Philip Stephenson

Chester bus exchange accomodates Crosville Cymru's SMM503, M503AJC, as it awaits departure on the A1 service to Rhyl. This service, branded MA1NLINE, replaced the eastern section of the former Crosville Coastliner which was abandoned in 1995 just short of its thirtieth anniversary. *Tim Deakin*

The main contributor towards the reduction of series 1 Nationals in North Wales were the Yorkshire Bus Group who have supplied fifteen National 2s. Pictured in Colwyn Bay was SNG215, EWX215Y, which arrived in December 1996 from South Yorkshire Road Transport. *Ralph Stevens*

SLG299	E299OMG	Leyland Lynx LX112TL11ZR1S	Leyland Lynx	B49F	1988	Ex Atlas Bus, 1994
SLC328	E328OMG	Leyland Lynx LX112TL11ZR1S	Leyland Lynx	B49F	1988	Ex Atlas Bus, 1994
SNL443	YPL443T	Leyland National 10351B/1R		B41F	1978	Ex London & Country, 1994
SMM501	M501AJC	MAN 11.190	Optare Vecta	B43F	1995	
SMM502	M502AJC	MAN 11.190	Optare Vecta	B43F	1995	
SMM503	M503AJC	MAN 11.190	Optare Vecta	B43F	1995	
SMM504	M504AJC	MAN 11.190	Optare Vecta	B43F	1995	
LDC521	R521UCC	Dennis Dart SLF	Plaxton Pointer 2	B39F	1997	
LDC522	R522UCC	Dennis Dart SLF	Plaxton Pointer 2	B39F	1997	
SNL574	JTU574T	Leyland National 10351B/1R		B44F	1979	Ex Crosville, 1986
CVV592	HIL7592	Volvo B10M-61	Duple 340	C51FT	1988	Ex Moor-Dale, 1994
CVV593	HIL7593	Volvo B10M-61	Duple 340	C51FT	1988	Ex Moor-Dale, 1994
SNL648	GMA648T	Leyland National 10351B/1R		B44F	1978	Ex Crosville, 1986
SLC677	E677DCU	Leyland Lynx LX112L10ZR1R	Leyland	B51F	1987	Ex Northumbria, 1997
SLC678	E678DCU	Leyland Lynx LX112L10ZR1R	Leyland	B51F	1987	Ex Northumbria, 1997
SNL722	MHJ722V	Leyland National 2 NL116L11/1R		B49F	1980	Ex Midland (Stevensons), 1997
SNL727	MHJ727V	Leyland National 2 NL116L11/1R		B49F	1980	Ex Midland (Stevensons), 1997
SLC733	H733HWK	Leyland Lynx LX2R11C15Z4S	Leyland Lynx 2	B51F	1990	Ex Clydeside (McGills), 1997
SNL820	CCY820V	Leyland National 2 NL116L11/1R		DP48F	1980	Ex Yorkshire Bus (WR), 1997
SNL824	SNS824W	Leyland National 2 NL116L11/1R		B49F	1980	Ex Yorkshire Bus (SY), 1996
SLC967	E967PME	Leyland Lynx LX112TL11ZR1R(L10)	Leyland Lynx	B49F	1988	Ex Atlas Bus, 1994
SLC968	E968PME	Leyland Lynx LX112TL11ZR1R(L10)	Leyland Lynx	B49F	1988	Ex Atlas Bus, 1994
CTL994	JSK994	Leyland Tiger TRCTL11/3RH	Berkhof Everest 370	C53F	1986	Ex Kentish Bus, 1997

Minibuses:

MMM33-46

| | | Mercedes-Benz L608D | Alexander AM | B20F | 1986 | Ex Hastings & District, 1987 |

33	D433UHC	**36**	D436UHC	**39**	D439UHC	**42**	D442UHC	**45**	D445UHC
34	D434UHC	**37**	D437UHC	**40**	D440UHC	**43**	D443UHC	**46**	D446UHC
35	D435UHC	**38**	D438UHC	**41**	D441UHC	**44**	D444UHC		

MMM59-67

| | | Mercedes-Benz L608D | Reeve Burgess | B20F | 1986 | Ex Hastings & District, 1987 |

59	D959UDY	**63**	D963UDY	**65**	D965UDY	**66**	D966UDY	**67**	D967UDY
60	D960UDY								

MMM79-99

| | | Mercedes-Benz L608D | Reeve Burgess | B20F* | 1986-87 | *99 is DP19F |

79	D79VCC	**85**	D85VCC	**89**	D89VCC	**92**	D92VCC	**98**	D98VCC
80	D80VCC	**86**	D86VCC	**91**	D91VCC	**94**	D94VCC	**99**	D99VCC
82	D82VCC	**88**	D88VCC						

MMM117	M943UDT	Mercedes-Benz 709D	Plaxton Beaver	B25F	1995	Ex Mercedes-Benz demonstrator, 1996
MMM118	P688KCC	Mercedes-Benz 709D	Plaxton Beaver	B27F	1997	
MMM119	P658KEY	Mercedes-Benz 711D	Plaxton Beaver	B27F	1997	

MMM154-189

| | | Mercedes-Benz L608D | Alexander AM | B20F* | 1986 | Ex Milton Keynes Citybus, 1988 *173 is DP19F |

154	D154VRP	**170**	D170VRP	**172**	D172VRP	**174**	D174VRP	**189**	D189VRP
167	D167VRP	**171**	D171VRP	**173**	D173VRP	**188**	D188VRP		

MMM210-228

| | | Mercedes-Benz 709D | Robin Hood | DP25F* | 1988-89 | *212/5/7/9/21 are B25F |

210	F210DCC	**214**	F214DCC	**218**	F218DCC	**222**	F222DCC	**226**	F426EJC
211	F211DCC	**215**	F215DCC	**219**	F219DCC	**223**	F223DCC	**227**	F427EJC
212	F212DCC	**216**	F216DCC	**220**	F220DCC	**224**	F424EJC	**228**	F428EJC
213	F213DCC	**217**	F217DCC	**221**	F221DCC	**225**	F425EJC		

Opposite:- **The single-deck fleet of Crosville Cymru has changed considerably of late. There are now only three first series Leyland Nationals remaining and only eight out of 62 vehicles were new to Crosville or Crosvile Cymru. One of the latest types to join the fleet is the DAF single deck bus bodied by Northern Counties. The pair joined the fleet via Hughes-DAF also a Cowie Group member - now known as Arriva Bus and Coach - who will be the agents for all new vehicles delivered to the company. Pictured at Mold bus station is SDD47, M647RCP.** *John Jones*
Two former South Yorkshire vehicles to join the fleet are Northern Counties-bodied Leyland Olympians, DOL103 and DOL104. Seen in Shoreline livery, the scheme employed for vehicles in use on former Alpine services for Conwy CC is the former, A103OUG. *John Jones*

Following the initial expansion of minibuses between 1985 and 1989, Crosville Cymru like many other companies, commenced replacing smaller minibuses with larger units. Some have been acquired in connection with particular contracts and the quartet MMM335-8 arrived for the National Grid plc contract at Llanberis. The first of these has now received fleet livery though MMM338, L38OKV, is seen here in contract livery of pale green. *Philip Stephenson*

MMM229-240

Mercedes-Benz 709D   Robin Hood   DP25F*   1989   *232/7/8 are B25F

229	G229FJC	233	G233FJC	235	G235FJC	237	G237FJC	239	G239FJC
230	G230FJC	234	G234FJC	236	G236FJC	238	G238FJC	240	G240FJC
232	G232FJC								

MMM241	G241GCC	Mercedes-Benz 709D	Phoenix	DP25F	1989	
MMM242	G242GCC	Mercedes-Benz 709D	Phoenix	DP25F	1989	
MMM243	G243GCC	Mercedes-Benz 709D	Phoenix	DP25F	1989	
MMM260	G160YRE	Mercedes-Benz 709D	LHE Commuter	B29F	1989	Ex Stevensons, 1994
MMM261	G161YRE	Mercedes-Benz 709D	LHE Commuter	B29F	1989	Ex Stevensons, 1994
MMM262	G162YRE	Mercedes-Benz 709D	LHE Commuter	B29F	1989	Ex Stevensons, 1994
MMM263	G163YRE	Mercedes-Benz 709D	LHE Commuter	B29F	1989	Ex Stevensons, 1994
MIF290	M290AJC	Iveco TurboDaily 59-12	Marshall C31	B27F	1994	
MIF291	M291AJC	Iveco TurboDaily 59-12	Marshall C31	B27F	1994	
MMM335	L35OKV	Mercedes-Benz 811D	Wright NimBus	B33F	1993	
MMM336	L36OKV	Mercedes-Benz 811D	Wright NimBus	B33F	1993	
MMM337	L37OKV	Mercedes-Benz 811D	Wright NimBus	B33F	1993	
MMM338	L38OKV	Mercedes-Benz 811D	Wright NimBus	B33F	1993	

MMM351-377

Mercedes-Benz 709D   Reeve Burgess Beaver   DP25F   1989

351	G151FJC	370	G170FJC	372	G172FJC	374	G174FJC	376	G176FJC
352	G152FJC	371	G171FJC	373	G173FJC	375	G175FJC	377	G177FJC
369	G169FJC								

MMM385	M385KVR	Mercedes-Benz 709D	Alexander Sprint	B27F	1995	Ex North Western (Bee Line), 1996
MMM394	M394KVR	Mercedes-Benz 709D	Alexander Sprint	B27F	1995	Ex North Western (Bee Line), 1996
MMM411	M411BEY	Mercedes-Benz 811D	Alexander Sprint	B33F	1995	
MMM412	M412BEY	Mercedes-Benz 811D	Alexander Sprint	B33F	1995	
MMM413	M413BEY	Mercedes-Benz 811D	Alexander Sprint	B33F	1995	
MMM638	L638DNA	Mercedes-Benz 709D	Alexander Sprint	B27F	1994	Ex AA, Ayr, 1996

The bus station and rail station buildings at Rhyl have had a considerable facelift over the last two years relying on Victorian-style street furnitue. Recently acquired is almost new MMM996, N996KUS which started operations in Preston with Redline. *Philip Stephenson*

MMM641-660			Mercedes-Benz 609D		Reeve Burgess		B20F	1987	Ex Maidstone & District, 1997
641	D441RKE	**649**	E49UKL	**651**	E51UKL	**659**	E59UKL	**660**	E60UKL
648	E48UKL	**650**	E50UKL						

MMM680	E980NMK	Mercedes-Benz 709D	Reeve Burgess		B20F	1988	Ex Maidstone & District, 1997
MMM687	G87SKR	Mercedes-Benz 609D	Reeve Burgess		B20F	1990	Ex Maidstone & District, 1997
MMM701	F701KMA	Mercedes-Benz 709D	Reeve Burgess Beaver		B27F	1989	Ex Midland, 1995
MMM702	F702KMA	Mercedes-Benz 709D	Reeve Burgess Beaver		B27F	1989	Ex Midland, 1995
MMM704	F704KMA	Mercedes-Benz 709D	Reeve Burgess Beaver		B27F	1989	Ex Midland, 1995
MMM711	M711YJC	Mercedes-Benz 709D	Marshall C19		B25F	1994	
MMM712	M712YJC	Mercedes-Benz 709D	Marshall C19		B25F	1994	
MMM713	M713YJC	Mercedes-Benz 709D	Marshall C19		B25F	1994	
MMM714	M714YJC	Mercedes-Benz 709D	Marshall C19		B25F	1994	
MMM715	L715WCC	Mercedes-Benz 709D	Marshall C19		B27F	1993	
MMM716	L716WCC	Mercedes-Benz 709D	Marshall C19		B27F	1993	
MMM717	L717WCC	Mercedes-Benz 709D	Marshall C19		B27F	1993	
MMM718	N718DJC	Mercedes-Benz 811D	Alexander Sprint		B33F	1995	
MMM719	N719DJC	Mercedes-Benz 811D	Alexander Sprint		B33F	1995	

MMM793-797			Mercedes-Benz 709D		Alexander Sprint		B27F	1995	
793	N993CCC	**794**	N994CCC	**795**	N995CCC	**796**	N996CCC	**797**	N997CCC

MMM886	R486UCC	Mercedes-Benz Vario O814	Plaxton Beaver 2		B27F	1997	
MMM887	R487UCC	Mercedes-Benz Vario O814	Plaxton Beaver 2		B27F	1997	
MIF935	N935ETU	Iveco TurboDaily 59-12	Mellor		B25F	1995	Ex Clydeside (GMS), 1997
MIF936	N936ETU	Iveco TurboDaily 59-12	Mellor		B25F	1995	Ex Clydeside (GMS), 1997
MMM996	N996KUS	Mercedes-Benz 709D	UVG Citistar		B29F	1995	Ex Redline, Penwortham, 1996

Double Deck Vehicles:

EVG49	UVT49X	Bristol VRT/SL3/6LXB	Eastern Coach Works	DPH41/29F	1981	Ex Midland Fox, 1992
EVG50	PFA50W	Bristol VRT/SL3/6LXB	Eastern Coach Works	DPH41/29F	1980	Ex Midland Fox, 1992
DOL103	A103OUG	Leyland Olympian ONTL11/1R	Northern Counties	H43/28F	1984	Ex Yorkshire Bus (WR), 1997
DOL104	A104OUG	Leyland Olympian ONTL11/1R	Northern Counties	H43/28F	1984	Ex Yorkshire Bus (SY), 1997
DOL112	TPD112X	Leyland Olympian ONTL11/1R	Roe	H43/29F	1982	Ex Londonlinks, 1997
DOL119	TPD119X	Leyland Olympian ONTL11/1R	Roe	H43/29F	1982	Ex Londonlinks, 1997
DOL120	TPD120X	Leyland Olympian ONTL11/1R	Roe	H43/29F	1982	Ex Londonlinks, 1997
DOL122	TPD122X	Leyland Olympian ONTL11/1R	Roe	H43/29F	1982	Ex Londonlinks, 1997
DOL125	TPD125X	Leyland Olympian ONTL11/1R	Roe	H43/29F	1982	Ex Londonlinks, 1997
DOL126	TPD126X	Leyland Olympian ONTL11/1R	Roe	H43/29F	1982	Ex Londonlinks, 1997
ODL190	JTD390P	Daimler Fleetline CRL6-33	Northern Counties	O49/29F	1975	Ex Southend, 1993
DOG191	B191BLG	Leyland Olympian ONLXB/1R	Eastern Coach Works	H45/32F	1985	Ex Crosville, 1986
DOG192	B192BLG	Leyland Olympian ONLXB/1R	Eastern Coach Works	H45/32F	1985	Ex Crosville, 1986
DOG193	B193BLG	Leyland Olympian ONLXB/1R	Eastern Coach Works	H45/32F	1985	Ex Crosville, 1986
DOG194	B194BLG	Leyland Olympian ONLXB/1R	Eastern Coach Works	H45/32F	1985	Ex Crosville, 1986
ODL195	JTD395P	Daimler Fleetline CRL6-33	Northern Counties	O49/29F	1976	Ex Southend, 1993
DOG196	B196BLG	Leyland Olympian ONLXB/1R	Eastern Coach Works	H45/32F	1985	Ex Crosville, 1986
DOG208	B208GTU	Leyland Olympian ONLXB/1R	Eastern Coach Works	H45/32F	1985	Ex Crosville, 1986
EOG209	B209GTU	Leyland Olympian ONLXB/1R	Eastern Coach Works	DPH42/29F	1985	Ex Crosville, 1986
EOG210	B210GTU	Leyland Olympian ONLXB/1R	Eastern Coach Works	DPH42/29F	1985	Ex Crosville, 1986
EOG211	B211GTU	Leyland Olympian ONLXB/1R	Eastern Coach Works	DPH42/29F	1985	Ex Crosville, 1986
EOG212	B212GTU	Leyland Olympian ONLXB/1R	Eastern Coach Works	DPH42/29F	1985	Ex Crosville, 1986

DOG220-232 Leyland Olympian ONLXB/1R Eastern Coach Works H45/32F* 1983 Ex Kentish Bus, 1995
*220 is H44/32F

220	WDC220Y	**222**	AEF222Y	**229**	AEF229Y	**230**	CEF230Y	**232**	CEF232Y
221	AEF221Y	**224**	AEF224Y				

DOG258	C258UAJ	Leyland Olympian ONLXB/1R	Eastern Coach Works	H45/32F	1985	Ex Kentish Bus, 1995
DOL401	YWX401X	Leyland Olympian ONTL11/1R	Northern Counties	H43/28F	1982	Ex Yorkshire Bus (SY), 1996
DOL402	YWX402X	Leyland Olympian ONTL11/1R	Northern Counties	H43/28F	1982	Ex Yorkshire Bus (SY), 1996
OVL429	RLG429V	Bristol VRT/SL3/501	Eastern Coach Works	O43/27F	1980	Ex Crosville, 1991

DVG446-478 Bristol VRT/SL3/6LXB Eastern Coach Works H43/31F* 1980-81 Ex Crosville, 1986
*467/78 are O43/31F (prefix OVG) and ex Midland 1994

446	UDM446V	**459**	VCA459W	**467**	WTU467W	**475**	WTU475W	**477**	WTU477W
447	UDM447V	**462**	VCA462W	**468**	WTU468W	**476**	WTU476W	**478**	WTU478W
449	UDM449V							

DVG500-534 Bristol VRT/SL3/6LXB Eastern Coach Works H43/31F* 1981 Ex Crosville, 1986
*512/9/28 are O43/31F (prefix OVG); 519/20 are ex Midland, 1994

500	YMB500W	**510**	YMB510W	**517**	YMB517W	**522**	BMA522W	**529**	DCA529X
501	YMB501W	**512**	YMB512W	**518**	YMB518W	**524**	BMA524W	**530**	DCA530X
502	YMB502W	**513**	YMB513W	**519**	YMB519W	**525**	DCA525X	**532**	DCA532X
503	YMB503W	**514**	YMB514W	**520**	BMA520W	**527**	DCA527X	**533**	DCA533X
504	YMB504W	**516**	YMB516W	**521**	BMA521W	**528**	DCA528X	**534**	DCA534X

DOG506	CWR506Y	Leyland Olympian ONLXB/1R	Eastern Coach Works	H45/32F	1982	Ex Yorkshire Bus (SY), 1997
DOG507	CWR507Y	Leyland Olympian ONLXB/1R	Eastern Coach Works	H45/32F	1982	Ex Yorkshire Bus (WR), 1997
DOG509	CWR509Y	Leyland Olympian ONLXB/1R	Eastern Coach Works	H45/32F	1982	Ex Yorkshire Bus (SY), 1997
DOG513	CWR513Y	Leyland Olympian ONLXB/1R	Eastern Coach Works	H45/32F	1983	Ex Yorkshire Bus (WR), 1997
DOG522	CWR522Y	Leyland Olympian ONLXB/1R	Eastern Coach Works	H45/32F	1983	Ex Yorkshire Bus (WR), 1997
DOG523	CWR523Y	Leyland Olympian ONLXB/1R	Eastern Coach Works	H45/32F	1983	Ex Yorkshire Bus (WR), 1997
DOG527	CWR527Y	Leyland Olympian ONLXB/1R	Eastern Coach Works	H45/32F	1983	Ex Yorkshire Bus (YB), 1997
OVG961	YCU961T	Bristol VRT/SL3/6LXB	Eastern Coach Works	O43/31F	1979	Ex Northumbria, 1994

Crosville Cymru's open-top fleet was updated during 1995 when the Fleetlines formerly with Southdown were sold. At the same time, the fleet identification codes were altered, replacing H with O for the open-top vehicles. OVG467, WTU467W, then still with its roof affixed, passed with Oswestry depot and services to Midland Red North in 1992 and returned home for open-top conversion in December 1994. *Tom Johnson*

Ancilliary:

G581r	HFM581D	Bristol MW6G	Eastern Coach Works	B00F	1966	Ex Crosville, 1986
M64r	D964UDY	Mercedes-Benz L608D	Eastern Coach Works	B00F	1966	Ex Hastimgs & Dirstict, 1987
REC2r	KKE739N	Bristol VRT/SL2/6LX	Eastern Coach Works	H43/34F	1975	Ex Maidstone & District, 1997
REC3r	C221EKJ	Mercedes-Benz L608D	Rootes	B00F	1986	Ex Maidstone & District, 1997
REC4r	D28KKP	Mercedes-Benz L608D	Rootes	B00F	1986	Ex Maidstone & District, 1997
TB1t	JTL804V	Bedford YLQ	Plaxton Supreme IV Exp	C45F	1979	Ex Lewis, Llanrhystyd, 1995
TB2t	GLS289N	Leyland Leopard PSU3/3R	Alexander AYS	B53F	1974	
TB3t	REU323S	Bristol LH6L	Eastern Coach Works	B43F	1978	Ex NE Bus (Tees), 1997
TB4t	MUP713T	Bristol LH6L	Eastern Coach Works	B43F	1979	Ex NE Bus (Tees), 1997

Previous Registrations:

HIL7592	E179FFT	SIB9492	A149EPA
HIL7593	E180FFT	SIB8583	A142EPA
JSK944	C153SPB	YCU961T	OBR774T, WSV571

The first, new generation, Mercedes-Benz Varios are entering service in quantity throughout the country. Crosville Cymru operate two dedicated to Conwy County Council 'Conwy Clipa' tendered services for which they carry a yellow livery with purple lettering. Plaxton's Beaver 2 coachwork is the re-styled model to supercede the earlier Beaver model. *Tom Johnson*

Allocations and liveries:-

Livery: Green and white; yellow ♥ (Conwy Clipa); green ♣(National Grid); white, yellow and blue ♦ (Shoreline); blue and yellow ♠(Route 5A)

Aberystwyth (Park Avenue)

Outstations - Llanrhystyd, New Quay and Tregaron

VR	EVG50	DVG447	DVG449	DVG501	DVG503	DVG516	DVG518	DVG520
	DVG524	DVG532	DVG533					
Olympian	DOL119	DOL122	DOL126					
National	SNL574	SNL648	SNL727					
Coach	CTL63	CVV592						
Mercedes-Benz	MMM210	MMM211	MMM701	MMM796	MMM797			
Iveco	MIF290	MIF291	MIF583	MIF935	MIF936			

Bangor (Beach Road)

Outstations - Amlwch, Caernarfon and Holyhead

VR	DVG468	DVG476	DVG502	DVG504	DVG506	DVG507	DVG509	DVG529
	DVG530							
Olympian	DOL103♠	DOL104♠	DOL402♠	DOG513	DOG527			
National	SNL209♠							
Lynx	SLG28	SLG29	SLC37	SLC66	SLC68	SLC69	SLC70	
Coach	CTL92	CVV593						
Mercedes-Benz	MMM59	MMM65	MMM66	MMM85	MMM86	MMM212	MMM214	MMM215
	MMM217	MMM238	MMM241	MMM243	MMM260	MMM261	MMM262	MMM263
	MMM335♣	MMM336♣	MMM337	MMM338♣	MMM411	MMM412	MMM413	

Corwen (London Road)

VR	DVG525
Lynx	SLC30

Dolgellau (Arran Road)

Outstation - Machynlleth

VR	EVG49	DVG500	DVG513	DVG517	DVG534		
National	SNL206	SNL722					
Lynx	SLC38	SLC39	SLC677	SLC678			
Coach	CTL83	CTL994					
Mercedes-Benz	MMM89	MMM154	MMM174	MMM216	MMM715	MMM716	MMM717

Holywell (Greenfield)

VR	DVG522						
National	SNG211						
Mercedes-Benz	MMM60	MMM67	MMM351	MMM352	MMM370	MMM373	MMM374	MMM376
	MMM704						

Llandudno Junction (Glan-y-mor Road) - includes Shoreline(♦)

Outstation - Llanrwst

Mercedes-Benz	MMM33	MMM91	MMM92	MMM98	MMM99	MMM117	MMM118♥	MMM119♥
	MMM170	MMM171	MMM172	MMM173	MMM189	MMM385	MMM394	MMM638
	MMM641	MMM648♦	MMM649♦	MMM650♦	MMM651♦	MMM659♦	MMM660	MMM680
	MMM687♦	MMM714	MMM718	MMM719	MMM886♥	MMM887♥		
Lynx	SLC33♦	SLC34♦	SLC67♦	SLG299♦	SLG328♦			
National	SNG91	SNG94	SNG207	SNG212	SNG213	SNG214	SNG215	SNL824
VR	DVG459	OVG467	OVG478	DVG514	OVG519	OVG961		

Mold (Ponterwyl)

Olympian	DOG191	DOG192	DOG193	DOG194	DOG196	
Lynx	SLC35	SLC36				
DAF	SDD24	SDD25	SDD47	SDD49		
Mercedes-Benz	MMM34	MMM60	MMM233	MMM235	MMM236	MMM237
Fleetline	ODL190	ODL195				

Pwllheli (West End Garage)

VR	DVG475		
National	SNL443		
Dart	LDC521	LDC522	
Mercedes-Benz	MMM213	MMM239	MMM240

Rhyl (Ffynnongroew Road)

Outstation - Denbigh

VR	OVL429	DVG462	OVG467	DVG477	DVG510	OVG512	OVG519	DVG520
	DVG521	DVG527	OVG528	OVG961				
Olympian	EOG209	EOG210	EOG211	EOG212				
National	SNG76	SNG84	SNG92	SNL820				
Lynx	SLL31	SLL32	SLC967	SLC968				
Vecta	SMM501	SMM502	SMM503	SMM504				
Mercedes-Benz	MMM63	MMM79	MMM80	MMM82	MMM94	MMM167	MMM242	MMM369
	MMM371	MMM372	MMM377	MMM711	MMM712	MMM713	MMM793	MMM996

Wrexham (BRS Yard, Caego)

VR	DVG524							
Olympian	DOG208	DOG220	DOG221	DOG222	DOG224	DOG229	DOG230	DOG232
	DOG258	DOL401	DOG522	DOG523				
Lynx	SLC27	SLC40	SLC733					
Mercedes-Benz	MMM35	MMM36	MMM37	MMM38	MMM39	MMM40	MMM41	MMM42
	MMM43	MMM44	MMM45	MMM46	MMM188	MMM218	MMM219	MMM220
	MMM221	MMM222	MMM223	MMM224	MMM225	MMM226	MMM227	MMM228
	MMM229	MMM230	MMM232	MMM702	MMM794	MMM795		

GREY-GREEN

Cowie Group plc, 53-55 Stamford Hill, London, N16 5TD

104	E104JYV	Volvo Citybus B10M-50	Alexander RV	CH41/34F	1987
105	E105JYV	Volvo Citybus B10M-50	Alexander RV	CH41/34F	1987
107	E107JYV	Scania K92CRB	East Lancashire	H45/31F	1987

109-114

Scania N112DRB — East Lancashire — H46/29F — 1988

| 109 | E109JYV | 111 | E111KYN | 112 | E112KYN | 113 | E113KYN | 114 | E114KYN |
| 110 | E110JYV | | | | | | | | |

115-158

Volvo Citybus B10M-55 — Alexander RV — H46/29D* — 1988-90 *149-54 are H46/33F

115	F115PHM	124	F124PHM	133	F133PHM	142	F142PHM	151	G151TYT
116	F116PHM	125	F125PHM	134	F134PHM	143	F143PHM	152	G152TYT
117	F117PHM	126	F126PHM	135	F135PHM	144	F144PHM	153	G153TYT
118	F118PHM	127	F127PHM	136	F136PHM	145	G145TYT	154	G154TYT
119	F119PHM	128	F128PHM	137	F137PHM	146	G146TYT	155	H155XYU
120	F120PHM	129	F129PHM	138	F138PHM	147	G147TYT	156	H156XYU
121	F121PHM	130	F130PHM	139	F139PHM	148	G148TYT	157	H157XYU
122	F122PHM	131	F131PHM	140	F140PHM	149	G149TYT	158	H158XYU
123	F123PHM	132	F132PHM	141	F141PHM	150	G150TYT		

159	L159GYL	Scania N113DRB	Northern Counties Palatine	H42/25D	1994
160	L160GYL	Scania N113DRB	Northern Counties Palatine	H42/25D	1994
161	L161GYL	Scania N113DRB	Northern Counties Palatine	H42/25D	1994

163-172

Volvo B10M-61 — East Lancashire (1992) — H44/30D — 1985

| 163 | B863XYR | 165 | B865XYR | 167 | B867XYR | 170 | B870XYR | 172 | B872XYR |
| 164 | B864XYR | 166 | B866XYR | 168 | B868XYR | 171 | B871XYR | | |

178	M178LYP	Scania N113DRB	Northern Counties Palatine	H42/25D	1995
179	M179LYP	Scania N113DRB	Northern Counties Palatine	H42/25D	1995
180	M180LYP	Scania N113DRB	Northern Counties Palatine	H42/25D	1995
181	N181OYH	Scania N113DRB	Northern Counties Palatine	H42/25D	1996
182	N182OYH	Scania N113DRB	Northern Counties Palatine	H42/25D	1996
183	N183OYH	Scania N113DRB	Northern Counties Palatine	H42/25D	1996

Opposite: - Grey Green now operate LRT service 67 using a batch of Dennis Darts with attractive Alexander ALX200 bodywork. Photographed at Loughton station is 959, P959RUL. *Tony Wilson* Grey Green came to prominence following their gain of route 24 under LRT tendering while the former London Buses companies were still state controlled. Pictured in Trafalgar Square in the spring of 1997 is 181, N181OYH, one of the 1996 delivery of double-deck Scania N113 buses. *Richard Godfrey*

The Grey-Green bus fleet received thirteen Volvo B10M buses with East Lancashire EL2000 bodywork to inaugurate their operation on LRT tendered route 210. Still seen on this route, 923, H923XYT, cruises through Archway in this view.
Philip Stephenson

401-415

Leyland Olympian ON2R50C13Z4 Northern Counties — H47/30F — 1990 — Ex County, 1991

401	H101GEV	404	H104GEV	407	H107GEV	410	H110GEV	414	H114GEV
402	H102GEV	405	H105GEV	408	H108GEV	412	H112GEV	415	H115GEV
403	H103GEV	406	H106GEV	409	H109GEV	413	H113GEV		

895	E895KYW	Scania K92CRB	Van Hool Alizée	C53F	1988
896	E896KYW	Scania K92CRB	Van Hool Alizée	C53F	1988
897	E897KYW	Scania K92CRB	Van Hool Alizée	C53F	1988
898	E898KYW	Scania K92CRB	Van Hool Alizée	C53F	1988

905-910

DAF MB230LB615 — Van Hool Alizée — C49FT* — 1990 — *905-7 are C53F

905	G905TYR	907	G907TYR	908	G908TYR	909	G909TYR	910	G910TYR
906	G906TYR								

912-925

Volvo Citybus B10M-55 — East Lancashire EL2000 — B41F — 1990

912	H912XYT	915	H915XYT	918	H918XYT	921	H921XYT	923	H923XYT
913	H913XYT	916	H916XYT	919	H919XYT	922	H922XYT	925	H925XYT
914	H914XYT	917	H917XYT	920	H920XYT				

932	K932VCP	DAF MB230LT615	Van Hool Alizée	C49FT	1993
933	K933VCP	DAF MB230LT615	Van Hool Alizée	C49FT	1993

934-941

Dennis Dart 9SDL3024 — Plaxton Pointer — B31F — 1993

934	L934GYL	936	L936GYL	938	L938GYL	940	L940GYL	941	L941GYL
935	L935GYL	937	L937GYL	939	L939GYL				

942-949

DAF SB3000WS601 — Van Hool Alizée — C49FT* — 1994-95 — *948/9 are C53F

942	M942LYR	944	M944LYR	946	M946LYR	948	M948LYR	949	M949LYR
943	M943LYR	945	M945LYR	947	M947LYR				

950	M950LYR	Dennis Dart 9.8SDL3040	Plaxton Pointer	B40F	1995

952-968

Dennis Dart SLF — Alexander ALX200 — B36F — 1997

952	P952RUL	956	P956RUL	960	P960RUL	963	P963RUL	966	P966RUL
953	P953RUL	957	P957RUL	961	P961RUL	964	P964RUL	967	P967RUL
954	P954RUL	958	P958RUL	962	P962RUL	965	P965RUL	968	P968RUL
955	P955RUL	959	P959RUL						

Grey Green 104 to 107 were four double-deck buses delivered during 1987-88 to provide higher capacity on London's commuter routes from Kent. They were initially fitted with high-back seating with the intention of down-grading them after a period in time. Seen working service 179 is Scania 107, E107JYV unusual in being based on the K92 coach chassis.
Malc McDonald

One of the main customers for the Volvo Citybus double-deck version of the B10M, Grey Green took some forty-six into stock up to 1990, including two finished with high-back seating. Number 143, F143PHM, is one of the large batch of thirty purchased for LRT route 24, although they now appear elsewhere as well. *Richard Godfrey*

Allocations and livery:

Livery: Green, grey and orange (buses); white, orange and green (coaches); red ✪ (LRT); white ✳ (Eurolines)

Barking (Ripple Road)

DAF Coach	905	906	907	910	932✳	933✳		
	942✳	943✳	944✳	945✳	946✳	947✳	948	949
Dart	934	935	936	937	938	939	940	941
	950	952	953	954	955	956	957	
	958	959	960	961	962	963	964	965
	966	967	968					
Volvo Citybus	104	105	149	150	151	152	153	154
Olympian	401	402	403	404	405	406	407	408
	409	410	411	412	413	414	415	
Scania DD	107	109	110	111	112	113	114	

Stamford Hill

Volvo B10M SD	**912**	**913**	**914**	**915**	**916**	**917**	**918**	**919**
	920	921	922	923	925			
Volvo Citybus	115✪	116✪	117✪	118✪	119✪	120	121	122
	123✪	124	125✪	126	127	128	129	130
	131	132	133	134	135	136	137	138
	139	140	141	142	143	144	145	146
	147	148	155	156	157	158	163	164
	165	166	167	168	170	171	172	
Scania DD	159	160	161	178	179	180	181	182
	183							

Outstationed for Essex Commuter Services:-

DAF Coach	908	909		
Scania Coach	895	896	897	898

KENTISH BUS

Kentish Bus & Coach Co Ltd, Invicta House, Armstrong Road, Maidstone, Kent, ME15 6TY

9	TIB5905	Leyland Tiger TRCTL11/3RH	Duple 320	C53F	1986	
30	TIB5903	Volvo B10M-61	Van Hool Alizée	C53F	1988	Ex Jason, St Mary Cray, 1996
31	TIB5904	Volvo B10M-61	Van Hool Alizée	C53F	1988	Ex Jason, St Mary Cray, 1996

87-98

Dennis Dart 9SDL3002 — Carlyle Dartline — B36F — 1990 — Ex R&I Buses, Harlesden, 1995

87	G217LGK	95	G125RGT	96	G126RGT	97	G127RGT	98	G128RGT
93	G123RGT								

112-159

Dennis Dart 9SDL3034 — Northern Counties Paladin 2 B35F — 1994

112	L112YVK	131	L131YVK	138	L138YVK	145	L145YVK	153	L153YVK
113	L113YVK	132	L132YVK	139	L139YVK	146	L146YVK	154	L154YVK
114	L114YVK	133	L133YVK	140	L140YVK	148	L148YVK	155	L155YVK
127	L127YVK	134	L134YVK	141	L141YVK	149	L149YVK	157	L157YVK
128	L128YVK	135	L135YVK	142	L142YVK	150	L150YVK	158	L158BFT
129	L129YVK	136	L136YVK	143	L143YVK	152	L152YVK	159	L159BFT
130	L130YVK	137	L137YVK	144	L144YVK				

184	P184LKL	Dennis Dart SLF	Plaxton Pointer 2	B37F	1997
185	P185LKL	Dennis Dart SLF	Plaxton Pointer 2	B37F	1997

Kent County Council subsidised the the purchase of ten low-floor Scania L113s which are fitted with Wright Pathfinder bodywork. These were delivered in 1995 are are normally used on service 480 for which they carry vinyl lettering as illustrated by 253, N253BKK, seen in Mackenzie Way, Gravesend.
Richard Godfrey

186-191

						Dennis Dart SLF		Plaxton Pointer 2		B40F	1997

186	P186LKJ	188	P188LKJ	189	P189LKJ	190	P190LKJ	191	P191LKJ
187	P187LKJ								

250-259

Scania L113CRL · Wright Axcess-ultralow · B43F · 1995

250	N250BKK	252	N252BKK	254	N254BKK	256	N256BKK	258	N258BKK
251	N251BKK	253	N253BKK	255	N255BKK	257	N257BKK	259	N259BKK

335	SIB6705	Leyland 10351A/1R	East Lancs Greenway(1992) B41F	1978	Ex Londonlinks, 1995
336	SIB6706	Leyland NL106AL11/1R	East Lancs Greenway(1992) B41F	1981	Ex Londonlinks, 1995
337	SIB6707	Leyland NL106AL11/1R	East Lancs Greenway(1992) B41F	1981	Ex Londonlinks, 1995
338	SIB6708	Leyland NL106AL11/1R	East Lancs Greenway(1992) B41F	1982	Ex Londonlinks, 1995
345	SIB6715	Leyland 1051/1R/0402	East Lancs Greenway(1993) B41F	1973	Ex Londonlinks, 1995
346	SIB6716	Leyland 1051/1R/0402	East Lancs Greenway(1993) B41F	1974	Ex Londonlinks, 1995
348w	SIB1279	Leyland 10351B/1R	East Lancs Greenway(1992) B41F	1979	
349w	SIB1280	Leyland 10351B/1R	East Lancs Greenway(1992) B41F	1979	
350w	SIB1281	Leyland 10351B/1R	East Lancs Greenway(1992) B41F	1979	
351w	SIB1282	Leyland 10351B/1R	East Lancs Greenway(1992) B41F	1978	
352w	SIB1283	Leyland 10351B/1R	East Lancs Greenway(1992) B41F	1979	
353w	SIB1284	Leyland 10351B/1R	East Lancs Greenway(1992) B41F	1978	
354w	SIB1285	Leyland 10351B/1R	East Lancs Greenway(1992) B41F	1979	
355w	SIB1286	Leyland 10351B/1R	East Lancs Greenway(1992) B41F	1979	
356w	SIB1287	Leyland 10351B/1R	East Lancs Greenway(1992) B41F	1979	
357w	SIB1288	Leyland 10351B/1R	East Lancs Greenway(1992) B41F	1979	
361	PDZ6261	Leyland 10351/1R	East Lancs Greenway(1994) B41F	1977	Ex Londonlinks, 1996
362	PDZ6262	Leyland 10351/1R	East Lancs Greenway(1994) B41F	1977	Ex Londonlinks, 1996

403-415

Leyland Lynx LX2R11C15Z4S · Leyland Lynx · B49F · 1989/91 Ex Boro'line, Maidstone, 1992

403	G36VME	406	G39VME	409	G42VME	411	G44VME	413	H813EKJ
404	G37VME	407	G40VME	410	G43VME	412	G45VME	415	H815EKJ
405	G38VME	408	G41VME						

444-453

Optare MetroRider MR17 · Optare · B29F · 1994 · 444/7-53 ex Londonlinks, 1997

444	M444HPF	446	M446HPF	448	M448HPF	450	M450HPF	452	M452HPG
445	M445HPF	447	M447HPF	449	M449HPF	451	M451HPF	453	M453HPG

492	RUF42R	Leyland National 11351/2R		B25DL	1977	Ex London Buses, 1993
493	THX202S	Leyland National 10351A/2R		B21DL	1978	Ex London Buses, 1993
494	YYE290T	Leyland National 10351A/2R		B21DL	1979	Ex London Buses, 1994

The original deliveries of the Dennis Dart were confined to Duple Dartline bodywork, with around forty examples being built before the Duple factory sold the design and components to the Birmingham-based firm Carlyle. Of these, fourteen were supplied to R&I buses for LRT tendered services. Six are now with Kentish Bus, including 96, G126RGT, caught in the green and cream livery at Sevenoaks.
Richard Godfrey

557-565 · Volvo Olympian YN2RC16Z4 · Northern Counties Palatine II H47/30F · 1994

557	L557YCU	559	L559YCU	562	L562YCU	564	L564YCU	565	L565YCU
558	L558YCU	561	L561YCU	563	L563YCU				

601-620 · Leyland Olympian ONLXB/1R · Eastern Coach Works · H45/32F* · 1983-85 Ex Londonlinks, 1997 · *601 is H44/32F

601	WDC219Y	611w	A241GHN	614w	A244GHN	617w	B247NVN	619w	B256RAJ
608	CEF231Y	612	A242GHN	615	B245NVN	618w	B248NVN	620	C257UAJ
610	A240GHN	613w	A243GHN	616w	B246NVN				

631-643 · Volvo Citybus B10M-50 · Northern Counties · H45/31F · 1989 · 639-43 ex Londonlinks, 1997

631	G631BPH	634	G634BPH	637	G637BPH	640	G640BPH	642	G642BPH
632	G632BPH	635	G635BPH	638	G638BPH	641	G641BPH	643	G643BPH
633	G633BPH	636	G636BPH	639	G639BPH				

702-709 · Volvo Citybus B10M-50 · East Lancashire · H49/39F · 1989-90 Ex North Western, 1996

702	G641CHF	706	G648EKA	707	G649EKA	708	G659DTJ	709	G660DTJ
703	G642CHF								

722	F102TML	Volvo Citybus B10M-50	Alexander RV	H47/29D	1989 Ex Londonlinks, 1997
731	F111TML	Volvo Citybus B10M-50	Alexander RV	H47/29D	1989 Ex Londonlinks, 1997
734	F114TML	Volvo Citybus B10M-50	Alexander RV	H47/29D	1989 Ex Londonlinks, 1997

751-762 · Leyland Olympian ONLXB/1RH · Optare · H47/29F · 1888/89 Ex Boro'line, Maidstone, 1992

751	E151OMD	754	E154OMD	757	E157OMD	759	E159OMD	761	E161OMD
752	E152OMD	755	E155OMD	758	E158OMD	760	E160OMD	762	F991UME
753	E153OMD	756	E156OMD						

764	E164OMD	Volvo Citybus B10M-50	Alexander RV	H47/37F	1988 Ex Boro'line, Maidstone, 1992

765-770 · Leyland Olympian ON2R50C13Z4 Northern Counties · H47/30F · 1991 Ex Boro'line, Maidstone, 1992

765	H765EKJ	767	H767EKJ	768	H768EKJ	769	H769EKJ	770	H770EKJ
766	H766EKJ								

801-808 · Optare MetroRider MR15 · Optare · B29F · 1996

801	N801BKN	803	N803BKN	805	N805BKN	807	N807BKN	808	N808BKN
802	N802BKN	804	N804BKN	806	N806BKN				

844	E34NEF	MCW MetroRider MF154/9	MCW	DP31F	1988	Ex Londonlinks, 1995
852	N852YKE	Optare MetroRider MR13	Optare	B25F	1995	Ex Londonlinks, 1995
862	F862LCU	MCW MetroRider MF158/15	MCW	B31F	1988	Ex Londonlinks, 1997
863	F863LCU	MCW MetroRider MF158/15	MCW	B31F	1988	Ex Londonlinks, 1997
864	F864LCU	MCW MetroRider MF158/15	MCW	B31F	1988	Ex Londonlinks, 1995
866	G866TCU	Optare MetroRider MR01	Optare	B31F	1989	Ex Londonlinks, 1995
869	F932LKE	MCW MetroRider MF154/13	MCW	B33F	1988	Ex Boro'line, Maidstone, 1992
886	H886CCU	Optare MetroRider MR03	Optare	B25F	1991	
887	H887CCU	Optare MetroRider MR03	Optare	B25F	1991	
889	H889CCU	Optare MetroRider MR03	Optare	B25F	1991	
890	H890CCU	Optare MetroRider MR03	Optare	B25F	1991	
891w	K981KGY	Mercedes-Benz 709D	Dormobile Routemaker	B29F	1993	Ex Transcity, Sidcup, 1993
892w	K982KGY	Mercedes-Benz 709D	Dormobile Routemaker	B29F	1993	Ex Transcity, Sidcup, 1993
893w	K983KGY	Mercedes-Benz 709D	Dormobile Routemaker	B29F	1993	Ex Transcity, Sidcup, 1993
894w	H149NOJ	Mercedes-Benz 709D	Carlyle	B29F	1991	Ex Transcity, Sidcup, 1993
895	J154NKN	Mercedes-Benz 814D	Dormobile Routemaker	B33F	1992	Ex Crossways Management, Swanley, 1996

Opposite, top:- **Kentish Bus caused comment by winning the LRT tender for route 19 as this included the loan of AEC Routemasters from London Buses. Recently, these moved with the route to South London following the change in operator as part of the Cowie/Arriva re-organisation, and are now listed in this book under that operator. Seen in the original cream and burgundy is RML2382, JJD382D.** *Gerald Mead*

Opposite, bottom:- **Kentish Bus 708 is one of six Dennis Dominator in the fleet that migrated south from sister company North Western. Carrying East Lancashire bodywork the vehicle is seen at Eltham rail station while operating service 132 to Beckenham.** *Gerald Mead*

961-975

		Optare MetroRider		Optare	B25F	1991				
961	J961JNL	**970**	J970JNL	**973**	J973JNL	**974**	J974JNL	**975**	J975JNL
962	J962JNL								

977	L837MWT	Optare MetroRider MR01	Optare	B31F	1993	Ex Darlington, 1995
978	L838MWT	Optare MetroRider MR01	Optare	B31F	1993	Ex Londonlinks, 1995

AN172	XPG172T	Leyland Atlantean AN68A/1R	Park Royal	H43/30F	1978	Ex Londonlinks, 1997

AN186-232

		Leyland Atlantean AN68A/1R		Roe		H43/30F	1979-80		
186	XPG186T	**210w**	EPH210V	**220**	EPH220V	**221w**	EPH221V	**232**	EPH232V

AN270-282

		Leyland Atlantean AN68B/1R		Roe		H43/30F	1981		
270	KPJ270W	**274**	KPJ274W	**276w**	KPJ276W	**277**	KPJ277W	**282**	KPJ282W
271	KPJ271W								

Named vehicles: 30 *Silver Fox*; 31 *Silver Link*

Previous Registrations:

PDZ6261	UPB310S		SIB1281	BPL489T
PDZ6262	UPB313S		SIB1282	YPL439T
SIB6705	YPF762T		SIB1283	BPL479T
SIB6706	LFR855X		SIB1284	YPL445T
SIB6707	JCK850W		SIB1285	BPL480T
SIB6708	LFR848X		SIB1286	BPL482T
SIB6715	TPD176M		SIB1287	BPL483T
SIB6716	UPE196M		SIB1288	EPD522V
SIB1279	BPL484T		TIB5903	E316OPR
SIB1280	EPD541V		TIB5904	E319OPR

Allocations and liveries

Livery: Yellow and green; red ♣ (LRT)

Dunton Green (London Road)

Atlantean	186							
Dart	159	184	185					
Lynx	404	405	407					
MetroRider	445	446	451	452	453	852	866	962
	974	978						

Dartford (Central Road)

Dart	112	114	127	128	129	130	131	132
	141	142	143	144	145	146	148	149
	150	152	153					
Greenway	335	336	337	338	345	346	361	362
Lynx	403	406	408	409	410	411	412	413
	415							
MetroRider	449	450	801	802	803	804	805	806
	807	808	844	869				
Olympian	612	615	751	752	753	754	755	756
	757	758	759	760	761	762	769	770
Mercedes	895							
Citybus	631	632	633	634	635	636	637	638
	639	640	641	642	643	702	703	706
	707	708	709	722	731	734	764	

Kentish Bus have several batches of MetroRiders, both original MCW and the later Optare examples. The newest are eight delivered in April 1996 and all of these, including 805, N805BNK, are based at Dartford. Kentish Bus are now administered by Invictaway, the parent company of Maidstone & District. Its days as a separate operator are limited
Richard Godfrey

Eight low-floor Dennis Darts were delivered to Kentish Bus during the 1996-97 winter and currently form the latest deliveries to the fleet. Number 184, P184LKL, illustrates the wider/lower version of the Plaxton Pointer bodywork as the bus leaves Sevenoaks bus station.
Richard Godfrey

Northfleet (London Road)

Atlantean	172	220	232	270	271	274	277	282
Coach	9	30	31					
Dart	87	93	95	96	97	98	113	133
	134	135	136	154	155	157	158	186
	187	188	189	190	191			
Scania	250	251	252	253	254	255	256	257
	258	259						
MetroRider	444	447	448	862	863	864	886	887
	889	890	961	970	973	975	977	
Greenway	492♣	493♣	494♣					
Olympian	557	558	559	561	562	563	564	565
	601	608	620	765	766	767	768	

Withdrawn and unallocated

Mercedes	891	892	893	894				
Greenway	348	349	350	351	352	353	354	355
	356	357						
Olympian	610*	611	613	614	616	617	618	619
Atlantean	210	221	276					
MetroRider	861							
Dart	137*	138*	139*	140*	*On loan to M&D			

LEASIDE

Leaside Bus Co Ltd, 16 Watsons Road, Wood Green, London N22 4TZ

DBS1-13

DAF DB250RS505* Northern Counties Palatine IIH47/30F 1995 11-13 are DE02RSSB250

1	N601DWY	4	N604DWY	7	N607DWY	10	N610DWY	12	N612DWY
2	N602DWY	5	N605DWY	8	N608DWY	11	N611DWY	13	N613DWY
3	N603DWY	6	N606DWY	9	N609DWY				

DN115-119

Dennis Dart 9SDL3034 Northern Counties Paladin B35F 1994 Ex Kentish Bus, 1998

115	L115YVK	116	L116YVK	117	L117YVK	118	L118YVK	119	L119YVK

DRL49	K549ORH	Dennis Dart 9SDL9016	Plaxton Pointer	B34F	1992	Ex London Buses, 1994
DRL50	K550ORH	Dennis Dart 9SDL9016	Plaxton Pointer	B34F	1992	Ex London Buses, 1994
DRL51	K551ORH	Dennis Dart 9SDL9016	Plaxton Pointer	B34F	1992	Ex London Buses, 1994
DRL52	K552ORH	Dennis Dart 9SDL9016	Plaxton Pointer	B34F	1992	Ex London Buses, 1994

DT58-64

Dennis Dart 8.5SDL3003 Carlyle Dartline B28F 1990 Ex South London, 1996

58	H458UGO	60	H460UGO	62	H462UGO	63	H463UGO	64	H464UGO
59	H459UGO	61	H461UGO						

L315-354

Leyland Olympian ON2R50C13Z4 Alexander RH H43/25D 1992 Ex London Buses, 1994

315	J315BSH	323	J323BSH	331	J331BSH	339	J339BSH	347	J347BSH
316	J316BSH	324	J324BSH	332	J332BSH	340	J340BSH	348	J348BSH
317	J317BSH	325	J325BSH	333	J433BSH	341	J341BSH	349	J349BSH
318	J318BSH	326	J326BSH	334	J334BSH	342	J342BSH	350	J350BSH
319	J319BSH	327	J327BSH	335	J335BSH	343	J343BSH	351	J351BSH
320	J320BSH	328	J328BSH	336	J336BSH	344	J344BSH	352	J352BSH
321	J321BSH	329	J329BSH	337	J337BSH	345	J345BSH	353	J353BSH
322	J322BSH	330	J330BSH	338	J338BSH	346	J346BSH	354	VLT32

L514-L556

Leyland Olympian ON2R50C13Z4* Northern Counties H47/27D 1990 Ex Kentish Bus, 1998
*514/41/3/4/6-54 are type ONCL10/1RZA

514	G514VBB	523	G523VBB	532	G532VBB	541	G541VBB	549	G549VBB
515	G515VBB	524	G524VBB	533	G533VBB	542	G542VBB	550	G550VBB
516	G516VBB	525	G525VBB	534	G534VBB	543	G543VBB	551	G551VBB
517	G517VBB	526	G526VBB	535	G535VBB	544	G544VBB	552	G552VBB
518	G518VBB	527	G527VBB	536	G536VBB	545	G545VBB	553	G553VBB
519	G519VBB	528	G528VBB	537	G537VBB	546	G546VBB	554	G554VBB
520	G520VBB	529	G529VBB	538	G538VBB	547	G547VBB	555	G555VBB
521	G521VBB	530	G530VBB	539	G539VBB	548	G548VBB	556	G556VBB
522	G522VBB	531	G531VBB	540	G540VBB				

Opposite:- **Following the purchase of Leaside Buses by Cowie, the London operation has been managed as a separate unit to the larger and more geographically spread British Bus operation. Leaside, along with South London, were the two operations to carry the Cowie name, in corporate style, on the vehicle sides. Both pictures here show the livery on vehicles taken before the name change occurred following the Board meeting in late November 1997. The upper picture shows Leyland Olympian L346, J346BSH, as it operated through Clapton. The lower picture illustrates the links with another Cowie partner, Hughes-DAF dealership who now handle all deliveries and orders for the group. Pictured at Archway, DBS13, N613DWY, is one of three vehicle in the 1995 batch to be supplied with the new version of the DB250 chassis.   Like the others in the batch it carries Northern Counties Palatine II bodywork.** *Gearld Mead/Tony Wilson*

Seven Dennis Darts were transferred from South London to Leaside's Enfield depot in 1996 to replace Optare StarRiders on route 192. Carlyle-bodied DT63, H463UGO, lays over at Little Park Gardens in Enfield in this view. *Philip Stephenson*

LDR1-21   Dennis Dart 9.8SDL3054   Plaxton Pointer   B40F   1995

1	N671GUM	6	N676GUM	10	N680GUM	14	N684GUM	18	N688GUM
2	N672GUM	7	N677GUM	11	N681GUM	15	N685GUM	19	N689GUM
3	N673GUM	8	N678GUM	12	N682GUM	16	N686GUM	20	N680GUM
4	N674GUM	9	N679GUM	13	N683GUM	17	N687GUM	21	N691GUM
5	N675GUM								

LDR40-55   Dennis Dart   Plaxton Pointer   B40F   1996

40	P840PWW	44	P844PWW	47	P847PWW	50	P850PWW	53	P853PWW
41	P841PWW	45	P845PWW	48	P848PWW	51	P851PWW	54	P854PWW
42	P842PWW	46	P846PWW	49	P849PWW	52	P852PWW	55	P855PWW
43	P843PWW								

M6	WYW6T	MCW Metrobus DR101/8	MCW	H43/28D	1978	Ex South London, 1996
M14	WYW14T	MCW Metrobus DR101/8	MCW	H43/28D	1978	Ex South London, 1995
M51	WYW51T	MCW Metrobus DR101/8	MCW	H43/28D	1978	Ex South London, 1996

M205-317   MCW Metrobus DR101/12   MCW   H43/28D   1979-80 Ex London Buses, 1994
205/20 ex South London, 1997

205	BYX205V	266	BYX266V	282	BYX282V	310	BYX310V	317	EYE317V
220	BYX220V							

The principal type of pay-as-you-board double-deck with Leaside is the MCW Metrobus with examples spanning eight years of production. M657, KYV657X, is from the large 1981-82 batch, most of which have operated in this area of London since they were first supplied to London Transport. *Richard Godfrey*

M353-493

MCW Metrobus DR101/12   MCW   H43/28D   1980   Ex London Buses, 1994
386 ex South London, 1997

353	GYE353W	389	GYE389W	426	GYE426W	450	GYE450W	485	GYE485W
382	GYE382W	419	GYE419W	441	GYE441W	469	GYE469W	491	GYE491W
386	GYE386W	422	GYE422W	445	GYE445W	478	GYE478W	493	GYE493W

M509-605

MCW Metrobus DR101/14   MCW   H43/28D   1981   Ex London Buses, 1994

509	GYE509W	538	GYE538W	551	GYE551W	581	GYE581W	593	GYE593W
510	GYE510W	540	GYE540W	557	GYE557W	582	GYE582W	596	GYE596W
529	GYE529W	543	GYE543W	559	GYE559W	585	GYE585W	600	GYE600W
530	GYE530W	544	GYE544W	562	GYE562W	586	GYE586W	602	GYE602W
531	GYE531W	547	GYE547W	567	GYE567W	587	GYE587W	603	GYE603W
533	GYE533W	548	GYE548W	569	GYE569W	590	GYE590W	604	GYE604W
535	GYE535W	549	GYE549W	575	GYE575W	591	GYE591W	605	GYE605W
536	GYE536W								

M609-631

MCW Metrobus DR101/14   MCW   H43/28D   1981   Ex London Buses, 1994

609	KYO609X	613	KYO613X	617	KYO617X	624	KYO624X	628	KYO628X
610	KYO610X	614	KYO614X	619	KYO619X	626	KYO626X	630	KYO630X
611	KYO611X	615	KYO615X	622	KYO622X	627	KYO627X	631	KYO631X
612	KYO612X								

M632-798 — MCW Metrobus DR101/14 — MCW — H43/28D — 1981-82 — Ex London Buses, 1994

No.	Reg	No.	Reg	No.	Reg	No.	Reg	No.	Reg
632	KYV632X	665	KYV665X	709	KYV709X	738	KYV738X	771	KYV771X
635	KYV635X	666	KYV666X	710	KYV710X	740	KYV740X	772	KYV772X
636	KYV636X	669	KYV669X	711	KYV711X	742	KYV742X	773	KYV773X
637	KYV637X	672	KYV672X	712	KYV712X	743	KYV743X	774	KYV774X
638	KYV638X	673	KYV673X	713	KYV713X	744	KYV744X	775	KYV775X
641	KYV641X	675	KYV675X	714	KYV714X	745	KYV745X	776	KYV776X
642	KYV642X	676	KYV676X	715	KYV715X	746	KYV746X	777	KYV777X
643	KYV643X	679	KYV679X	716	KYV716X	747	KYV747X	778	KYV778X
644	KYV644X	681	KYV681X	717	KYV717X	748	KYV748X	780	KYV780X
645	KYV645X	684	KYV684X	718	KYV718X	749	KYV749X	781	KYV781X
646	KYV646X	686	KYV686X	719	KYV719X	750	KYV750X	782	KYV782X
647	KYV647X	688	KYV688X	720	KYV720X	751	KYV751X	783	KYV783X
648	KYV648X	689	KYV689X	721	KYV721X	752	KYV752X	784	KYV784X
649w	KYV649X	692	KYV692X	723	KYV723X	753	KYV753X	785	KYV785X
650	KYV650X	694	KYV694X	726	KYV726X	754	KYV754X	786	KYV786X
651	KYV651X	698	KYV698X	727	KYV727X	756	KYV756X	787	KYV787X
652	KYV652X	699	KYV699X	728	KYV728X	757	KYV757X	788	KYV788X
653	KYV653X	700	KYV700X	729	KYV729X	758	KYV758X	789	KYV789X
657	KYV657X	701	KYV701X	730	KYV730X	761	KYV761X	790	KYV790X
658	KYV658X	702	KYV702X	731	KYV731X	762	KYV766X	791	KYV791X
659	KYV659X	703	KYV703X	732	KYV732X	765	KYV765X	792	KYV792X
660	KYV660X	704	KYV704X	733	KYV733X	766	KYV766X	793	KYV793X
661	KYV661X	705	KYV705X	734	KYV734X	767	KYV767X	795	KYV795X
663	KYV663X	707	KYV707X	736	KYV736X	768	KYV768X	796	KYV796X
664	KYV664X	708	KYV708X	737	KYV737X	770	KYV770X	798	KYV798X

M891-1044 — MCW Metrobus DR101/16* — MCW — H43/28D — 1983-84 Ex London Buses, 1994
*988-1000 are DR101/17; 1044 is DR101/19

No.	Reg	No.	Reg	No.	Reg	No.	Reg	No.	Reg
891	OJD891Y	919	A919SUL	936	A936SUL	988	A988SYF	1000	A700THV
903	A903SUL	929	A929SUL	939	A939SUL	996	A996SYF	1044	A744THV

Among the first buses to receive the Arriva branding were those Leaside buses in the red and yellow colour scheme. This was applied in advance of the official name change which occurred on 6th November for the group and from January 1998 for the Arriva Passenger Services division. Metrobus M712, KYV712X, leaves Edmonton Green on trunk route 279. *Colin Lloyd*

M1070-1303

MCW Metrobus DR101/17   MCW   H43/28D   1984-85 Ex London Buses, 1994

1070	B70WUL	1134	B134WUL	1175	B175WUL	1233	B233WUL	1283	B283WUL
1074	B74WUL	1135	B135WUL	1176	B176WUL	1239	B239WUL	1285	B285WUL
1075	B75WUL	1136	B136WUL	1179	B179WUL	1249	B249WUL	1286	B286WUL
1109	B109WUL	1137	B137WUL	1182	B182WUL	1252	B252WUL	1288	B288WUL
1112	B112WUL	1138	B138WUL	1209	B209WUL	1253	B253WUL	1289	B289WUL
1121	B121WUL	1139	B139WUL	1210	B210WUL	1254	B254WUL	1290	B290WUL
1122	B122WUL	1140	B140WUL	1213	B213WUL	1255	B255WUL	1291	B291WUL
1123	B123WUL	1152	B152WUL	1214	B214WUL	1263	B263WUL	1293	B293WUL
1124	B124WUL	1154	B154WUL	1216	B216WUL	1265	B265WUL	1294	B294WUL
1126	B126WUL	1155	B155WUL	1217	B217WUL	1275	B275WUL	1295	B295WUL
1127	B127WUL	1162	B162WUL	1219	B219WUL	1276	B276WUL	1296	B296WUL
1128	B128WUL	1164	B164WUL	1221	B221WUL	1278	B278WUL	1297	B297WUL
1129	B129WUL	1165	B165WUL	1227	B227WUL	1279	B279WUL	1298	B298WUL
1130	B130WUL	1169	B169WUL	1228	B228WUL	1280	B280WUL	1299	B299WUL
1131	B131WUL	1170	B170WUL	1229	B229WUL	1281	B281WUL	1300	B300WUL
1132	B132WUL	1173	B173WUL	1231	B231WUL	1282	B282WUL	1303	B303WUL
1133	B133WUL								

M1307-1424

MCW Metrobus DR101/17   MCW   H43/28D   1985   Ex London Buses, 1994

1307	C307BUV	1314	C314BUV	1321	C321BUV	1332	C332BUV	1405	C405BUV
1308	C308BUV	1316	C316BUV	1322	C322BUV	1362	C362BUV	1406	C406BUV
1309	C309BUV	1317	C317BUV	1323	C323BUV	1399	C399BUV	1413	C413BUV
1310	C310BUV	1318	C318BUV	1324	C324BUV	1401	C401BUV	1417	C417BUV
1312	C312BUV	1319	C319BUV	1326	C326BUV	1402	C402BUV	1424	C424BUV
1313	C313BUV	1320	C320BUV	1327	C327BUV	1404	C404BUV		

MR102	F102YVP	MCW MetroRider MF150/115	MCW	B23F	1988	Ex London Buses, 1994
MR104	F104YVP	MCW MetroRider MF150/116	MCW	DP23F	1988	Ex London Buses, 1994
MR105	F105YVP	MCW MetroRider MF150/116	MCW	DP23F	1988	Ex London Buses, 1994

Standard Leaside Metrobus M657, KYV657X, is seen with Cowie lettering at Waltham Cross. Only the London-based Cowie fleet used that name which took the corporate style as also shown on the cover of this edition. Interestingly, several of the London buses were the first to carry the Arriva name and 'wheels' motif in any quantity, though this arrangement was affixed to the old livery. *Richard Godfrey*

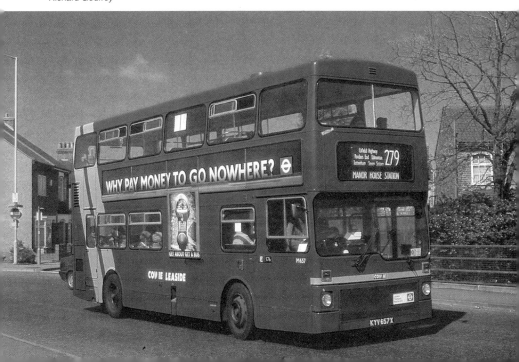

Leaside are still responsible for two LRT routes that require Routemaster operation on Monday through Saturday. Tottenham's RMLs are found on route 73 while Clapton's are the principal type on service 38 illustrated here by RML2758, SMK758F, seen at St. Giles Circus. *Ralph Stevens*

RM5	VLT5	AEC Routemaster R2RH	Park Royal	H36/28R	1959	Ex London Buses, 1994	
RM295	VLT295	AEC Routemaster R2RH	Park Royal	H36/28R	1960	Ex London Buses, 1997	
RM311	KGJ142A	AEC Routemaster R2RH(Iveco)	Park Royal	H36/28R	1960	Ex Cowie South London, 1996	
RM736	XYJ418	AEC Routemaster R2RH	Park Royal	H36/28R	1961	Ex London Buses, 1997	

RML882-901

	AEC Routemaster R2RH/1(Cummins) Park Royal					H40/32R	1961	Ex London Buses, 1994	
882	WLT882	888	WLT888	896	WLT896	897	WLT897	901	WLT901
884	WLT884								

RM1125	KGH858A	AEC Routemaster R2RH(Iveco)	Park Royal	H36/28R	1962	Ex Cowie South London, 1996	
RM1330	KGH975A	AEC Routemaster R2RH	Park Royal	H36/28R	1962	Ex London Buses, 1997	
RM1725	725DYE	AEC Routemaster R2RH(Iveco)	Park Royal	H36/28R	1963	Ex Cowie South London, 1996	
RM2185	CUV185C	AEC Routemaster R2RH(Iveco)	Park Royal	H36/28R	1965	Ex Cowie South London, 1996	

RML2261-2359

	AEC Routemaster R2RH/1(Cummins) Park Royal					H40/32R	1965	Ex London Buses, 1994	
2261	CUV261C	2292	CUV292C	2325	CUV325C	2334	CUV334C	2354	CUV354C
2267	CUV267C	2294	CUV294C	2326	CUV326C	2340	CUV340C	2355	CUV355C
2277	CUV277C	2304	CUV304C	2328	CUV328C	2344	CUV344C	2356	CUV356C
2280	CUV280C	2315	CUV315C	2329	CUV329C	2346	CUV346C	2359	CUV359C
2287	CUV287C	2323	CUV323C	2330	CUV330C	2350	CUV350C		

Leaside Buses received fourteen Scania N113CRL low-floor buses for the LRT low-floor bus trials. LRT route 144 was the chosen service and SLW10, RDZ1710, is seen on that service in this picture taken near Wood Green underground station. *Richard Godfrey*

RML2370-2597   AEC Routemaster R2RH/1   Park Royal   H40/32R   1966   Ex London Buses, 1994

2370	JJD370D	2406	JJD406D	2468	JJD468D	2525	JJD525D	2562	JJD562D
2372	JJD372D	2408	JJD408D	2483	JJD483D	2526	JJD526D	2567	JJD567D
2373	JJD373D	2409	JJD409D	2492	JJD492D	2528	JJD527D	2571	JJD571D
2380	JJD380D	2416	JJD416D	2494	JJD494D	2534	JJD534D	2588	JJD588D
2386	JJD386D	2418	JJD418D	2503	JJD503D	2544	JJD544D	2589	JJD589D
2391	JJD391D	2434	JJD424D	2504	JJD504D	2546	JJD546D	2595	JJD595D
2394	JJD394D	2457	JJD457D	2510	JJD510D	2552	JJD552D	2597	JJD597D
2401	JJD401D	2460	JJD460D	2518	JJD518D				

RML2611-2655   AEC Routemaster R2RH/1   Park Royal   H40/32R   1967   Ex London Buses, 1994

2611	NML611E	2625	NML625E	2632	NML632E	2638	NML638E	2655	NML655E
2617	NML617E	2628	NML628E	2635	NML635E	2643	NML643E		

RML2658-2758   AEC Routemaster R2RH/1   Park Royal   H40/32R   1968   Ex London Buses, 1994

2658	SMK658F	2678	SMK678F	2688	SMK688F	2742	SMK742F	2750	SMK750F
2660	SMK660F	2682	SMK682F	2708	SMK708F	2746	SMK746F	2754	SMK754F
2666	SMK666F	2684	SMK684F	2716	SMK716F	2747	SMK747F	2758	SMK758F
2675	SMK675F	2685	SMK685F						

SLW1-14   Scania N113CRL   Wright Pathfinder   B37D   1994   Ex London Buses, 1994

1	RDZ1701	4	RDZ1704	7	RDZ1707	10	RDZ1710	13	RDZ1713
2	RDZ1702	5	RDZ1705	8	RDZ1708	11	RDZ1711	14	RDZ1714
3	RDZ1703	6	RDZ1706	9	RDZ1709	12	RDZ1712		

T95w	CUL95V	Leyland Titan TNLXB2RRSp	Park Royal	H44/26D	1979	Ex London Buses, 1994

V721-733   Volvo Citybus B10M-50   Alexander RV   H47/29D   1989   Ex Kentish Bus, 1998

721	F101TML	**725**	F105TML	**727**	F107TML	**729**	F109TML	**732**	F112TML
723	F103TML	**726**	F106TML	**728**	F108TML	**730**	F110TML	**733**	F113TML
724	F104TML								

On order - 3 DAF B220 - Northern Counties.

Previous Registrations:

KGH975A	330CLT		VLT32	J354BSH
KGJ142A	WLT311		XYJ418	WLT736
KGH858A	125CLT			

Allocations and liveries:

Livery   Red and yellow

Cambridge Heath (Ash Grove) - *Transfers from Kentish Bus in January 1998*

Dart	DN115	DN116	DN117	DN118	DN119			
Olympian	L514	L515	L516	L517	L518	L519	L520	L521
	L522	L523	L524	L525	L526	L527	L528	L529
	L530	L531	L532	L533	L534	L535	L536	L537
	L538	L539	L540	L541	L542	L543	L544	L545
	L546	L547	L548	L549	L550	L551	L552	L553
	L554	L555	L556					
Citybus	721	723	724	725	726	727	728	729
	730	732	733					

Clapton (Bohemia Place, Hackney)

Olympian	L315	L316	L317	L318	L319	L320	L321	L322
	L323	L324	L325	L326	L327	L328	L329	L330
	L331	L332	L333	L334	L335	L336	L337	L338
	L339	L340	L341	L342	L343	L344	L345	L346
	L347	L348	L349	L350	L351	L352	L353	L354
Metrobus	M14t	M282t	M422t	M445t	M469t	M478t	M562	M632
	M660	M730	M777	M782 *	M786	M788	M790	M988
	M1000	M1075	M1112	M1182	M1229	M1296	M1298	
	* On loan to County							
MetroRider	MR102	MR104	MR105					
Routemaster RM	RM5	RM311	RM1125	RM1725	RM2185			
RML	RML882	RML884	RML888	RML896	RML897	RML901	RML2280	RML2287
	RML2304	RML2325	RML2326	RML2328	RML2329	RML2334	RML2344	RML2354
	RML2355	RML2356	RML2359	RML2370	RML2386	RML2401	RML2406	RML2409
	RML2416	RML2457	RML2483	RML2492	RML2494	RML2526	RML2534	RML2552
	RML2567	RML2597	RML2675	RML2682	RML2685	RML2688	RML2716	RML2750
	RML2754	RML2758						

Enfield (Southbury Road, Ponders End)

Dart	DT58	DT59	DT60	DT61	DT62	DT63	DT64	LDR1
	LDR2	LDR3	LDR4	LDR5	LDR6	LDR7	LDR8	LDR9
	LDR10	LDR11	LDR12	LDR13	LDR14	LDR40	LDR41	LDR42
	LDR43	LDR44	LDR45					
Metrobus	M6t	M205t	M220t	M336	M533	M543	M569	M590
	M593	M604	M619	M622	M624	M630	M643	M644
	M646	M648	M652	M657	M659	M661	M666	M672
	M689	M694	M698	M700	M701	M702	M703	M704
	M707	M709	M712	M713	M715	M717	M718	M720
	M721	M723	M726	M727	M728	M729	M731	M733
	M734	M736	M737	M738	M740	M742	M743	M744
	M747	M748	M749	M751	M752	M761	M762	M765
	M770	M774	M778	M780	M781	M783	M785	M787
	M791	M798	M903	M1170	M1179	M1231	M1249	M1253
	M1279	M1320						

Stamford Hill (Rookwood Road) - *withdrawn vehicles*

Routemaster	RM295	RM736	RM1330
Titan	T95		

Palmers Green (Regents Avenue) - *sub-depot of Wood Green*

Dart	DRL49	DRL50	DRL51	DRL52				
Metrobus	M493	M510	M529	M530	M531	M535	M536	M538
	M540	M547	M548	M549	M551	M557	M567	M581
	M582	M585	M587	M591	M596	M600	M602	M603
	M605	M609	M610	M611	M612	M613	M614	M615
	M617	M626	M627	M628	M631	M635	M636	M637
	M638	M641	M642	M645	M647	M651	M653	M658
	M664	M669	M673	M746				

Tottenham (Philip Lane)

Metrobus	M266	M310	M317	M441	M491	M509	M544	M754
	M382t	M426t	M450t	M485t	M996	M1121	M1129	M1131
	M1132	M1133	M1134	M1135	M1137	M1138	M1139	M1140
	M1152	M1154	M1155	M1162	M1164	M1165	M1175	M1176
	M1210	M1213	M1227	M1228	M1233	M1263	M1275	M1280
	M1281	M1283	M1285	M1286	M1288	M1289	M1290	M1293
	M1294	M1295	M1297	M1299	M1307	M1308	M1309	M1399
	M1401	M1402	M1404	M1405	M1406	M1413	M1417	M1424
RML	RML2261	RML2267	RML2277	RML2292	RML2294	RML2315	RML2323	RML2330
	RML2340	RML2346	RML2350	RML2372	RML2373	RML2380	RML2391	RML2394
	RML2408	RML2418	RML2434	RML2460	RML2468	RML2503	RML2504	RML2510
	RML2518	RML2525	RML2528	RML2544	RML2546	RML2562	RML2571	RML2588
	RML2589	RML2595	RML2611	RML2617	RML2625	RML2628	RML2632	RML2635
	RML2638	RML2643	RML2655	RML2658	RML2660	RML2666	RML2678	RML2684
	RML2708	RML2742	RML2746	RML2747				

Wood Green (High Road)

DAF Bus	DBS1	DBS2	DBS3	DBS4	DBS5	DBS6	DBS7	DBS8
	DBS9	DBS10	DBS11	DBS12	DBS13			
Dart	LDR15	LDR16	LDR17	LDR18	LDR19	LDR20	LDR21	LDR46
	LDR47	LDR48	LDR49	LDR50	LDR51	LDR52	LDR53	LDR54
	LDR55							
Metrobus	M51	M353	M389	M419	M559			
	M575	M586	M650	M663	M665	M675	M676	M679
	M681	M684	M686	M688	M692	M699	M705	M708
	M710	M711	M714	M716	M719	M732	M745	M750
	M753	M756	M757	M758	M766	M767	M768	M771
	M772	M773	M775	M776	M784	M789	M792	M793
	M795	M796	M891	M919	M929	M936	M939	M1044
	M1070	M1074	M1109	M1122	M1123	M1124	M1126	M1127
	M1128	M1130	M1136	M1169	M1173	M1209	M1214	M1216
	M1217	M1219	M1221	M1239	M1252	M1254	M1255	M1265
	M1276	M1278	M1282	M1300	M1303	M1310	M1312	M1313
	M1314	M1316	M1317	M1318	M1319	M1321	M1322	M1323
	M1324	M1326	M1327	M1332	M1362			
Lance	SLW1	SLW2	SLW3	SLW4	SLW5	SLW6	SLW7	SLW8
	SLW9	SLW10	SLW11	SLW12	SLW13	SLW14		

LONDON & COUNTRY

London & Country Ltd; Guildford & West Surrey Buses Ltd; Horsham Buses Ltd;
Gem Fairtax (1991) Ltd Linden Court, Lesbourne Road, Reigate, Surrey, RH2 7LE
Londonlinks Buses Ltd; Invicta House; Armstrong Road, Maidstone, Kent ME15 6TY

Main series:

113	G113TND	Mercedes-Benz 811D	Carlyle	B20FL	1990	Ex Bee Line Buzz, 1992
120	G120TJA	Mercedes-Benz 814D	Carlyle	B33F	1990	Ex C-Line, 1991

120-126   Dennis Dart 9SDL3034   Northern Counties Paladin   B35F   1994   Ex Londonlinks, 1997

120	L120YVK	122	L122YVK	124	L124YVK	125	L125YVK	126	L126YVK
121	L121YVK	123	L123YVK						

132	K132XRE	Mercedes-Benz 709D	Dormobile	B29F	1992	Ex Stevensons, 1995
133	J480XHL	Mercedes-Benz 709D	Alexander AM	DP25F	1991	Ex Stevensons, 1995
151	L151YVK	Dennis Dart 9SDL3034	Northern Counties Paladin	B35F	1994	Ex Londonlinks, 1997
154	K154BRF	Mercedes-Benz 709D	Dormobile Routemaker	B29F	1993	Ex Stevensons, 1995
155	K155CRE	Mercedes-Benz 709D	Dormobile Routemaker	B27F	1993	Ex Stevensons, 1995
156	K156BRF	Mercedes-Benz 709D	Dormobile Routemaker	B27F	1993	Ex Stevensons, 1995
157	K157BRF	Mercedes-Benz 709D	Dormobile Routemaker	B27F	1993	Ex Stevensons, 1995
160	M160SKR	Dennis Dart 9SDL3053	Plaxton Pointer	B35F	1995	Ex Londonlinks, 1997
161	APM113T	AEC Reliance 6U3ZR	Plaxton Supreme III	C53F	1979	Ex Eagle, Bristol, 1994
161	M161SKR	Dennis Dart 9SDL3053	Plaxton Pointer	B35F	1995	Ex Londonlinks, 1997
162	M162SKR	Dennis Dart 9SDL3053	Plaxton Pointer	B35F	1995	Ex Londonlinks, 1997
163	M163SKR	Dennis Dart 9SDL3053	Plaxton Pointer	B35F	1995	Ex Londonlinks, 1997

164-172   Dennis Dart 9SDL3053   Plaxton Pointer   B34F   1995   Ex Londonlinks, 1997

164	N701GUM	166	N703GUM	168	N705GUM	170	N707GUM	172	N709GUM
165	N702GUM	167	N704GUM	169	N706GUM	171	N708GUM		

168	E168OMD	Volvo B10M-61	Plaxton Paramount 3500 II	C57F	1988	Ex Moon, Warnham, 1994
189	G689OHE	Mercedes-Benz 811D	Reeve Burgess Beaver	B20FL	1990	Ex Metrowest, Coseley, 1992
190	G690OHE	Mercedes-Benz 811D	Reeve Burgess Beaver	B20FL	1990	Ex Metrowest, Coseley, 1992
201	G101TND	Mercedes-Benz 811D	Carlyle	B33F	1990	Ex C-Line, 1991

201-212   Volvo B6-9.9M   Northern Counties Paladin   B39F   1994   Ex Londonlinks, 1997

201	L201YCU	204	L204YCU	207	L207YCU	209	L209YCU	211	L211YCU
202	L202YCU	205	L205YCU	208	L208YCU	210	L210YCU	212	L212YCU
203	L203YCU	206	L206YCU						

202	HPK504N	Leyland National 11351/1R	Urban Bus	B49F	1975	Ex Alder Valley, 1990
221	KPA372P	Leyland National 11351/1R		B49F	1975	Ex Alder Valley, 1990
242	LPF600P	Leyland National 11351/1R(Cummins) Urban Bus		DP21FL	1976	Ex Alder Valley, 1990
246	KPA367P	Leyland National 11351/1R		DP21FL	1975	Ex Alder Valley, 1990
252	JCK852W	Leyland 2 NL106AL11/1R	East Lancs Greenway (1991) B44F		1981	Ex North Western, 1991
257	NPJ478R	Leyland National 11351A/1R		B49F	1976	Ex Alder Valley, 1990
258	NPJ479R	Leyland National 11351A/1R		B49F	1976	Ex Alder Valley, 1990
265	PPM892R	Leyland 11351A/1R(Cummins)	Urban Bus	B49F	1976	Ex Alder Valley, 1990
270	GFR799W	Leyland National 116690/1R		B52F	1979	Ex North Western, 1992
302	G302DPA	Dennis Falcon HC SDA421	East Lancashire EL2000	B48F	1990	
303	G303DPA	Dennis Falcon HC SDA421	East Lancashire EL2000	B48F	1990	
304	G304DPA	Dennis Falcon HC SDA421	East Lancashire EL2000	B48F	1990	
305	G305DPA	Dennis Falcon HC SDA421	East Lancashire EL2000	B48F	1990	

311-316   Leyland Lynx LX2R11G15Z4S   Leyland Lynx   B49F   1990   Ex Londonlinks, 1997

311	G311DPA	313	G313DPA	314	G314DPA	315	G315DPA	316	G316DPA
312	G312DPA								

331	UPB331S	Leyland National 10351A/1R(Volvo)		B41F	1977	Ex Londonlinks, 1997
339	SIB6709	Leyland NL106AL11/1R	East Lancs Greenway(1992)	B41F	1981	Ex Londonlinks, 1997
341	SIB6711	Leyland 10351/1R/SC	East Lancs Greenway(1992)	B41F	1975	Ex Londonlinks, 1997
343	SIB6713	Leyland 1051/1R/0402	East Lancs Greenway(1992)	B41F	1974	Ex Londonlinks, 1997
344	SIB6714	Leyland 10351/R/SC	East Lancs Greenway(1992)	B41F	1974	Ex Londonlinks, 1997
353	JIL2193	Leyland 11351/1R	East Lancs Greenway(1994)	B49F	1974	Ex South Coast Buses, 1994
356	JIL2196	Leyland 11351/1R	East Lancs Greenway(1994)	B49F	1975	Ex Westbus, Ashford, 1994
357	JIL2197	Leyland 1151/1R	East Lancs Greenway(1994)	B49F	1973	Ex Midland Fox, 1994
358	JIL2198	Leyland 11351A/1R	East Lancs Greenway(1994)	B49F	1976	Ex Midland Fox, 1994
359	JIL2199	Leyland 11351A/1R	East Lancs Greenway(1994)	B49F	1976	Ex Midland Fox, 1994
360	JIL2190	Leyland 11351/1R	East Lancs Greenway(1994)	B49F	1976	Ex Midland, 1994
363	PDZ6263	Leyland 11351A/1R	East Lancs Greenway(1994)	B49F	1977	Ex Tellings Golden-Miller, 1992
364	PDZ6264	Leyland 11351A/1R	East Lancs Greenway(1994)	B49F	1979	Ex Tellings Golden-Miller, 1994
365	PDZ6265	Leyland 11351A/1R	East Lancs Greenway(1994)	B49F	1975	Ex Alder Valley, 1990
366	SJI5066	Leyland 11351A/1R	East Lancs Greenway(1994)	B49F	1977	Ex Tellings Golden-Miller, 1994
367	JIL5367	Leyland 11351A/1R	East Lancs Greenway(1994)	B49F	1977	Ex Tellings Golden-Miller, 1994
368	LIL2168	Leyland 11351A/1R	East Lancs Greenway(1994)	B49F	1977	Ex Tellings Golden-Miller, 1994
369	SJI5569	Leyland 11351A/1R	East Lancs Greenway(1994)	B49F	1977	Ex The Bee Line, 1994
370	SJI5570	Leyland 11351/1R	East Lancs Greenway(1994)	B49F	1976	Ex Midland Fox, 1994
371	SJI5571	Leyland 11351/1R	East Lancs Greenway(1994)	B49F	1976	Ex Midland Fox, 1994
372	SJI5572	Leyland 11351/1R	East Lancs Greenway(1994)	B49F	1976	Ex The Bee Line, 1994
373	PDZ6273	Leyland 11351/1R	East Lancs Greenway(1994)	DP49F	1976	Ex Midland Fox, 1994
374	PDZ6274	Leyland 11351A/1R	East Lancs Greenway(1994)	DP49F	1976	Ex Midland Fox, 1994
375	PDZ6275	Leyland 11351A/2R	East Lancs Greenway(1994)	DP49F	1977	Ex Panther, Crawley, 1991
376	PDZ6276	Leyland 11351A/1R	East Lancs Greenway(1994)	DP49F	1975	Ex Northumbria, 1994
377	PDZ6277	Leyland 11351A/1R	East Lancs Greenway(1994)	DP49F	1978	Ex Alder Valley, 1990
378	RDZ4278	Leyland 11351/1R	East Lancs Greenway(1995)	B49F	1975	Ex Shamrock & Rambler, 1988
379	RDZ4279	Leyland 11351/1R	East Lancs Greenway(1995)	B49F	1975	Ex Alder Valley, 1990
380	LIL2180	Leyland 11351/1R	East Lancs Greenway(1995)	B49F	1975	Ex Alder Valley, 1990
381	SIB1278	Leyland 10351B/1R	East Lancs Greenway(1994)	B41F	1979	Ex Londonlinks, 1997
399	D101NDW	Leyland Lynx LX112TL11ZR1R	Leyland Lynx	B49F	1987	Ex Londonlinks, 1997
400	D102NDW	Leyland Lynx LX112TL11ZR1R	Leyland Lynx	B49F	1987	Ex Londonlinks, 1997
401	G34VME	Leyland Lynx LX2R11C15Z4S	Leyland Lynx	B49F	1989	Ex Londonlinks, 1997
402	G35VME	Leyland Lynx LX2R11C15Z4S	Leyland Lynx	B49F	1989	Ex Londonlinks, 1997
402	K402VPK	Mercedes-Benz 709D	Dormobile Routemaker	B25FL	1992	
403	K403VPK	Mercedes-Benz 709D	Dormobile Routemaker	B25FL	1992	
404	K404VPK	Mercedes-Benz 709D	Dormobile Routemaker	B25FL	1992	
405	K405VPK	Mercedes-Benz 709D	Dormobile Routemaker	B25FL	1992	
418	D156HML	Leyland Lynx LX112TL11ZR1S	Leyland Lynx	B49F	1987	Ex Londonlinks, 1997

421-427

Mercedes-Benz 709D Dormobile Routemaker B25F* 1993-94 *425-7 are B27F

421	L421CPB	423	L423CPB	425	L425CPB	426	L426CPB	427	L427CPB
422	L422CPB	424	L424CPB						

428	L428CPC	Mercedes-Benz 709D	Danescroft	B27F	1994	
429	L429CPC	Mercedes-Benz 709D	Danescroft	B27F	1994	

430-437

Mercedes-Benz 811D Plaxton Beaver B31F 1994 Ex Londonlinks, 1997

430	L430CPJ	433	L433CPJ	435	L435CPJ	436	L436CPJ	437	L437CPJ
431	L431CPJ	434	L434CPJ						

438	P438HKN	Mercedes-Benz 811D	Plaxton Beaver	B31F	1996	Ex Londonlinks, 1997
438	L438FPA	Mercedes-Benz 709D	Plaxton Beaver	B23F	1994	
439	L439FPA	Mercedes-Benz 709D	Plaxton Beaver	B27F	1994	
440	M440HPF	Optare MetroRider MR17	Optare	B29F	1994	Ex Londonlinks, 1997
441	M441HPF	Optare MetroRider MR17	Optare	B29F	1994	Ex Londonlinks, 1997
442	M442HPF	Optare MetroRider MR17	Optare	B29F	1994	Ex Londonlinks, 1997
443	M443HPF	Optare MetroRider MR17	Optare	B29F	1994	Ex Londonlinks, 1997

454-460

Mercedes-Benz 709D Alexander Sprint B23F 1994

454	M454HPG	456	M456HPG	458	M458JPA	459	M459JPA	460	M460JPA
455	M455HPG	457	M457HPG						

461	M461JPA	Mercedes-Benz 811D	Plaxton Beaver	B31F	1995	
462	M462JPA	Mercedes-Benz 811D	Plaxton Beaver	B31F	1995	
463	M463JPA	Mercedes-Benz 709D	Plaxton Beaver	B23F	1995	
464	M464JPA	Mercedes-Benz 709D	Plaxton Beaver	B23F	1995	
465	M465LPG	Mercedes-Benz 709D	Alexander Sprint	B29F	1995	

June 1995 saw the arrival with London & Country of two additional Mercedes-Benz 709Ds. These Plaxton 21-seater bodies were painted into a new style livery of mainly white with green and red relief. Number 467, M467MPM, here carries *Airporter* names and wording for route X38 to which it is dedicated in order to serve Gatwick Airport. *Richard Godfrey*

466	M466MPM	Mercedes-Benz 709D	Plaxton Beaver	B21F	1995				
467	M467MPM	Mercedes-Benz 709D	Plaxton Beaver	B21F	1995				
468	N468SPA	Mercedes-Benz 709D	Alexander Sprint	B27FL	1995				
469	N469SPA	Mercedes-Benz 709D	Alexander Sprint	B27FL	1995				
470	N470SPA	Mercedes-Benz 709D	Alexander Sprint	B27FL	1995				

512-516
		Volvo B6-9.9M		Plaxton Pointer	B41F	1994			
512	L512CPJ	513	L513CPJ	514	L514CPJ	515	L515CPJ	516	L516CPJ

610-622
		Volvo Citybus B10M-50		East Lancashire		H49/39F	1989		
610	G610BPH	613	G613BPH	616	G616BPH	619	G619BPH	621	G621BPH
611	G611BPH	614	G614BPH	617	G617BPH	620	G620BPH	622	G622BPH
612	G612BPH	615	G615BPH	618	G618BPH				

623-630
		Volvo Citybus B10M-50		Northern Counties		H45/31F	1989	Ex Londonlinks, 1997	
623	G623BPH	625	G625BPH	627	G627BPH	629	G629BPH	630	G630BPH
624	G624BPH	626	G626BPH	628	G628BPH				

685-704
		Volvo Olympian YN2RV16Z4		East Lancashire		H44/30F	1994	685-700 Ex Londonlinks, 1997	
685	M685HPF	689	M689HPF	693	M693HPF	697	M697HPF	701	M701HPF
686	M686HPF	690	M690HPF	694	M694HPF	698	M698HPF	702	M702HPF
687	M687HPF	691	M691HPF	695	M695HPF	699	M699HPF	703	M703HPF
688	M688HPF	692	M692HPF	696	M696HPF	700	M700HPF	704	M704HPF

Opposite, top:- **Twelve Volvo B6s with Northern Counties Paladin bodywork are included in the London & Country operation having moved from the Londonlinks unit. Pictured at Purley while working service 289 is 211, L211YCU. The Londonlinks unit closes in 1998 with transfer of work to other units within the group.** *Richard Godfrey*
Opposite, bottom:- **London and Country were keen players in the Greenway programme with many vehicles being acquired for conversion. Before its conversion 377, PDZ6277, was latterly with Alder Valley and is seen here on Green Line duties.** *Gerald Mead*

London Transport Buses contracted route 85 from Kingston to Putney is operated by Volvo Citybuses from London & Country's Leatherhead base. These B10M vehicles have longer 88-seat bodies dwhich are needed for this very busy suburban route and which date from 1989. Representing the batch is 612, G612BPH. *Richard Godfrey*

701	G640CHF	Volvo Citybus B10M-50	East Lancashire	H49/39F	1989	Ex Londonlinks, 1997
704	G643CHF	Volvo Citybus B10M-50	East Lancashire	H49/39F	1989	Ex Londonlinks, 1997
705	G647EKA	Volvo Citybus B10M-50	East Lancashire	H49/39F	1990	Ex Londonlinks, 1997
710	G661DTJ	Volvo Citybus B10M-50	East Lancashire	H49/39F	1990	Ex Londonlinks, 1997
847	E136KYW	MCW MetroRider MF150/38	MCW	B25F	1987	Ex Londonlinks, 1997
849	E141KYW	MCW MetroRider MF150/38	MCW	B25F	1987	Ex Londonlinks, 1997
850	E145KYW	MCW MetroRider MF150/38	MCW	B25F	1987	Ex Londonlinks, 1997
860	F860LCU	MCW MetroRider MF158/15	MCW	B31F	1988	Ex Londonlinks, 1997
861	F861LCU	MCW MetroRider MF158/15	MCW	B31F	1988	Ex Londonlinks, 1997
865	F865LCU	MCW MetroRider MF158/15	MCW	B31F	1988	Ex Londonlinks, 1997
901	F571SMG	Leyland Olympian ONLXB/1RZ	Alexander RL	H47/32F	1988	Ex Alder Valley, 1990
907	F577SMG	Leyland Olympian ONLXB/1RZ	Alexander RL	H47/32F	1988	Ex Alder Valley, 1990
908	F578SMG	Leyland Olympian ONLXB/1RZ	Alexander RL	H47/32F	1988	Ex Alder Valley, 1990
910	F580SMG	Leyland Olympian ONLXB/1RZ	Alexander RL	H47/32F	1988	Ex Alder Valley, 1990
969	J969JNL	Optare MetroRider MR03	Optare	B25F	1991	Ex Londonlinks, 1997
3713	TOF713S	Leyland National 11351A/1R		B49F	1978	Ex Tellings Golden-Miller, 1992
4555	A144EPA	Leyland Tiger TRCTL11/2R	Plaxton Paramount 3200	C57F	1984	
4556	A156EPA	Leyland Tiger TRCTL11/2R	Plaxton Paramount 3200	C57F	1984	
4721	GGE165T	Leyland National 10351A/1R		B41F	1979	Ex Southend, 1993
25107	H107JAR	Volvo B10M-62	Ikarus Blue Danube	C49FT	1990	

The 1998 Cowie Bus Handbbook

Five Wright Pathfinder bodied Dennis Lances operate major route 408 between Guildford and Croydon. The old fleet livery sits nicely on LSL9, N527SPA, as it pauses outside the company's Leatherhead garage for a crew change while heading towards Croydon. *Colin Lloyd*

Classified series:-

AD1-8

Dennis Arrow   East Lancashire Pyoneer   H45/35F   1996

AD1	N801TPK	AD3	N803TPK	AD5	N805TPK	AD7	N807TPK	AD8	N808TPK
AD2	N802TPK	AD4	N804TPK	AD6	N806TPK				

AD9	N809TPK	Dennis Arrow	East Lancashire Pyoneer	DPH45/31F	1996
AD10	N810TPK	Dennis Arrow	East Lancashire Pyoneer	DPH45/31F	1996

AN135-182

Leyland Atlantean AN68A/1R   Park Royal   H43/30F   1978-79

135	UPK135S	147	UPK147S	149	VPK149S	152	VPA152S	175	XPG175T
146	UPK146S	148	VPK148S	151	VPK151S	153	VPA153S	182	XPG182T

AN184-229

Leyland Atlantean AN68A/1R   Roe   H43/30F   1979-80

184	XPG184T	201	XPG201T	223	EPH223V	228	EPH228V	229	EPH229V
187	XPG187T								

AN258-288

Leyland Atlantean AN68B/1R   Roe   H43/30F   1980-81 262 ex Londonlinks, 1997

258	KPJ258W	262	KPJ262W	281	KPJ281W	284	KPJ284W	286	KPJ286W
259	KPJ259W	267	KPJ267W	283	KPJ283W	285	KPJ285W	288	KPJ288W

BTL44	C144SPB	Leyland Tiger TRCTL11/3RH	Berkhof Everest 370	C53F	1986	
DD1	F201OPD	Dennis Dominator DDA1020	East Lancashire	H51/33F	1988	Ex County, 1990

DD2-9

Dennis Dominator DDA1026   East Lancashire   H45/31F*   1989   *9 is H49/35F

DD2	F602RPG	DD4	F604RPG	DD6	F606RPG	DD8	F608RPG	DD9	F609RPG
DD3	F603RPG	DD5	F605RPG	DD7	F607RPG				

DD10-16

Dennis Dominator DDA2005*   East Lancashire   H45/31F   1993-96 *13-16 are DDA2004

DD10	K36XNE	DD12	K38XNE	DD14	N714TPK	DD15	N715TPK
DD11	K37XNE	DD13	N713TPK				

(DD16   N716TPK)

DD17-22

Dennis Dominator DDA1031*   East Lanacshire   H43/25F*   1989-90 Ex North Western, 1997
*19 is type DDA1026 and DPH43/25F

DD17	G626EKA	DD19	F631BKD	DD20	G663FKA	DD21	G664FKA
DD18	G628EKA						

(DD22   G665FKA)

DFC1	OYD693	DAF MB230LT615	Van Hool Alizée	C53FT	1989	Ex London Coaches, 1997
DFC2	F619HGO	DAF MB230LB615	Van Hool Alizée	C53FT	1989	Ex London Coaches, 1997
DFC3	G974KJX	DAF MB230LB615	Van Hool Alizée	C53FT	1990	Ex London Coaches, 1997
DFC4	J16AMB	DAF SB3000DKV601	Van Hool Alizée	C46FT	1992	Ex Kentish Bus, 1997

DS1-24

Dennis Dart 9.8SDL3035*   East Lancashire EL2000   B40F*   1993-96 *10-3/6-18 are B30FL
*14/15 are 9.8SDL3054; *10-3/6-8 are 9.8SDL3053

1	L503CPB	6	L508CPJ	11	M522MPF	16	N528SPA	21	N541TPF
2	L504CPB	7	L509CPJ	12	M523MPF	17	N529SPA	22	N542TPK
3	L505CPJ	8	L510CPJ	13	M524MPF	18	N530SPA	23	N543TPK
4	L506CPJ	9	L511CPJ	14	M525MPM	19	N539TPF	24	N544TPK
5	L507CPJ	10	M521MPF	15	M526MPM	20	N540TPF		

DSL37-55

Dennis Dart SLF   East Lancashire Spryte   B31F   1996-97

37	N237VPH	41	N241VPH	45	N245VPH	49	N249VPH	53	P253APM
38	N238VPH	42	N242VPH	46	N246VPH	50	P250APM	54	P254APM
39	N239VPH	43	N243VPH	47	N247VPH	51	P251APM	55	P255APM
40	N240VPH	44	N244VPH	48	N248VPH	52	P252APM		

DSL68-96

Dennis Dart SLF   Plaxton Pointer 2   B39F   1997

68	P268FPK	74	P274FPK	80	P380FPK	86	P286FPK	92	P292FPK
69	P269FPK	75	P275FPK	81	P281FPK	87	P287FPK	93	P293FPK
70	P270FPK	76	P276FPK	82	P282FPK	88	P288FPK	94	P294FPK
71	P271FPK	77	P277FPK	83	P283FPK	89	P289FPK	95	P295FPK
72	P272FPK	78	P278FPK	84	P284FPK	90	P290FPK	96	P296FPK
73	P273FPK	79	P279FPK	85	P285FPK	91	P291FPK		

DSL97-108

Dennis Dart SLF   Plaxton Pointer 2   B39F   1997

97	R297CMV	100	R310CMV	103	R303CMV	105	R305CMV	107	R307CMV
98	R298CMV	101	R301CMV	104	R304CMV	106	R296CMV	108	R308CMV
99	R299CMV	102	R302CMV						

LNB28	JOX528P	Leyland National 11351A/1R		B25F	1976	Ex Shamrock & Rambler, 1988
LNB36	NOE536R	Leyland National 11351A/1R		B49F	1976	Ex Midland, 1990
LNB546	PKP546R	Leyland National 11351A/1R		B49F	1976	Ex Maidstone & District, 1995
LNB553	MEL553P	Leyland National 11351A/1R		B49F	1976	Ex Hampshire Bus, 1993
LNB600	NOE600R	Leyland 11351A/1R(Cummins)	Urban Bus	B49F	1977	Ex Midland, 1994
LNC362	KDW362P	Leyland National 11351A/1R		DP48F	1975	Ex Rhondda, 1992

LR8-50

Leyland Olympian ONLXB/1R   Roe   H43/29F   1982-83 *21/4 ex Londonlinks, 1997

8	TPD108X	18	TPD118X	27	TPD127X	29	TPD129X	48	A148FPG
13	TPD113X	21	TPD121X	28	TPD128X	46	A146FPG	50	A150FPG
14	TPD114X	24	TPD124X						

Opposite:- **While London & Country and East Lancashire were associated companies within British Bus many of the buses were supplied by the bodybuilder. Here are two examples of the bodywork that show the change in styles over just a short time frame. The upper picture shows AD5, N805TPK, which has been built on the Dennis Arrow chassis, here seen running through the Epsom Downs on service 406. The lower picture shows an earlier East Lancashire style fitted to a Volvo B10M chassis. Here, Norwood-based 671, H671GPF, is seen in Waterloo on Londonlinks duties. Since the picture was taken, the first changes in the group reorganisation has seen this batch transferred to South London where they continue to operate the LRT service.** *Gerald Mead*

LR74	B274LPH	Leyland Olympian ONTL11/1R	Eastern Coach Works	H43/29F	1985	
LR75	B275LPH	Leyland Olympian ONTL11/1R	Eastern Coach Works	H43/29F	1985	
LR501	G501SFT	Leyland Olympian ONCL10/1R	Northern Counties	H47/30F	1989	Ex Kentish Bus, 1992
LR502	G502SFT	Leyland Olympian ONCL10/1R	Northern Counties	H43/29F	1989	Ex Kentish Bus, 1992
LR503	G503SFT	Leyland Olympian ONCL10/1R	Northern Counties	H43/29F	1989	Ex Kentish Bus, 1992
LR504	G504SFT	Leyland Olympian ONCL10/1R	Northern Counties	H43/29F	1989	Ex Kentish Bus, 1992

LSL5-9
Dennis Lance SLF — Wright Pathfinder — B40F* — 1994-95 *9 is B39F

5	M517KPA	6	M518KPA	7	M519KPA	8	M520KPA	9	N527SPA

LS10-24
Dennis Lance 11SDA3113 — East Lancashire — B49F — 1996

10	N210TPK	13	N213TPK	16	N216TPK	19	N219TPK	22	N322TPK
11	N211TPK	14	N214TPK	17	N217TPK	20	N220TPK	23	N223TPK
12	N212TPK	15	N215TPK	18	N218TPK	21	N221TPK	24	N224TPK

MBM236	M236KNR	Mercedes-Benz 811D	Alexander AM	B29FL	1995
MM471	N671TPF	Mercedes-Benz 709D	Plaxton Beaver	B23F	1996
MR472	P472APJ	Optare MetroRider MR17	Optare	B29F	1996
MM473	P473APJ	Mercedes-Benz 711D	Plaxton Beaver	B23F	1996
MM474	P474APJ	Mercedes-Benz 811D	Plaxton Beaver	B18FL	1996

MM475-480
Mercedes-Benz 711D — Plaxton Beaver — B27F — 1997

475	P475DPE	476	P476DPE	477	P477DPE	479	P479DPE	480	P480DPE

SNB348	UPB348S	Leyland National 10351A/1R		B41F	1977
SNB349	UPB349S	Leyland National 10351A/1R		B41F	1977

SNB376-502
Leyland National 10351B/1R — B41F — 1978-79

SNB420 had an UrbanBus re-build and is fitted with Cummins engine

376	YPL376T	380	YPL380T	393w	YPL393T	427	YPL427T	475	BPL475T
377w	YPL377T	382	YPL382T	394	YPL394T	440	YPL440T	491	BPL491T
378	YPL378T	385	YPL385T	420	YPL420T	459	BPL459T	502w	DPH502T

SNB511	EPD511V	Leyland National 10351B/1R		B41F	1979	
SNB530	EPD530V	Leyland National 10351B/1R		B41F	1979	
SNB538	EPD538V	Leyland National 10351B/1R		B41F	1979	
SNB543	EPD543V	Leyland National 10351B/1R		B41F	1979	
SR88	E88OJT	Leyland Tiger TRCTL11/3RZ	Plaxton Paramount 3200 III	C48FT	1988	Ex Shamrock & Rambler, 1989
SR89	E89OJT	Leyland Tiger TRCTL11/3RZ	Plaxton Paramount 3200 III	C53F	1988	Ex Speedlink, 1990
SR90	E90OJT	Leyland Tiger TRCTL11/3RZ	Plaxton Paramount 3200 III	C48FT	1988	Ex Shamrock & Rambler, 1989
TC426	HBH426Y	Leyland Tiger TRCTL11/3RZ	Plaxton Paramount 3200	C53F	1983	Ex Blue Saloon, Guildford, 1996
TDL46	C246SPC	Leyland Tiger TRCTL11/3RH	Duple 320	C53F	1986	
TDL66	ESK987	Leyland Tiger TRCTL11/2RH	Duple 320	C50F	1985	Ex Maidstone & District, 1997
TDL67	ESK988	Leyland Tiger TRCTL11/2RH	Duple 320	C50F	1985	Ex Maidstone & District, 1997
TP74	B274KPF	Leyland Tiger TRCTL11/2R	Plaxton Paramount 3200 2	C49F	1985	
TP91	AEF990Y	Leyland Tiger TRCTL11/2R	Plaxton Paramount 3200	C53F	1983	Ex Shamrock & Rambler, 1988
TPL54	A154EPA	Leyland Tiger TRCTL11/2R	Plaxton Paramount 3200	C57F	1984	
TPL85	B285KPF	Leyland Tiger TRCTL11/2R	Plaxton Paramount 3200 2	C50FT	1985	
TPL88	B288KPF	Leyland Tiger TRCTL11/2R	Plaxton Paramount 3200 2	C50FT	1985	
VCB89	C89NNV	Volvo B10M-61	Caetano Stagecoach	B57F	1986	Ex Tellings-Golden Miller, 1995
ZGF58	UFG58S	Leyland National 11351A/2R		B49F	1977	Ex Panther, Crawley, 1991
ZGF60	UFG60S	Leyland National 11351A/2R		B49F	1977	Ex Panther, Crawley, 1991
ZGF180	THX180S	Leyland National 10351A/2R		B41F	1978	Ex Panther, Crawley, 1991
ZGF313	AYR313T	Leyland National 10351A/2R		B41F	1979	Ex Panther, Crawley, 1991

Heritage fleet:-

GS13	MXX313	Guy Special NLLVP	Eastern Coach Works	B26F	1953	Ex Sussex Bus, Ford, 1992
RMA16	KGJ614D	AEC Routemaster	Park Royal	H31/24F	1966	Ex preservation, 1996
RMC4	SLT59	Leyland Routemaster	Eastern Coach Works	H32/25RD	1970	Ex London Transport, 1970
RT3775	NLE882	AEC Regent III O961	Park Royal	H30/26R	1953	Ex preservation, 1994
RP21	JPA121K	AEC Reliance 6U3ZR	Park Royal	DP45F	1972	Ex AML, Hounslow, 1994

London & Country for a few years in the early to mid 1990s proudly boasted a vintage fleet of both single and double-deckers. Restored in as near original liveries as possible to the former London Transport country area era and later London Country, the vehicles were mostly used in service during the Summer seasonal periods. GS13, MXX313, a Guy Special was one these special event vehicles.
Richard Godfrey

Ancilliary vehicles:-

160	CPG160T	AEC Reliance 6U3ZR	Plaxton Supreme III Express	C53F	1979	
BS407	YPH407T	Bedford YMT	Plaxton Supreme III	C53F	1978	Ex Blue Saloon, Guildford, 1996
BS820	YPB820T	Bedford YMT	Plaxton Supreme III	C53F	1978	Ex Blue Saloon, Guildford, 1996
DT9	SFJ132R	Bristol LH6L	Plaxton Supreme III Express	C41F	1977	
4713	LPB218P	Leyland National 10351/1R		B41F	1976	
4716	GGE156T	Leyland National 10351A/1R		B41F	1979	Ex Southend, 1997
SNB381	YPL381T	Leyland National 10351B/1R		B41F	1978	Ex Londonlinks, 1997
A4	OLS540P	Leyland Leopard PSU3C/4R	Alexander AYS	DP53F	1975	Ex Londonlinks, 1997
A26	TSJ64S	Leyland Leopard PSU3D/4R	Alexander AY	DP53F	1977	Ex Londonlinks, 1997
A27	TSJ83S	Leyland Leopard PSU3D/4R	Alexander AY	DP53F	1977	Ex Londonlinks, 1997
A33	CKE168Y	Leyland Leopard PSU3G/4R	Eastern Coach Works B51	DP49F	1982	Ex Londonlinks, 1997
A34	CKE169Y	Leyland Leopard PSU3G/4R	Eastern Coach Works B51	DP49F	1982	Ex Londonlinks, 1997
954	D954VCN	Freight Rover Sherpa	Dormobile	B16F	1986	Ex Londonlinks, 1997

Previous Registrations:

776WME	F619HGO	PDZ6273	JOX490P
B23PGX	776WME	PDZ6274	UHG744S
ESK987	B812JPN	PDZ6275	UFG54S
ESK988	B815JPN	PDZ6276	GOL403N
JIL2190	JOX499P	PDZ6277	TPE161S
JIL2193	RKE520M	RDZ4278	JOX481P
JIL2196	KDW332P	RDZ4279	KPA380P
JIL2197	BCD808L	SIB1278	BPL481T
JIL2198	SCK703P	SIB6709	LFR865X
JIL2199	UHG736R	SIB6711	HPF310N
JIL5367	NOE598R	SIB6713	UPE215M
LIL2168	SGR134R	SIB6714	WPG216M
LIL2180	KPA375P	SJI5066	NEN961R
OYD693	F618HGO	SJI5569	NPJ471R
PDZ6263	NOE562R	SJI5570	JOX491P
PDZ6264	ERP551T	SJI5571	SCK709P
PDZ6265	GPJ891N	SJI5572	LPF601P

Allocations and liveries:-

Livery: Two-tone green, white and red; red and white ♥ (Gem Fairtax)

Cranleigh (Mansfield Park) - Guildford & West Surrey

Lance	LS19	LS20	LS21	LS22	LS23	LS24
Greenway	370					
Dominator	DD13	DD14				
Heritage	RMA16.					

Crawley (Wheatstone Close) - London & Country

Tiger	SR88	TPL85	TPL88					
Mercedes-Benz	422	428	461	466	467	468	470	MM471
Dart	DSL97	DSL98	DSL99	DSL100	DSL101	DSL102		
National	221	3713	4721	SNB348	SNB349	SNB376	SNB378	SNB380
	SNB382	SNB385	SNB427	SNB530	SNB538	LNB36	ZGF58♥	
	ZGF60♥	ZGF180♥	ZGF313♥					
Lance	LS10	LS11	LS12					
Atlantean	AN147	AN148	AN149	AN151	AN152	AN153	AN182	AN201
	AN223	AN229	AN283	AN284	AN286			
Dominator	DD17	DD18	DD19	DD20	DD21	DD22		
Arrow	AD1	AD2	AD3	AD4	AD5	AD6	AD7	AD8
	AD9	AD10						
Heritage	RT3775	RP21						

Croydon (Beddington Farm Road) - Londonlinks

Mercedes-Benz	430	431	433	434	435	436	437	438
MetroRider	440	441	442	443	847	850	865	969
Volvo B6	201	202	203	204	205	206	207	208
	209	210	211	212				
Dart	120	121	122	123	124	125	126	151
	160	161	162	163	164	165	166	167
	168	169	170	171	172			
National	331							
Lynx	311	312	313	314	315	316	399	400
	401	402	418					
Atlantean	AN262							
Olympian	685	686	687	688	689	690	691	692
	693	694	695	696	697	698	699	700
	LR21	LR24						
Volvo Citybus	623	624	625	626	627	628	629	630
	701	704	705	710				

Guildford (Leas Road) - Guildford & West Surrey

Mercedes-Benz	403	404	405	421	438	454	455	458
	459	460	469	MBM236				
Dart	DS7	DS9	DS14	DS15	DS21	DSL68	DSL69	DSL70
	DSL71	DSL72	DSL73	DSL74	DSL75	DSL76	DSL77	DSL78
	DSL79	DSL80	DSL81	DSL82	DSL97	DSL98	DSL99	DSL100
National	242	246						
Greenway	373	374	375	376	377			
Falcon	302	303	304	305				
Lance	LS13	LS14	LS15	LS16	LS17	LS18		
Dominator	DD10	DD11	DD12	DD16				
Olympian	901	907	908	910				
Heritage	GS13							

Horsham (Parsonage Way) - Horsham Buses

Tiger	4555	TP91			
Mercedes-Benz	132	154	155	156	157
Reliance	161				
Dart	DSL37	DSL50	DSL53	DSL54	DSL55
National	257	LNB553			
Greenway	363	364	365	366	
Atlantean	AN175	AN281	AN288		

Hounslow (Albion Road) - London & Country

Mercedes-Benz	113	189	190	402	425	MM473	MM474
MetroRider	MR472						
Dart	DS10	DS11	DS12	DS13	DS16	DS17	DS18
Atlantean	AN135	AN267	AN285				

Leatherhead (Guildford Road) - London & Country

Mercedes-Benz	201	426	429					
Dart	DS1	DS2	DS4	DS23	DS24	DSL90	DSL91	DSL92
	DSL93	DSL94	DSL95	DSL96				
National	270	LNB28	LNC362	SNB394	SNB459	SNB475S	SNB491	SNB511
	SNB543	LNB546						
Greenway	378	379						
Lance	LSL5	LSL6	LSL7	LSL8	LSL9			
Atlantean	AN258							
Volvo Citybus	610	611	612	613	614	615	616	617
	618	619	620	621	622			
Dominator	DD1	DD2	DD3	DD4	DD5	DD6	DD7	DD8
	DD9							
Olympian	LR8	LR13	LR18	LR29	LR46	LR48	LR50	LR75

Merstham (Station Road) - London & Country

Tiger	SR89							
Mercedes-Benz	464	475	476					
Volvo B6	512	513	514	515	516			
Dart	DS6	DS8						
National	202	252	265	LNB600	SNB377	SNB420		
Greenway	339	341	343	344	353	356	357	358
	359	360	367	368	369	380	381	
Atlantean	AN146	AN184	AN187	AN228	AN259			
Olympian	701	702	703	704				
Heritage	RMC4							

Slyfield (Westfield Road) - London & Country

DAF	DFC1	DFC2	DFC3	DFC4				
Tiger	BTL44	SR90	TC426	TDL46	TDL66	TDL67	TP74	TPL54
Mercedes-Benz	133							
National	258							
Volvo B10M	168	25107	VCB89					

Woking (Goldsworth Park Industrial Estate) - Guildford & West Surrey

Mercedes-Benz	120	423	424	427	439	456	457	462
	463	465	MM477	MM479	MM480			
Dart	DS3	DS5	DS19	DS20	DS22	DSL38	DSL39	DSL40
	DSL41	DSL42	DSL43	DSL44	DSL45	DSL46	DSL47	DSL48
	DSL49	DSL51	DSL52	DSL83	DSL84	DSL85	DSL86	DSL87
	DSL88	DSL89	DSL101	DSL102				
Greenway	371	372						
Dominator	DD15							

MAIDSTONE & DISTRICT

Maidstone & District Motor Services Ltd; New Enterprise Coaches (Tonbridge) Ltd;
Invicta House; Armstrong Road, Maidstone, Kent ME15 6TY

1041-1086   Mercedes-Benz 609D   Reeve Burgess   B20F   1987-90 *1077/8 are B19F

1041	E41UKL	1052	E52UKL	1063	E63UKL	1071	G71PKR	1078	G78SKR
1042	E42UKL	1053	E53UKL	1064	E64UKL	1072	G72PKR	1079	G79SKR
1043	E43UKL	1054	E54UKL	1065	E65KXE	1073	G73PKR	1080	G80SKR
1044	E44UKL	1055	E55UKL	1066	F66BKK	1074	G74PKR	1082	G82SKR
1045	E45UKL	1056	E56UKL	1067	F67BKK	1075	G75PKR	1084	G84SKR
1046	E46UKL	1057	E57UKL	1069	G69PKR	1076	G76PKR	1085	G85SKR
1047	E47UKL	1058	E58UKL	1070	G70PKR	1077	G77PKR	1086	G86SKR

1201	G201RKK	Mercedes-Benz 709D	Reeve Burgess Beaver	B25F	1989
1202	G202RKK	Mercedes-Benz 709D	Reeve Burgess Beaver	B25F	1989
1203	G203RKK	Mercedes-Benz 709D	Reeve Burgess Beaver	B25F	1989
1204	H204EKO	Mercedes-Benz 709D	Carlyle	B25F	1991
1205	M205SKE	Mercedes-Benz 709D	Plaxton Beaver	B23F	1995
1206	M206SKE	Mercedes-Benz 709D	Plaxton Beaver	B23F	1995

1207-1217   Mercedes-Benz 709D   Plaxton Beaver   B27F   1996

1207	N207CKP	1210	P210JKL	1212	P212JKL	1214	P214JKL	1216	P216JKL
1208	N208CKP	1211	P211JKL	1213	P213JKL	1215	P215JKL	1217	P217JKL
1209	N209CKP								

1218-1230   Mercedes-Benz 711D   Plaxton Beaver   B27F   1997

1218	P218LKK	1221	P221LKK	1225	P225LKK	1227	P227LKK	1229	P229LKK
1219	P219LKK	1223	P223LKK	1226	P226LKK	1228	P228LKK	1230	P230LKK
1220	P220LKK	1224	P224LKK						

1301	H301FKL	Mercedes-Benz 709D	Reeve Burgess Beaver	DP25F	1991	Ex New Enterprises, 1996
1351	N351YKE	Mercedes-Benz 709D	Plaxton Beaver	DP16FL	1995	
1352	N352BKK	Mercedes-Benz 709D	Plaxton Beaver	DP16FL	1995	

Opposite:- **This operation is the original Maidstone and District Motor Services Ltd founded in 1911, though in NBC days it did share common management with East Kent from 1972 to 1983. Representing the fleet here are two recently delivered buses, a Super-low-floor Dart 3180, P180LKL photographed at Chatham, and a Volvo Olympian 5937, P937MKL, currently allocated to Maidstone.** *Malc McDonald/Martin Smith*

Between 1987 and 1990 the standard minibuses for Maidstone & District were Mercedes-Benz 609Ds with panel van bodywork converted for bus use by Reeve Burgess. The majority still remain in service as illustrated by 1075, G75PKR at Chatham.
Colin Lloyd

Maidstone & District have acquired Dennis Darts, both new and second hand. Until the recent influx of over sixty low-floor variety there have been three small batches placed in service. Number 3465, J465MKL, is from the first batch that was delivered in November 1991 and currently carries a predominately green livery. *Richard Godfrey*

1713	L287EKK	Iveco TurboDaily 59-12	Dormobile Routemaker	B25F	1994	Ex Kentish Bus, 1996
1714	L714EKO	Iveco TurboDaily 59-12	Dormobile Routemaker	B25F	1994	Ex Kentish Bus, 1996
1836	F393DOA	Peugeot-Talbot Pullman	Talbot	B17FL	1989	Ex Kentish Bus, 1997
1840	M40MPS	Iveco TurboDaily 59-12	Marshall C31	B26FL	1995	Ex Mercury, Hoo, 1996
1860	J60MPS	Mercedes-Benz 811D	PMT Ami	DP33F	1992	Ex Mercury, Hoo, 1996
1870w	L70MPS	Peugeot-Talbot Pullman	TBP	B22F	1993	Ex Mercury, Hoo, 1996
1880	L80MPS	Peugeot-Talbot Pullman	TBP	B22F	1994	Ex Mercury, Hoo, 1996
1885w	G885SKE	Peugeot-Talbot Pullman	Talbot	B22F	1989	Ex Kentish Bus, 1997
2172	YSU895	Leyland Tiger TRCTL11/2R	Plaxton Paramount 3200E	C53F	1983	Ex Kentish Bus, 1997
2173	YSU896	Leyland Tiger TRCTL11/2R	Plaxton Paramount 3200E	C53F	1984	Ex London County NE, 1990
2174	YSU897	Leyland Tiger TRCTL11/2R	Plaxton Paramount 3200E	C53F	1984	Ex Kentish Bus, 1990
2186	YSU870	Leyland Tiger TRCTL11/3ARZA	Plaxton Paramount 3500 III	C53F	1988	
2187	YSU871	Leyland Tiger TRCTL11/3ARZA	Plaxton Paramount 3500 III	C53F	1988	
2188	F188HKK	Leyland Tiger TRCL10/3RZA	Duple 340	C53F	1989	
2189	F189HKK	Leyland Tiger TRCL10/3RZA	Duple 340	C53F	1989	
2192	YSU872	Leyland Tiger TRCL10/3RZ	Duple 320	C53F	1989	Ex Park's, Hamilton, 1993
2193	YSU873	Leyland Tiger TRCL10/3RZ	Duple 320	C53F	1989	Ex Park's, Hamilton, 1993
2195	J26UNY	Leyland Tiger TRCL10/3ARZM	Plaxton 321	C53F	1992	Ex Bebb, Llantwit Fardre, 1993
2196	J27UNY	Leyland Tiger TRCL10/3ARZM	Plaxton 321	C53F	1992	Ex Bebb, Llantwit Fardre, 1993
2197	IIL9168	Leyland Tiger TRCL10/3ARZM	Plaxton Paramount 3200 III	C53F	1989	Ex Kentish Bus, 1997
2198	IIL9169	Leyland Tiger TRCL10/3ARZM	Plaxton Paramount 3200 III	C53F	1989	Ex Kentish Bus, 1997
2199	XSV691	Leyland Tiger TRCTL11/3ARZA	Plaxton Paramount 3200 III	C53F	1988	Ex London & Country, 1997
2200	TSU644	Leyland Tiger TRCTL11/3R	Plaxton Paramount 3200E	C53F	1983	
2841	HIL2279	Volvo B10M-61	Plaxton Paramount 3500 III	C50F	1988	Ex Kentish Bus, 1997
2844	TIB5901	Volvo B10M-61	Plaxton Paramount 3500 III	C50F	1988	Ex Kentish Bus, 1996
2845	A14GTA	Volvo B10M-60	Plaxton Paramount 3500 III	C49FT	1990	Ex Kentish Bus, 1996
2846	H846AHS	Volvo B10M-60	Plaxton Paramount 3500 III	C49FT	1991	Ex Express Travel, Liverpool, 1995
2847	H847AHS	Volvo B10M-60	Plaxton Paramount 3500 III	C51F	1991	Ex Express Travel, Liverpool, 1995
2848	H616UWR	Volvo B10M-60	Plaxton Paramount 3500 III	C50F	1991	Ex Wallace Arnold, 1996
2849	H618UWR	Volvo B10M-60	Plaxton Paramount 3500 III	C50F	1991	Ex Wallace Arnold, 1996
2850	H637UWR	Volvo B10M-60	Plaxton Paramount 3500 III	C50F	1991	Ex Westbus, Hounslow, 1996
2851w	G801BPG	Volvo B10M-60	Plaxton Paramount 3500 III	C37FT	1989	Ex Speedlink, 1997
2852w	G802BPG	Volvo B10M-60	Plaxton Paramount 3500 III	C37FT	1989	Ex Speedlink, 1997
3040	D108NDW	Leyland Lynx LX112TL11ZR1R	Leyland Lynx	B49F	1987	Ex London Coaches (Kent), 1996
3041	E885KYW	Leyland Lynx LX112TL11ZR1S	Leyland Lynx	B49F	1987	Ex London Coaches (Kent), 1996
3042	E886KYW	Leyland Lynx LX112TL11ZR1S	Leyland Lynx	B47F	1987	Ex London Coaches (Kent), 1996
3043	E887KYW	Leyland Lynx LX112TL11ZR1S	Leyland Lynx	B47F	1987	Ex London Coaches (Kent), 1996
3044	E890KYW	Leyland Lynx LX1126LXCTZR1S	Leyland Lynx	B47F	1987	Ex London Coaches (Kent), 1996

The 1998 Cowie Bus Handbook

Following de-regulation, Wigan-based Shearings established commercial bus operations in Kent, Shropshire, Yorkshire, South Wales and Manchester, though these were subsequently sold following a change of policy. Maidstone & District purchased the Kent workings along with four Leyland Lynx, the one seen here being 3046, F46ENF. *Richard Godfrey*

3045	F45ENF	Leyland Lynx LX112L10ZR1R	Leyland Lynx	B49F	1988	Ex Shearings, 1991
3046	F46ENF	Leyland Lynx LX112L10ZR1R	Leyland Lynx	B49F	1988	Ex Shearings, 1991
3047	F47ENF	Leyland Lynx LX112L10ZR1R	Leyland Lynx	B49F	1988	Ex Shearings, 1991
3048	F48ENF	Leyland Lynx LX112L10ZR1R	Leyland Lynx	B49F	1988	Ex Shearings, 1991
3049	H256YLG	Leyland Lynx LX2R11V18Z4R	Leyland Lynx 2	B49F	1990	Ex Aintree Coachline, 1995
3051	H814EKJ	Leyland Lynx LX2R11C15Z4S	Leyland Lynx 2	B49F	1991	Ex Kentish Bus, 1997
3052	H816EKJ	Leyland Lynx LX2R11C15Z4S	Leyland Lynx 2	B49F	1991	Ex Kentish Bus, 1997
3066	D155HML	Leyland Lynx LX112TL11ZR1S	Leyland Lynx	B49F	1987	Ex Kentish Bus, 1997
3067	D157HML	Leyland Lynx LX112TL11ZR1S	Leyland Lynx	B49F	1987	Ex Kentish Bus, 1997
3149	J220HGY	Dennis Dart 9SDL3011	Plaxton Pointer	B35F	1992	Ex Londonlinks, 1997
3150	J221HGY	Dennis Dart 9SDL3011	Plaxton Pointer	B35F	1992	Ex Londonlinks, 1997
3151	L500DKT	Dennis Dart 9SDL3032	WSC Portsdown	B43F	1994	Ex Wealden Beeline, 1997
3152	M501PKJ	Dennis Dart 9SDL3032	WSC Portsdown	B43F	1994	Ex Wealden Beeline, 1997
3153	M502RKO	Dennis Dart 9SDL3032	WSC Portsdown	B43F	1995	Ex Wealden Beeline, 1997
3154	L503HKM	Dennis Dart 9SDL3032	WSC Portsdown	B43F	1994	Ex Wealden Beeline, 1997
3155	L766DPE	Dennis Dart 9.8SDL3034	Wadham Stringer Winchester	C39F	1993	Ex Wealden Beeline, 1997
3156	L156YVK	Dennis Dart 9SDL3034	Northern Counties Paladin	B35F	1994	Ex Kentish Bus, 1997

3176-3183

Dennis Dart SLF		Plaxton Pointer		B40F	1996		
3176	P176LKL	3178	P178LKL	3180	P180LKL	3182	P182LKL	3183	P183LKL
3177	P177LKL	3179	P179LKL	3181	P181LKL		

3192-3247

Dennis Dart SLF Plaxton Pointer 2 B40F 1997

3192	P192LKJ	3204	P204LKJ	3215	P215LKJ	3227	P227MKL	3238	P238MKN
3193	P193LKJ	3205	P205LKJ	3216	P216LKJ	3228	P228MKL	3239	P239MKN
3194	P194LKJ	3206	P206LKJ	3217	P217MKL	3229	P229MKL	3240	P240MKN
3195	P195LKJ	3207	P207LKJ	3218	P218MKL	3230	P230MKL	3241	P241MKN
3196	P196LKJ	3208	P208LKJ	3219	P219MKL	3231	P231MKL	3242	P242MKN
3197	P197LKJ	3209	P209LKJ	3220	P220MKL	3232	P232MKL	3243	P243MKN
3198	P198LKJ	3210	P210LKJ	3221	P221MKL	3233	P233MKN	3244	P244MKN
3199	P199LKJ	3211	P211LKJ	3223	P223MKL	3234	P234MKN	3245	P245MKN
3201	P201LKJ	3212	P212LKJ	3224	P224MKL	3235	P235MKN	3246	P246MKN
3202	P202LKJ	3213	P213LKJ	3225	P225MKL	3236	P236MKN	3247	P247MKN
3203	P203LKJ	3214	P214LKJ	3226	P226MKL	3237	P237MKN		

3461	G218LGK	Dennis Dart 9SDL3002	Duple Dartline	B36F	1990	Ex Kentish Bus, 1996
3462	G122RGT	Dennis Dart 9SDL3002	Duple Dartline	B36F	1990	Ex R&I Buses, Harlesden, 1995
3463	J463MKL	Dennis Dart 9.8SDL3012	Plaxton Pointer	B40F	1991	
3464	J464MKL	Dennis Dart 9.8SDL3012	Plaxton Pointer	B40F	1991	
3465	J465MKL	Dennis Dart 9.8SDL3012	Plaxton Pointer	B40F	1991	

3466-3471

Dennis Dart 9.8SDL3017 — Plaxton Pointer — B40F — 1992 — 3470 was rebodied in 1995

3466	J466OKP	3468	J468OKP	3469	K469SKO	3470	K470SKO	3471	K471SKO
3467	J467OKP						

3474	M100CBB	Dennis Dart 9.8SDL3040	Plaxton Pointer	B40F	1995	Ex Cardiff Bluebird, 1996
3475	M200CBB	Dennis Dart 9.8SDL3040	Plaxton Pointer	B40F	1995	Ex Cardiff Bluebird, 1996

3601-3618

Volvo B6-9.9M — Plaxton Pointer — B40F — 1994-95

3601	L601EKM	3605	L605EKM	3609	L609EKM	3613	M613PKP	3616	M616PKP
3602	L602EKM	3606	L606EKM	3610	L610EKM	3614	M614PKP	3617	M617PKP
3603	L603EKM	3607	L607EKM	3611	M611PKP	3615	M615PKP	3618	M618PKP
3604	L604EKM	3608	L608EKM	3612	M612PKP			

3810	SIB6710	Leyland NL106L11/1R	East Lancs Greenway(1992)	B41F	1981	Ex Kentish Bus, 1997
3812	SIB6712	Leyland 10351A/2R	East Lancs Greenway(1992)	B41F	1979	Ex Kentish Bus, 1997
3820	M20MPS	Dennis Dart 9.8SDL3054	Marshall C37	B40F	1994	Ex Mercury, Hoo, 1996
3830	M30MPS	Dennis Dart 9.8SDL3054	Marshall C37	DP40F	1995	Ex Mercury, Hoo, 1996
5111	PKM111R	Bristol VRT/SL3/6LXB	Eastern Coach Works	H43/31F	1976	
5112	PKM112R	Bristol VRT/SL3/6LXB	Eastern Coach Works	H43/31F	1976	
5116	PKM116R	Bristol VRT/SL3/6LXB	Eastern Coach Works	H43/31F	1977	
5125	WKO125S	Bristol VRT/SL3/6LXB	Eastern Coach Works	H43/31F	1978	
5133	WKO133S	Bristol VRT/SL3/6LXB	Eastern Coach Works	H43/31F	1978	
5137	WKO137S	Bristol VRT/SL3/6LXB	Eastern Coach Works	H43/31F	1978	
5138	WKO138S	Bristol VRT/SL3/6LXB	Eastern Coach Works	H43/31F	1978	

5201-5210

MCW Metrobus DR102/42 — MCW — H45/31F — 1984

5201	A201OKJ	5203	A203OKJ	5205	A205OKJ	5208	A208OKJ	5210	A210OKJ
5202	A202OKJ	5204	A204OKJ	5207	A207OKJ	5209	A209OKJ		

5827	WRC833S	Bristol VRT/SL3/501(6LXB)	Eastern Coach Works	H43/31F	1978	Ex Trent, 1993
5828	BRC834T	Bristol VRT/SL3/6LXB	Eastern Coach Works	H43/31F	1979	Ex Trent, 1993
5829	BRC835T	Bristol VRT/SL3/6LXB	Eastern Coach Works	H43/31F	1979	Ex Trent, 1993
5830	BRC837T	Bristol VRT/SL3/6LXB	Eastern Coach Works	H43/31F	1979	Ex Trent, 1993

5831-5853

Bristol VRT/SL3/6LXB — Eastern Coach Works — H43/31F — 1978-79

5831	BKE831T	5837	BKE837T	5843w	BKE843T	5846	BKE846T	5852	BKE852T
5832	BKE832T	5840	BKE840T	5845	BKE845T	5848	BKE848T	5853	BKE853T
5833	BKE833T	5842	BKE842T					

5863-5869

Bristol VRT/SL3/6LXB — Eastern Coach Works — H43/31F — 1979

5863	FKM863V	5864	FKM864V	5867	FKM867V	5868	FKM868V	5869	FKM869V

5870	ODC470W	Bristol VRT/SL3/6LXB	Eastern Coach Works	H43/31F	1981	Ex West Riding, 1995

5873-5886

Bristol VRT/SL3/6LXB — Eastern Coach Works — H43/31F — 1979-80

5873w	FKM873V	5878	FKM878V	5881	FKM881V	5883	HKM883V	5885	HKM885V
5875	FKM875V	5879	FKM879V	5882	FKM882V	5884	HKM884V	5886	HKM886V
5877	FKM877V	5880	FKM880V					

5887w	GHB84W	Bristol VRT/SL3/6LXB	East Lancashire	H44/32F	1981	Ex Mercury, Hoo, 1996
5888	A888PKR	Leyland Olympian ONLXB/1R	Eastern Coach Works	DPH42/27F	1984	
5889	A889PKR	Leyland Olympian ONLXB/1R	Eastern Coach Works	DPH42/27F	1984	
5890	A890PKR	Leyland Olympian ONLXB/1R	Eastern Coach Works	DPH42/27F	1984	

5891-5900

Leyland Olympian ONLXB/1RH — Northern Counties — H45/30F — 1988

5891	E891AKN	5893	F893BKK	5895	F895BKK	5897	F897DKK	5899	F899DKK
5892	F892BKK	5894	F894BKK	5896	F896DKK	5898	F898DKK	5900	F900DKK

Maidstone and District acquired Wealden Beeline bus operations during August 1997 along with seven vehicles, and these included one of the few Wadham Stringer Winchester-bodied Dennis Darts. Now numbered 3155, L766DPE, it is seen in the final Maidstone and District livery in Tunbridge Wells. *Terry Blackman*

Only three 'standard' NBC Olympians were taken by Maidstone & District, although the coach versions were supplied for Invictaway duties. All three have now been upgraded with high-back seating, just visible in this view of 5890, A890PKR, taken in Maidstone. *Malc McDonald*

5901-5905
Leyland Olympian ON2R50G13Z4 Northern Counties Palatine H45/30F 1990

5901	G901SKP	5902	G902SKP	5903	G903SKP	5904	G904SKP	5905	G905SKP

5906-5910
Leyland Olympian ON2R50G13Z4 Northern Counties Palatine H45/30F 1993

5906	K906SKR	5907	K907SKR	5908	K908SKR	5909	K909SKR	5910	K910SKR

5911-5925
Volvo Olympian YN2R50C16Z4 Northern Counties Palatine H47/30F 1994-95 5913 rebodied 1995

5911	M911MKM	5914	M914MKM	5917	M917MKM	5920	M920MKM	5923	M923PKN
5912	M912MKM	5915	M915MKM	5918	M918MKM	5921	M921PKN	5924	M924PKN
5913	M913MKM	5916	M916MKM	5919	M919MKM	5922	M922PKN	5925	M925PKN

5926-5943
Volvo Olympian Northern Counties Palatine H47/30F* 1997 *5938-43 are H45/30F

5926	P926MKL	5930	P930MKL	5934	P934MKL	5938	P938MKL	5941	P941MKL
5927	P927MKL	5931	P931MKL	5935	P935MKL	5939	P939MKL	5942	P942MKL
5928	P928MKL	5932	P932MKL	5936	P936MKL	5940	P940MKL	5943	P943MKL
5929	P929MKL	5933	P933MKL	5937	P937MKL				

6666	THX291S	Leyland Fleetline FE30ALR	MCW	O44/24F	1977	Ex Cowie Leaside, 1997

As well as the Dennis Dart, Maidstone & District have eighteen Volvo B6s. When delivered in 1995 these carried a different livery than that applied to the later examples. Pictured in Park and Ride livery is 3611, M611PKP, which is currently with New Enterprise. The base colour for this contract is yellow with green relief.
Richard Godfrey

Since 1988, Maidstone & District received regular batches of Leyland Olympians with Northern Counties bodywork. One of the 1997 deliveries, 5942, P942MKL, illustrates its dedicated branding for route 101.
Gerald Mead

New Enterprise:-

7003	M619PKP	Volvo B6-9.9M	Plaxton Pointer	B40F	1995	
7006	F68BKK	Mercedes-Benz 609D	Reeve Burgess Beaver	DP19F	1988	
7018w	LSK643	Bedford YNV Venturer	Plaxton Paramount 3200 II	C53F	1986	Ex Excelsior, Bournemouth, 1988
7023	TSU645	Leyland Tiger TRCTL11/3R	Plaxton Paramount 3200 E	C53F	1983	
7024	494WYA	Leyland Tiger TRCTL11/3R	Plaxton Paramount 3500	C57F	1984	Ex PMT, 1990
7025	LSK641	Leyland Tiger TRCTL11/3R	Plaxton Paramount 3200	C53F	1983	Ex Mercers, Longridge, 1991
7026	NTK611	Leyland Tiger TRCTL11/3R	Duple Laser	C53F	1983	
7027	544XVW	Leyland Tiger TRCTL11/3R	Duple Laser	C53F	1983	
7028	J25UNY	Leyland Tiger TRCL10/3ARZM	Plaxton 321	C53F	1992	Ex Bebb, Llantwit Fardre, 1993
7030	A222DRM	Bedford YNT	Plaxton Paramount 3200	C57F	1984	Ex Clarke, Elmswell, 1994
7031	UJI2338	Scania K113CRB	Plaxton Paramount 3500 III	C49FT	1990	Ex Happy Days, Woodseaves, 1994
7033w	GGM69W	Leyland Leopard PSU3F/4R	Plaxton Supreme IV Express	C53F	1981	Ex Alder Valley, 1994
7034	UJI2339	Leyland Tiger TRCTL11/3RH	Plaxton Paramount 3500 II	C49FT	1985	Ex Kentish Bus, 1995
7035	UJI2337	Leyland Tiger TRCTL11/3RH	Plaxton Paramount 3500 II	C49FT	1985	Ex Kentish Bus, 1995
7036	F621HGO	DAF MB230LT615	Van Hool Alizée	C53FT	1989	Ex London Coaches (Kent), 1997
7040	F899GUM	DAF MB230LB615	Plaxton Paramount 3500 III	C53F	1989	Ex O'Sullivan, Killarney, 1997
7041	F901GUM	DAF MB230LB615	Plaxton Paramount 3500 III	C53F	1989	Ex O'Sullivan, Killarney, 1996
7042	J36GCX	DAF SB2305DHS585	Duple 320	C57F	1992	Ex Eagle, Bristol, 1997
7050	A11GTA	Volvo B10M-60	Plaxton Paramount 3500 III	C53F	1991	Ex Kentish Bus, 1997
7051	G546NKJ	Volvo B10M-60	Caetano Algarve	C53F	1989	
7052	G998RKN	Volvo B10M-60	Caetano Algarve	C53F	1990	
7059	WKO139S	Bristol VRT/SL3/6LXB	Eastern Coach Works	H43/31F	1978	
7060	VCA461W	Bristol VRT/SL3/6LXB	Eastern Coach Works	H43/31F	1980	Ex Crosville Cymru, 1996
7061	YNW401S	Bristol VRT/SL3/6LXB	Eastern Coach Works	H43/31F	1978	Ex Southend, 1996
7062	YUM515S	Bristol VRT/SL3/6LXB	Eastern Coach Works	H43/31F	1978	Ex Southend, 1996

Heritage Vehicles:-

LC1	NKN650	Commer Avenger 1	Harrington	C16F	1951	Knight Rider
3456	EKL456K	Leyland Leopard PSU4B/4R	Marshall	B52F	1972	
5558	558LKP	Leyland Atlantean PDR1/1	Metro Cammell	H44/33F	1960	

Ancilliary vehicles:

A4	CTN637V	Bedford YMT	Duple Dominant	B55F	1980	Ex Kentish Bus, 1997
P5	CVA110V	Bedford YMT	Plaxton Supreme IV	C53F	1980	Ex New Enterprise, Tonbridge, 1995
P8	JUR818V	Bedford YMT	Duple Dominant II	C53F	1979	Ex New Enterprise, Tonbridge, 1995
P9	AKP430T	Bedford YMT	Plaxton Supreme IV	C53F	1978	Ex New Enterprise, Tonbridge, 1995
P10	FKM713L	Leyland Atlantean PDR1/1	MCW	O45/33F	1972	
P40	A829JLT	Mercedes-Benz L609D	Mercedes-Benz	M10	1984	Ex private owner, 1987
P43	D387VKJ	Renault-Dodge S56	?	B/F	1986	
P44	E836BKL	Renault-Dodge S56	?	B/F	1987	

Previous Registrations:

494WYA	A268MEH, 507EXA, A420HND	NTK611	A181MKE
544XVW	A184MKE	SIB6710	DBV844W
A11GTA	H832AHS	SIB6712	BYW425V
A14GTA	G89RGG	TIB5901	E301UUB, HIL2280, E848WWU
F899GUM	F236RJX, 89KY1320	TSU644	FKL174Y
F901GUM	F235RJX, 89KY1321	TSU645	FKL173Y
HIL2279	E300UUB	UJI2337	C204PPE, XSV691, C895YKJ
IIL9168	F714ENE	UJI2338	G897DEH
IIL9169	F710ENE	UJI2339	C202PPE, XSV689, C894YKJ
J60MPS	J457UFS, J10FTG	XSV691	E91OJT
L70MPS	L464DOA	YSU870	E186XKO
L80MPS	L140FOJ	YSU871	E187XKO
L503HKM	L10FUG	YSU872	G795RNC
LSK641	KGS494Y	YSU895	A114EPA
LSK643	C112AFX	YSU896	A135EPA

Allocations and liveries

Livery: Green and cream; cream and blue ⊕ (New Enterprise).

Gillingham (Nelson Road)

Mercedes-Benz	1041	1042	1044	1045	1046	1047	1052	1053
	1054	1057	1063	1064	1065	1066	1067	1069
	1070	1071	1072	1074	1075	1076	1077	1078
	1079	1080	1082	1084	1085	1086	1211	1212
	1213	1214	1215	1216	1217	1860		
Talbot	1836	1880						
Iveco	1713	1714	1840					
Dart	3178	3179	3180	3181	3182	3183	3213	3214
	3215	3216	3218	3219	3220	3221	3223	3224
	3225	3226	3227	3228	3229	3230	3231	3232
	3233	3234	3235	3236	3237	3238	3239	3240
	3241	3242	3243	3244	3245	3462	3474	3475
	3820	3830						
Greenway	3810	3812						
Bristol VR	5111	5112	5116	5137	5848	5853	5868	5875
	5878	5880	5884	5886				
Metrobus	5201	5202	5203	5204	5205	5207	5208	5209
	5210							
Olympian	5911	5912	5913	5914	5915	5916	5917	5918
	5919	5920	5921	5938	5939	5940	5941	5942
	5943							

Hawkhurst (Sandhurst Road)

Outstation at Tenterden♣

Tiger	2174							
Mercedes-Benz	1351	1352						
Lynx	3047⊕							
Dart	3155	3217♣	3467♣	3468♣	3469♣			
	139*	140*		*On loan from Kentish Bus.				
Volvo B6	3614♣	3615♣						
Bristol VR	5840	5881	5882	5883				
Olympian	5888♣	5889♣	5890♣	5898♣	5899♣	5900♣	5924♣	5925♣
	610*	*On loan from Kentish Bus.						

Maidstone (Armstrong Road)

Mercedes-Benz	1201	1202	1203	1210				
Tiger	2173	2186	2187	2188	2189	2197	2198	2199
Volvo	2841	2844	2845	2846	2847	2848	2849	
Dart	3149	3176	3177	3192	3193	3194	3195	3196
	3201	3202	3203	3204	3205	3206	3207	3208
	3209	3210	3211	3212	3246	3247	3461	3463
	3464	3466	3470	3471				
Volvo B6	3611⊕	3612⊕	3613⊕	3618				
Lynx	3045⊕	3046⊕	3048⊕	3049⊕				
Bristol VR	5125	5133	5138	5831	5837	5852	5867	5869
	5877	5885						
Olympian	5891	5909	5910	5922	5923	5926	5927	5928
	5929	5930	5931	5932	5933	5934	5935	5936
	5937							

Opposite, top:- **The hilly terrain surrounding the Medway Towns was viewed as an ideal testing ground by NBC and experimental batches of vehicles were supplied to Maidstone & District for this purpose. Following five early examples, Maidstone took a batch of ten mark2 Metrobus in 1984. The first, 5201, A201OKJ, is seen in Chatham.** *Gerald Mead*
Opposite, bottom:- **Maidstone & District's 6666, THX291S, was transferred from Leaside during 1997 and entered service in red with M&D lettering. The vehicle is seen in Chatham on the tourist service to which it is dedicated, details of which can be read on the advertisement. It is generally stored over winter months.** *Gerald Mead*

Tunbridge Wells (St John's Road)

Mercedes-Benz	1204	1205	1206	1218	1219	1220	1221	1223
	1224	1225	1226	1227	1228	1229	1230	
Volvo B6	3601	3602	3603	3604	3605	3606	3607	3608
	3609	3610	3616	3617				
Dart	3150	3151	3152	3153	3154	3156		
	137*	138*	*On loan from Kentish Bus.					
Lynx	3040	3041	3042	3043	3044	3051	3052	3066
	3067							
Bristol VR	5842	5845	5879					
Olympian	5892	5893	5894	5895	5896	5897	5901	5902
	5903	5904	5905	5906	5907	5908		

Sheerness (Bridge Road)

Tiger	2172	2200						
Bristol VR	5827	5828	5829	5830	5832	5833	5846	5863
	5864	5870						

Sittingbourne (Crown Quay Lane)

Mercedes-Benz	1043	1055	1056	1058	1073	1207	1208	1209
	1301							
Dart	3197	3198	3199	3465				

Tonbridge (Cannon Bridge Works, Cannon Lane) - New Enterprise

Olympian	7059	7060	7061	7062				
Mercedes-Benz	7006							
Volvo Bus	7003							
Coach	2193	2195	2196	2850	7023	7024	7025	7026
	7027	7028	7030	7031	7034	7035	7036	7040
	7041	7042	7050	7051	7052	2195	2850	

Withdrawn and unlicenced

Talbot	1870	1885		
Coach	2851	2852	7018	7033
Bristol VR	5843	5873	5881	5887
On loan to Midland Fox	2192			

A link from the Medway Towns to Gatwick airport is marketed as a non-stop service. Volvo B10M 2850, H637UWR, carries the dedicated ivery for the service on its Plaxton Paramount body, and working harder than when it was a Wallace Arnold touring coach.
Richard Godfrey

MIDLAND FOX

Midland Fox Ltd, P.O.Box 613, Leicester, LE4 8ZN
Derby City Transport Ltd, Ascot Drive, Derby, DE24 8ND

1	URH657	Leyland Tiger TRCTL11/3R	Plaxton Paramount 3200	C51F	1983	
2	FAZ2784	Leyland Tiger TRCTL11/3RH	Plaxton Paramount 3200 IIE	C53F	1986	Ex Crosville Cymru, 1996
4	FIL3452	Leyland Tiger TRCTL11/3RH	Plaxton Paramount 3200 II	C50FT	1985	
8	A108EPA	Leyland Tiger TRCTL11/2R	Plaxton Paramount 3200 E	C53F	1983	Ex London Country NE, 1989
9	A125EPA	Leyland Tiger TRCTL11/2R	Plaxton Paramount 3200 E	C53F	1983	Ex London Country NE, 1989
19	109CRC	Leyland Tiger TRCTL11/3R	Plaxton Paramount 3200	C48FT	1983	Ex London & Country, 1990
20	LJI5632	Leyland Tiger TRCTL11/3R	Plaxton Paramount 3200	C48FT	1983	Ex London & Country, 1990
21	111XKT	Leyland Tiger TRCTL11/3R	Plaxton Paramount 3200	C46FT	1983	Ex London & Country, 1990
22	JDE972X	Leyland Tiger TRCTL11/3R	Plaxton Supreme VI Express	C53F	1982	Ex Hills, Nuneaton, 1991
23	BPR103Y	Leyland Tiger TRCTL11/3R	Duple Laser	C50F	1983	Ex London & Country, 1990
24	A37SMA	Leyland Tiger TRCTL11/2R	Duple Laser	C49F	1984	Ex Crosville Cymru, 1993
26	B146ALG	Leyland Tiger TRCTL11/2RH	Duple Laser 2	C49F	1984	Ex Crosville Cymru, 1993
27	B151ALG	Leyland Tiger TRCTL11/2R	Duple Laser 2	C49F	1985	Ex Crosville Cymru, 1993
28	BPR108Y	Leyland Tiger TRCTL11/3R	Duple Laser	C50F	1983	Ex London & Country, 1990
71	81SVO	Leyland Leopard PSU5D/4R	Plaxton Supreme IV	C57F	1981	Ex Bedminster Coaches, 1983
75	YCF826	Leyland Leopard PSU5/4R	Plaxton Elite III	C57F	1975	Ex Orsborn, Wollaston, 1989
86	LJI8156	DAF MB200DKFL600	Van Hool Alizée	C49FT	1984	Ex Orsborn, Wollaston, 1989
87	LJI8157	DAF MB200DKFL600	Van Hool Alizée	C49FT	1984	Ex Orsborn, Wollaston, 1989
153	662NKR	DAF MB200DKFL615	Plaxton Supreme VI	C57F	1982	Ex Bland, Stamford, 1990
192	C632PAU	DAF MB230DKFL615	Plaxton Paramount 3200 II	C53F	1986	Ex Trent, 1991
211	N211TBC	Volvo B10M-62	Plaxton Expressliner 2	C49FT	1996	
212	N212TBC	Volvo B10M-62	Plaxton Expressliner 2	C49FT	1996	
213	FIL3451	Volvo B10M-60	Van Hool Alizée	C50F	1989	Ex Tellings-Golden Miller, Byfleet, 1992
214	XPA110	Volvo B10M-60	Van Hool Alizée	C52F	1989	Ex Tellings-Golden Miller, Byfleet, 1992
236	F406DUG	Volvo B10M-60	Plaxton Paramount 3200 III	C50F	1989	Ex Wallace Arnold, 1992
237	F407DUG	Volvo B10M-60	Plaxton Paramount 3200 III	C50F	1989	Ex Wallace Arnold, 1992
246	J246MFP	Volvo B10M-60	Plaxton Expressliner	C46FT	1992	Ex Express Travel, Liverpool, 1995
247	J247MFP	Volvo B10M-60	Plaxton Expressliner	C46FT	1992	Ex Express Travel, Liverpool, 1995
784	BVP784V	Leyland Leopard PSU3E/4R	Plaxton Supreme IV	C53F	1980	Ex Midland Red, 1981
785	BVP785V	Leyland Leopard PSU3E/4R	Plaxton Supreme IV	C53F	1980	Ex Midland Red, 1981
839	LOA839X	Leyland Leopard PSU3F/4R	Willowbrook 003	C49F	1982	Ex Midland Red Coaches, 1986

Much, in marketing terms, has been made of the connection between Midland Fox's home, Leicestershire, and the county emblem, the fox. Coaches carry the Foxhound name and this is shown here on Duple Laser-bodied Leyland Tiger 28, BPR108Y which is seen in Coventry while heading north on express service X66.
Richard Godfrey

Tellings-Golden Miller had been taken over by Midland Fox to become part of British Bus. In 1993 TGM was sold back to its original owners. However, one of the consequences was the retention in the Midland Fox fleet of two Volvo B10M-s with Van Hool Alizée bodywork. Photographed in Parliament Square, London, is 214, XPA110, one of the pair. *Richard Godfrey*

2152	STW18W	Leyland National 2 NL116L11/1R		B49F	1980	Ex Frontline, 1996
2153	BVP813V	Leyland National 2 NL116L11/1R		B49F	1980	Ex London & Country, 1997
2154	EON831V	Leyland National 2 NL116L11/1R		B49F	1980	Ex London & Country, 1997
2155	GNV656N	Leyland National 11351/1R		B49F	1974	Ex The Shires, 1996
2156	JIL2156	Leyland National 11351/1R	East Lancs Greenway (1994)	B49F	1974	Ex National Welsh, 1989
2157	JIL2157	Leyland National 1151/1R/0402	East Lancs Greenway (1994)	B49F	1973	Ex Kinch, Barrow-on-Soar, 1989
2158	JIL2158	Leyland National 11351A/1R	East Lancs Greenway (1994)	B49F	1977	Ex Midland Red, 1981
2159	JIL2159	Leyland National 11351A/1R	East Lancs Greenway (1994)	B49F	1977	Ex Midland Red, 1981
2160	JIL2160	Leyland National 11351/1R	East Lancs Greenway (1994)	B49F	1975	Ex London & Country, 1994
2161	JIL2161	Leyland National 11351/1R	East Lancs Greenway (1994)	B49F	1974	Ex Kinch, Barrow-on-Soar, 1989
2162	JIL2162	Leyland National 1151/1R/0102	East Lancs Greenway (1994)	B49F	1974	Ex Kinch, Barrow-on-Soar, 1989
2163	JIL2163	Leyland National 11351/1R	East Lancs Greenway (1994)	B49F	1974	Ex National Welsh, 1989
2164	JIL2164	Leyland National 11351A/1R	East Lancs Greenway (1994)	B49F	1978	Ex London & Country, 1994
2165	JIL2165	Leyland National 11351A/1R	East Lancs Greenway (1994)	B49F	1976	Ex London & Country, 1994

2166-2179   Scania L113CRL   East Lancashire European   B51F   1996

2166	N166PUT	2169	N169PUT	2172	N172PUT	2175	N175PUT	2178	N178PUT
2167	N167PUT	2170	N170PUT	2173	N173PUT	2176	N176PUT	2179	N179PUT
2168	N168PUT	2171	N171PUT	2174	N174PUT	2177	N177PUT		

2201-2206   Dennis Dart SLF   Plaxton Pointer   B39F   1997

2201	P201HRY	2203	P203HRY	2204	P204HRY	2205	P205HRY	2206	P206HRY
2202	P202HRY								

2445	JHE145W	MCW Metrobus DR104/6	MCW	H46/31F	1981	Ex Stevensons, 1994
2453	JHE153W	MCW Metrobus DR104/6	MCW	H46/31F	1981	Ex South Yorkshire's Transport, 1991
2460	JHE160W	MCW Metrobus DR104/6	MCW	H46/31F	1981	Ex South Yorkshire's Transport, 1991
2467	JHE167W	MCW Metrobus DR104/6	MCW	H46/31F	1981	Ex South Yorkshire's Transport, 1991

2474	EWF474V	MCW Metrobus DR102/13	MCW	H46/27D	1980	Ex Stevensons, 1988
2477	JHE177W	MCW Metrobus DR104/6	MCW	H46/31F	1981	Ex South Yorkshire's Transport, 1991
2479	JHE179W	MCW Metrobus DR104/6	MCW	H46/31F	1981	Ex South Yorkshire's Transport, 1991
2480	JHE189W	MCW Metrobus DR104/6	MCW	H46/31F	1981	Ex Stevensons, 1994
2482	JHE192W	MCW Metrobus DR104/6	MCW	H46/31F	1981	Ex Stevensons, 1994
2483	JHE193W	MCW Metrobus DR104/6	MCW	H46/31F	1981	Ex Stevensons, 1994
2484	EWF484V	MCW Metrobus DR102/13	MCW	H46/27D	1980	Ex Stevensons, 1988
2485	ULS615X	MCW Metrobus DR102/28	Alexander RL	H45/33F	1982	Ex Midland Red North, 1993
2486	CKS386X	MCW Metrobus DR102/24	Alexander RL	H45/33F	1981	Ex North Western, 1992
2488	EWF488V	MCW Metrobus DR102/13	MCW	H46/27D	1980	Ex Stevensons, 1988
2490	CKS390X	MCW Metrobus DR102/24	Alexander RL	H45/33F	1981	Ex Midland Red North, 1993
2493	JWF493W	MCW Metrobus DR102/13	MCW	H46/30F	1980	Ex Stevensons, 1994
2494	JWF494W	MCW Metrobus DR102/13	MCW	H46/30F	1980	Ex Stevensons, 1994
2534	PWE534R	Leyland Fleetline FE30AGR	Alexander AL	H45/29D	1977	Ex South Yorkshire's Transport, 1990
2539	GTO49V	Leyland Fleetline FE30AGR	Northern Counties	H43/29F	1980	Ex City Rider, 1997
2547	GTO307V	Leyland Fleetline FE30AGR	Northern Counties	H43/30F	1980	Ex City Rider, 1997
2559	SHE559S	Leyland Fleetline FE30AGR	Alexander AL	H45/29D	1978	Ex South Yorkshire's Transport, 1990
2560	SHE560S	Leyland Fleetline FE30AGR	Alexander AL	H45/29D	1978	Ex South Yorkshire's Transport, 1990
2561	FTU382T	Bristol VRT/SL3/501	Eastern Coach Works	H43/31F	1978	Ex North Western, 1996
2562	RLG427V	Bristol VRT/SL3/501	Eastern Coach Works	H43/31F	1980	Ex North Western, 1996
4151	E701XKR	Scania N112DRB	Alexander RH	H47/31F	1988	Ex Kentish Bus, 1996
4152	E702XKR	Scania N112DRB	Alexander RH	H47/31F	1988	Ex Kentish Bus, 1996

4153-4158

Scania N113DRB   Alexander RH   H47/33F   1989   Ex BTS, Borehamwood, 1993

4153	F153DET	4155	F155DET	4156	F156DET	4157	F157DET	4158	F158DET
4154	F154DET								

4159-4178

Scania N113DRB   East Lancashire   H47/33F   1994-95

4159	M159GRY	4163	M163GRY	4167	M167GRY	4171	M171GRY	4175	M175GRY
4160	M160GRY	4164	M164GRY	4168	M168GRY	4172	M172GRY	4176	M176GRY
4161	M161GRY	4165	M165GRY	4169	M169GRY	4173	M173GRY	4177	M177GRY
4162	M162GRY	4166	M166GRY	4170	M170GRY	4174	M174GRY	4178	M178GRY

4478	D80UTF	Leyland Olympian ONLXCT/1RH	Eastern Coach Works	CH39/27F	1986	Ex Reading, 1994
4479	D81UTF	Leyland Olympian ONLXCT/1RH	Eastern Coach Works	CH39/27F	1986	Ex Reading, 1994
4480	C42HHJ	Leyland Olympian ONLXCT/1RH	Eastern Coach Works	H47/31F	1985	Ex Colchester, 1994
4481	D44RWC	Leyland Olympian ONLXCT/1RH	Eastern Coach Works	H47/31F	1985	Ex Colchester, 1994
4482	C286BBP	Leyland Olympian ONLXB/1R	East Lancashire	DP43/27F	1986	Ex Sheffield Omnibus, 1993
4483	A280ROW	Leyland Olympian ONLXB/1R	East Lancashire	H45/31F	1984	Ex Sheffield Omnibus, 1993
4484	A278ROW	Leyland Olympian ONTL11/1R	East Lancashire	H47/29F	1984	Ex Sheffield Omnibus, 1993

4485-4489

Leyland Olympian ONT11/1R   Eastern Coach Works   H46/31   1981-82 Ex Merseybus, 1993

4485	ACM705X	4486	ACM706X	4487	ACM707X	4488	ACM710X	4489	ACM711X

4490-4494

Leyland Olympian ONLXB/1R   Eastern Coach Works   H45/32F   1983   Ex Crosville Cymru, 1989

4490	MTU116Y	4491	MTU117Y	4492	MTU118Y	4493	MTU119Y	4494	MTU121Y

4501-4514

Leyland Olympian ONLXB/1R   Eastern Coach Works   H45/32F   1983-84

4501	A501EJF	4504	A504EJF	4508	A508EJF	4511	A511EJF	4513	B513LFP
4502	A502EJF	4505	A505EJF	4509	A509EJF	4512	A512EJF	4514	B514LFP
4503	A503EJF	4507	A507EJF	4510	A510EJF				

4516	A132SMA	Leyland Olympian ONLXB/1R	Eastern Coach Works	H45/32F	1983	Ex Crosville Cymru, 1989
4517	A133SMA	Leyland Olympian ONLXB/1R	Eastern Coach Works	H45/32F	1983	Ex Crosville Cymru, 1989
4518	A134SMA	Leyland Olympian ONLXB/1R	Eastern Coach Works	H45/32F	1983	Ex Crosville Cymru, 1989
4519	A135SMA	Leyland Olympian ONLXB/1R	Eastern Coach Works	H45/32F	1983	Ex Crosville Cymru, 1989
4520	C30EUH	Leyland Olympian ONTL11/2R	East Lancashire	CH47/31F	1985	Ex Stevensons, 1989

4521-4525

Leyland Olympian ONCL10/1RZ   Alexander RL   H45/30F   1989

4521	G521WJF	4522	G522WJF	4523	G523WJF	4524	G524WJF	4525	G525WJF

4526	B186BLG	Leyland Olympian ONLXB/1RZ	Eastern Coach Works	H45/32F	1984	Ex Crosville Cymru, 1990
4527	B187BLG	Leyland Olympian ONLXB/1RZ	Eastern Coach Works	H45/32F	1984	Ex Crosville Cymru, 1990
4528	B190BLG	Leyland Olympian ONLXB/1RZ	Eastern Coach Works	H45/32F	1984	Ex Crosville Cymru, 1990

Between 1994 and 1995, twenty East Lancashire-bodied Scania double-deck buses were placed in service with Midland Fox and these are currently shared between Leicester Southgates depot and Wigston. Seen in Leicester is M162GRY. *Richard Godfrey*

4529-4533
Leyland Olympian ONCL10/1RZ Northern Counties H47/30F 1989 Ex Kentish Bus, 1992

4529	G506SFT	4530	G508SFT	4531	G509SFT	4532	G512SFT	4533	G513SFT

4601-4613
Volvo Olympian YN2RV18Z4 Northern Counties Palatine H47/29F 1996

4601	P601CAY	4604	P604CAY	4607	P607CAY	4610	P610CAY	4612	P612CAY
4602	P602CAY	4605	P605CAY	4608	P608CAY	4611	P611CAY	4613	P613CAY
4603	P603CAY	4606	P606CAY	4609	P609CAY				

8006	LJI5631	DAF MB200DKFL600	Plaxton Paramount 3500	C49F	1985

C001-C020
Carbodies Taxi Carbodies Fairway Driver M5 1994

C001	M901DHP	C005	M905DHP	C009	M909DHP	C013	M913DHP	C017	M917DHP
C002	M890DHP	C006	M906DHP	C010	M910DHP	C014	M914DHP	C018	M918DHP
C003	M903DHP	C007	M907DHP	C011	M911DHP	C015	M915DHP	C019	M919DHP
C004	M904DHP	C008	M908DHP	C012	M912DHP	C016	M916DHP	C020	M920DHP

C022	P95HOF	Carbodies Taxi	Carbodies	M5	1996
C023	P96HOF	Carbodies Taxi	Carbodies	M5	1996
C024	P58LOE	Carbodies Taxi	Carbodies	M5	1997

Opposite:- In 1996 Midland Fox introduced high quality services under the **Urban Fox** brand in a striking new blue livery. Several vehicles now carry this attractive scheme. Shown here are East Lancashire-bodied Scania 2176, N176PUT and Volvo Olympian 4607, P607CAY which carries Northern Counties bodywork. *Malc McDonald/Tony Wilson*

D021-D026
Scania K92CRB — Alexander PS — B51F — 1988

D021	E21ECH	D023	E23ECH	D024	E24ECH	D025	E25ECH	D026	E26ECH

D027	F27JRC	Scania K93CRB	Alexander PS	B51F	1989
D028	F28JRC	Scania K93CRB	Alexander PS	B51F	1989

D029-D033
Scania L113CRL — East Lancashire European — B51F — 1996

D029	N429XRC	D030	N430XRC	D031	N431XRC	D032	N432XRC	D033	N433XRC

D034-D038
Dennis Dart 9.8SDL3040 — East Lancashire EL2000 — B40F — 1994

D034	L34PNN	D035	L35PNN	D036	L36PNN	D037	L37PNN	D038	L38PNN

D048	GTO48V	Leyland Fleetline FE30AGR	Northern Counties	H43/29F	1980	
D064	D154RAK	Renault-Dodge S56	Reeve Burgess	B25F	1987	Ex Red & White, 1993
D068	K390NGG	Mercedes-Benz 811D	Dormobile Routemaker	DP33F	1992	Ex Irving & McIntyre, Greenock, 1995
D070	G64SNN	Mercedes-Benz 709D	Carlyle	C29F	1990	Ex Midland Red North, 1995
D071	J401FNS	Mercedes-Benz 709D	Dormobile Routemaker	B29F	1991	Ex Irving & McIntyre, Greenock, 1995

D072-D081
Mercedes-Benz 709D — Alexander Sprint — B27F — 1996

D072	N472XRC	D074	N474XRC	D076	N476XRC	D078	N478XRC	D080	N480XRC
D073	N473XRC	D075	N475XRC	D077	N477XRC	D079	N479XRC	D081	N481XRC

D082-D092
Mercedes-Benz 709D — Plaxton Beaver — B27F — 1996

D082	P482CAL	D085	P485CAL	D087	P487CAL	D089	P489CAL	D091	P491CAL
D083	P483CAL	D086	P486CAL	D088	P488CAL	D090	P490CAL	D092	P492CAL
D084	P484CAL								

D109-D121
Ailsa B55-10 — Northern Counties — H38/35F — 1982

D109	SRC109X	D112	SRC112X	D115	SRC115X	D118	TCH118X	D120	TCH120X
D110	SRC110X	D113	SRC113X	D116	TCH116X	D119	TCH119X	D121	TCH121X
D111	SRC111X	D114	SRC114X	D117	TCH117X				

D122	STV122X	Ailsa B55-10	Marshall	H44/35F	1982
D123	STV123X	Ailsa B55-10	Marshall	H44/35F	1982
D126	YAU126Y	Volvo Citybus B10M-50	Marshall	H45/33F	1983
D127	YAU127Y	Volvo Citybus B10M-50	Marshall	H45/33F	1983
D128	YAU128Y	Volvo Citybus B10M-50	Marshall	H43/33F	1983

Opposite:- **Derby came within British Bus in 1994 after the acquisition of Luton and District. After a period of autonomy the business was relaunched under the City Rider brand name and a yellow red and blue livery. In January 1996 Derby City Transport was incorporated into the Midland Fox group. Shown here are Plaxton-bodied Mercedes-Benz numbered D081, N481XRC and Northern Counties-bodied Volvo Olympian D166, P166XVO, both vehicle being new to this fleet,** *Tony Wilson*

The Derby fleet currently operates without the D-prefix, which, on paper avoids confusion with vehicles from the main fleet. Showing number 136, B136GAU, is seen in its home city of Derby.
Roy Marshall

D129-D133

Volvo Citybus B10M-50 — East Lancashire — H45/31F — 1984

D129	A129DTO	D130	A130DTO	D131	A131DTO	D132	A132DTO	D133	A133DTO

D134-D143

Volvo Citybus B10M-50 — Marshall — H45/33F — 1984

D134	B134GAU	D136	B136GAU	D138	B138GAU	D140	B140GAU	D142	B142GAU
D135	B135GAU	D137	B137GAU	D139	B139GAU	D141	B141GAU	D143	B143GAU

D144-D153

Volvo Citybus B10M-50 — Northern Counties — H42/33F — 1986/88

D144	C144NRR	D146	C146NRR	D148	C148NRR	D150	E150BTO	D152	E152BTO
D145	C145NRR	D147	C147NRR	D149	E149BTO	D151	E151BTO	D153	E153BTO

D160-D164

Scania N113DRB — East Lancashire — H45/33F — 1995

D160	N160VVO	D161	N161VVO	D162	N162VVO	D163	N163VVO	D164	N164VVO

D165-D169

Volvo Olympian YN2RV18Z4 — Northern Counties Palatine I — H47/30F — 1996

D165	N165XVO	D166	N166XVO	D167	P167BTV	D168	P168BTV	D169	P169BTV

D299-D315

Leyland Fleetline FE30AGR — Northern Counties — H43/30F — 1978-81

D299	GTO299V	D304	GTO304V	D309	MTV309W	D312	MTV312W	D314	MTV314W
D301	GTO301V	D305	GTO305V	D310	MTV310W	D313	MTV313W	D315	MTV315W
D302	GTO302V	D306	GTO306V	D311	MTV311W				

M101-M126

Mercedes-Benz Vario O810 — Alexander ALX100 — B29F — 1997

M101	P101HCH	M106	P106HCH	M112	P112HCH	M117	P117HCH	M122	P122HCH
M102	P102HCH	M107	P107HCH	M113	P113HCH	M118	P118HCH	M123	P123HCH
M103	P103HCH	M108	P108HCH	M114	P114HCH	M119	P119HCH	M124	P124HCH
M104	P104HCH	M109	P109HCH	M115	P115HCH	M120	P120HCH	M125	P125HCH
M105	P105HCH	M110	P110HCH	M116	P116HCH	M121	P121HCH	M126	P126HCH

M201-M214

Iveco Daily 49.10 — Carlyle Dailybus 2 — B25F — 1988

M201	E201HRY	M203	E203HRY	M208	E208HRY	M212	E212HRY	M214	E214HRY
M202	E202HRY	M206	E206HRY	M209	E209HRY	M213	E213HRY		

M222-M229

Iveco Daily 49.10 — Carlyle Dailybus 2 — B25F* — 1988 — *M223-5 are DP25F

M222	F22XVP	M224	F24XVP	M226	F26XVP	M228	F28XVP	M229	F29XVP
M223	F23XVP	M225	F25XVP	M227	F27XVP				

M230-M240

Iveco Daily 49.10 — Carlyle Dailybus 2 — B25F — 1989

M230	G230EOA	M232	G232EOA	M236	G236EOA	M239	G239EOA	M240	G240EOA
M231	G231EOA	M235	G235EOA						

M245	H245MOE	Iveco Daily 49.10	Carlyle Dailybus 2	B25F	1990	
M257	G87OTU	Iveco Daily 49.10	Carlyle Dailybus	B25F	1989	Ex Bee Line Buzz, 1990
M258	E188CNE	Iveco Daily 49.10	Northern Counties	B22F	1988	Ex Bee Line Buzz, 1990
M263	G245GCC	Iveco Daily 49.10	Carlyle Dailybus 2	B25F	1989	Ex North Western, 1994
M264	G247GCC	Iveco Daily 49.10	Carlyle Dailybus 2	B25F	1989	Ex North Western, 1994
M265	G249GCC	Iveco Daily 49.10	Carlyle Dailybus 2	DP25F	1989	Ex North Western, 1994
M266	G250GCC	Iveco Daily 49.10	Carlyle Dailybus 2	B25F	1989	Ex North Western, 1994
M276	F660KNL	Iveco Daily 49.10	Carlyle Dailybus 2	B23F	1989	Ex The Shires, 1996
M281	E61UKL	Mercedes-Benz 609D	Reeve Burgess Beaver	B20F	1988	Ex Maidstone & District, 1997
M282	E62UKL	Mercedes-Benz 609D	Reeve Burgess Beaver	B20F	1988	Ex Maidstone & District, 1997
M289	F379UCP	Mercedes-Benz 609D	Reeve Burgess Beaver	B20F	1988	Ex Edinburgh Transport, 1994
M291	D906MVU	Mercedes-Benz 609D	Mercedes	B27F	1987	Ex
M292	D222SKD	Mercedes-Benz L608D	Alexander	B20F	1986	Ex North Western 1992
M293	D223SKD	Mercedes-Benz L608D	Alexander	B20F	1986	Ex North Western 1992
M294	D224SKD	Mercedes-Benz L608D	Alexander	B20F	1986	Ex North Western 1992
M296	D226SKD	Mercedes-Benz L608D	Alexander	B20F	1986	Ex North Western 1992
M299	D209SKD	Mercedes-Benz L608D	Reeve Burgess	B20F	1986	Ex North Western, 1992
M301	F301RUT	Mercedes-Benz 709D	Robin Hood	B26F	1989	
M302	F302RUT	Mercedes-Benz 709D	Robin Hood	B26F	1989	

The use of Scania products by Derby first occurred in 1988 with the arrival of six K92 buses with Alexander bodywork. These were followed by a pair of the K93 model in 1989. First of the 1998 delivery, D021, E21ECH, is seen in City Rider livery on service 41. *Philip Stephenson*

Derby took an liking to the double-deck version of the Volvo B10M coach chassis which, for a period was marketed as both the D10M or B10MD. Seen with Northern Counties 'standard' bodywork is D153, E153BTO. *Tony Wilson*

The minibuses of Midland Fox are operated as Fox Cubs and mostly carry a similar livery to the big buses. The initial dominance of the Ford Transit has been changed as larger minibuses have been added to the fleet, both new and transfers from other group members. Seen in St Margaret's bus station is M293, D223SKD which was part of the order placed for Ribble, but delivered to the then new North Western company at Bootle. *Richard Godfrey*

M303-M322 — Mercedes-Benz 709D — Alexander Sprint — B25F — 1994

M303	L303AUT	M307	L307AUT	M311	L311AUT	M315	L315AUT	M319	L319AUT
M304	L304AUT	M308	L308AUT	M312	L312AUT	M316	L316AUT	M320	L320AUT
M305	L305AUT	M309	L309AUT	M313	L313AUT	M317	L317AUT	M321	L321AUT
M306	L306AUT	M310	L310AUT	M314	L314AUT	M318	L318AUT	M322	L322AUT

M323	L323AUT	Mercedes-Benz 709D	Leicester Carriage Builders	B25F	1994
M324	L324AUT	Mercedes-Benz 709D	Leicester Carriage Builders	B25F	1994
M325	L325AUT	Mercedes-Benz 709D	Leicester Carriage Builders	B25F	1994
M326	N331OFP	Mercedes-Benz 709D	Leicester Carriage Builders	B25F	1995	Ex Leicester Carriage demonstrator, 1996
M329	L227HRF	Mercedes-Benz 709D	Dormobile Routemaker	B29F	1993	Ex Stevensons, 1994
M330	L228HRF	Mercedes-Benz 709D	Dormobile Routemaker	B29F	1993	Ex Stevensons, 1994
M331	L231HRF	Mercedes-Benz 709D	Dormobile Routemaker	B27F	1993	Ex Stevensons, 1994
M333	L233HRF	Mercedes-Benz 709D	Dormobile Routemaker	B27F	1993	Ex Stevensons, 1994
M335	G65SNN	Mercedes-Benz 709D	Carlyle	B29F	1990	Ex Stevensons, 1994
M336	J151WEH	Mercedes-Benz 709D	Dormobile Routemaker	B29F	1992	Ex Stevensons, 1994
M337	K148BRF	Mercedes-Benz 709D	Dormobile Routemaker	B27F	1992	Ex Stevensons, 1994
M338	K158HRF	Mercedes-Benz 709D	Dormobile Routemaker	B27F	1993	Ex Stevensons, 1994
M339	G301RJA	Mercedes-Benz 709D	Reeve Burgess Beaver	B25F	1990	Ex Stevensons, 1994
M341	K131XRE	Mercedes-Benz 709D	Dormobile Routemaker	B29F	1992	Ex Stevensons, 1994
M342	G142GOL	Mercedes-Benz 709D	Carlyle	B29F	1990	Ex Stevensons, 1994
M343	G143GOL	Mercedes-Benz 709D	Carlyle	B29F	1990	Ex Stevensons, 1994

M344-M358 — Mercedes-Benz 709D — Alexander Sprint — B27F — 1995

M344	N344OBC	M347	N347OBC	M350	N350OBC	M353	N353OBC	M356	N356OBC
M345	N345OBC	M348	N348OBC	M351	N351OBC	M354	N354OBC	M357	N357OBC
M346	N346OBC	M349	N349OBC	M352	N352OBC	M355	N355OBC	M358	N358OBC

The main 1994 intake of minibuses was a batch of twenty Mercedes -Benz 709Ds with Alexander Sprint bodywork. Representing this batch is M317, L317AUT, photographed in Leicester with spring blossom much in evidence. The vehicle is allocated to Fox's depot in the Thurmaston district of Leicester which is currently the head office site of the British Bus division of Cowie. *Richard Godfrey*

M359	P111MML	Mercedes-Benz 709D	Reeve Burgess Beaver	B27F	1996	
M360	P222MML	Mercedes-Benz 709D	Reeve Burgess Beaver	B27F	1996	
M402	F272OPX	Mercedes-Benz 811D	Robin Hood	B22F	1988	
M411	D111OWG	Renault-Dodge S56	Reeve Burgess	B25F	1986	Ex Stevensons, 1992
M413	E413EPE	Renault-Dodge S56	Northern Counties	B27F	1987	Ex Stagecoach South, 1992
M415	E415EPE	Renault-Dodge S56	Northern Counties	B27F	1987	Ex Stagecoach South, 1992
M417	E417EPE	Renault-Dodge S56	Northern Counties	B27F	1987	Ex Stagecoach South, 1992

M460-M468 Renault-Dodge S56 Reeve Burgess DP25F* 1986/7 Ex South Yorkshire's Transport, 1992
436 ex Deeward, 1993; *461-3 B25F

| M460 | D130OWG | **M462** | D124OWG | **M463** | D162RAK | **M464** | D134OWG | **M468** | D138OWG |
| M461 | D118OWG | | | | | | | | |

M470	E181UWF	Renault-Dodge S56	Reeve Burgess	B25F	1987	Ex City Rider, 1996
M471	E188UWF	Renault-Dodge S56	Reeve Burgess	B25F	1987	Ex City Rider, 1996
M472	E933UBO	Renault-Dodge S56	Northern Counties	B25F	1988	Ex City Rider, 1997
M473	D152RAK	Renault-Dodge S56	Reeve Burgess	B25F	1987	Ex City Rider, 1997
M474	E332LHN	Renault-Dodge S56	Northern Counties	B20F	1988	Ex City Rider, 1997
M475	E334LHN	Renault-Dodge S56	Northern Counties	B25F	1987	Ex City Rider, 1997
M476	E326LHN	Renault-Dodge S56	Northern Counties	B20F	1988	Ex City Rider, 1996
M477	E327LHN	Renault-Dodge S56	Northern Counties	B25F	1987	Ex City Rider, 1996
M478	E328LHN	Renault-Dodge S56	Northern Counties	B25F	1987	Ex City Rider, 1996
M480	E330LHN	Renault-Dodge S56	Northern Counties	B20F	1988	Ex City Rider, 1996
M481	E331LHN	Renault-Dodge S56	Northern Counties	B25F	1987	Ex City Rider, 1996

T01	J255TJW	Reliant Metrocab	Reliant	M5	1991

T15-T30

		Carbodies Taxi	Carbodies FX4	M5	1990

T15	H912KUD	T23	J655OWK	T25	J651OWK	T27	J656OWK	T29	J473RDU
T19	H695KKV	T24	J650OWK	T26	J649OWK	T28	J657OWK	T30	J474RDU
T21	H697KKV								

T31	J766SOC	Reliant Metrocab	Reliant	M5	1991
T32	J961TOF	Reliant Metrocab	Reliant	M5	1991
T33	J963TOF	Reliant Metrocab	Reliant	M5	1991

T34-T52

		Carbodies Taxi	Carbodies FX4	M5	1992-94

T34	J248SHP	T38	J917VHP	T42	K745CWK	T46	L143NHP	T50	L149NHP
T35	J249SHP	T39	J918VHP	T43	K746CWK	T47	L145NHP	T51	M651ERW
T36	J658UDU	T40	K741CWK	T44	L132NHP	T48	L146NHP	T52	M652ERW
T37	J659UDU	T41	K742CWK	T45	L133NHP	T49	L148NHP		

T57	M331MRW	Carbodies Taxi	Carbodies Fairway Driver	M5	1994
T58	M332MRW	Carbodies Taxi	Carbodies Fairway Driver	M5	1994

T59-T67

		Carbodies Taxi	Carbodies FX	M5	1997

T59	P36LOE	T61	P28LOE	T63	P57LOE	T66	P95MOX	T67	P96MOX
T60	P37LOE	T62	P29LOE	T65	P94MOX				

T68	R278VOK	Reliant Metrocab	Metrocab	M5	1997
T69	R279VOK	Reliant Metrocab	Metrocab	M5	1997
T70	R288VOK	Reliant Metrocab	Metrocab	M5	1997
T71	R289VOK	Reliant Metrocab	Metrocab	M5	1997

Ancilliary vehicles:-

317t	TVC402W	Leyland Leopard PSU5C/4R	Plaxton Supreme IV	C51F	1981	Ex Hills, Nuneaton, 1991
612t	796UHT	Leyland Leopard PSU5D/5R	Plaxton Supreme IV	C50F	1981	Ex Fen Travel, Syston, 1992
9045	D59TLV	Freight Rover Sherpa	Carlyle	B2F	1987	Ex North Western, 1991
9047	RBC500W	Bedford YMT	Plaxton Supreme IV	C53F	1981	
D350	JDJ350N	Bedford YRT	Plaxton Elite III	C53F	1975	Ex Grayway, Wigan, 1996
D395	SVL830R	Bristol LH6L	Eastern Coach Works	B43F	1977	Ex RoadCar, 1994
M75	C475TAY	Ford Transit 190	Robin Hood	B16F	1985	

Named vehicles: -
D034 *John Barton*; D035 *Peter Varley*

Previous Registrations:

109CRC	A103HNC		JIL2162	SEO208M
111XKT	A102HNC		JIL2163	GHB790N
662NKR	OWA23X		JIL2164	XNG760S
796UHT	NMV612W		JIL2165	JOX516P
81SVO	HHW471X		LJI5631	B568NJF
FAZ2784	B282KPF		LJI5632	A104HNC, XPA110, A927KFP
FIL3451	F803TMD		LJI8156	B310CRP
FIL3452	B104LJU		LJI8157	B310LUT
JIL2156	GHB677N		TVC402W	PWK5W, DJI8467
JIL2157	NPD142L		URH657	BRY1Y
JIL2158	PUK649R		XPA110	F804TMD
JIL2159	PUK643R		YCF826	JNK550N
JIL2160	JOX482P			
JIL2161	HWC87N			

Midland Fox's 4520, C30EUH, has had a colourful past. Latterly with Stevensons, the vehicle was new to Rhymney Valley District Council which became Inter Valley Link on deregulation in 1986. It is seen in departing Leicester for Wigston while its two sisters are with Badgerline. *Richard Godfrey*

Allocations and liveries

Livery : Yellow and red; blue (Urban Fox & County Fox); white ⅃National Express ; yellow,blue and red (City Rider); silver & blue ⁑ (Park & Ride); red or black (Taxi fleet)

Coalville (Ashby Road)

Tiger	2	22	24	26	27			
Mercedes-Benz	M289	M291	M293	M294	M296	M301	M302	M303
	M304	M305	M306	M311	M312	M335	M339	M342
	M343	M348	M349	M402				
Leopard	784							
National	2152	2154						
Greenway	2164	2165						
Dart	2205	2206						
Olympian	4482	4501	4502	4503	4504	4505	4508	4512
	4527							

Leicester (St Ives Road) - Foxhound

Tiger	4	9	20	21			
DAF	86	87	192	8006			
Volvo	211⅃	212⅃	213	214	236	237	246⅃	247⅃

Hinckley (Jacknell Road, Dodwells Bridge)

Iveco	M245							
Mercedes-Benz	M292	M299	M310	M326	M329	M338	M344	
Renault-Dodge	M472	M473	M474	M475	M476	M477	M478	M480
	M481							
Tiger	19							
Leopard	71	785						
DAF	153							
National	2155							
Greenway	2156	2157	2158					
Fleetline	2534							

Southgates (Peacock Lane, Leicester)

Iveco	M201	M202	M203	M206	M208	M209	M212	M213
	M214	M258	M330	M331	M333	M350	M351	M357
	358							
Greenway	2159	2160	2161	2162	2163			
Scania L	2166	2167	2168	2169	2170	2171	2172	2173
	2174	2175						
Metrobus	2445	2453	2460	2467	2474	2477	2479	2480
	2482	2483	2484	2485	2486	2488	2490	2493
	2494							
Scania N	4168	4169	4170	4171	4172	4173	4174	4175
	4176	4177	4178					

Stamford

Tiger	28		
Leopard	75		
Fleetline	2547	D48	D302
Bristol VR	2561		

Wigston (Station Street, South Wigston)

Mercedes	M123	M124	M125	M126	M281	M282	M345	M346
	M347	M359	M360					
Iveco	M264	M276						
Renault-Dodge	M470							
Tiger	1	8	23					
Leopard	839							
Fleetline	2559	2560						
Scania N	4151	4152	4153	4154	4155	4156	4157	4158
	4159	4160	4161	4162	4163	4164	4165	4166
	4167							
Olympian	4478	4480	4481	4490	4491	4492	4493	4494
	4510	4516	4517	4520	4521	4522	4523	4524
	4525	4529	4530	4531	4532	4533	4601	4602
	4603	4604	4605	4606	4607	4608	4609	4610
	4611	4612	4613					

Thurmaston (Melton Road, Thurmaston, Leicester)

Mercedes-Benz	M107	M108	M109	M110	M112	M113	M114	M115
	M116	M117	M118	M119	M120	M121	M122	M307
	M308	M309	M313	M314	M315	M316	M317	M318
	M319	M320	M321	M322	M323	M324	M325	M336
	M337	M341	M352	M353	M354	M355	M356	
Iveco	M222	M223	M224	M225	M226	M227	M228	M229
	M230	M231	M232	M235	M236	M239	M240	M257
	M263	M265	M266					
Dart	2201:	2202:	2203:	2204:				
National	2153							
Bristol VR	2562							
Scania L	2176	2177	2178	2179				
Olympian	4479	4483	4484	4485	4486	4487	4488	4489
	4507	4509	4511	4513	4514	4518	4519	4526
	4528							

The 1998 Cowie Bus Handbbook

Delivered to Midland Fox for the City Rider operation in 1996 were five low-floor Scania L113 buses which carry the East Lancashire European bodywork. Photographed in Melbourne is D031, N431XRC. *Richard Godfrey*

Derby (London Road) - City Rider *(The D-prefix is not carried on the vehicles)*

Mercedes-Benz	D68	D70	D71	D72	D73	D74	D75	D76
	D77	D78	D79	D80	D81	D82	D83	D84
	D85	D86	D87	D88	D89	D90	D91	D92
Dart	D34	D35	D36	D37	D38			
Scania K	D21	D23	D24	D25	D26	D27	D28	D29
	D30	D31	D32	D33				
Ailsa	D109	D110	D111	D112	D113	D114	D115	D116
	D117	D118	D119	D120	D121	D122	D123	
Fleetline	2539	D299	D301	D304	D305	D306	D309	D310
	D311	D312	D313	D314	D315			
Volvo Citybus	D126	D127	D128	D129	D130	D131	D132	D133
	D134	D135	D136	D137	D138	D139	D140	D141
	D142	D143	D144	D145	D146	D147	D148	D149
	D150	D151	D152	D153				
Scania N	D160	D161	D162	D163	D164			
Olympian	D165	D166	D167	D168	D169			

Foxcabs

C001-C020/2-4

Derby 75 Taxis

T01/15/9/21/3-52/7-63/5-71

MIDLAND RED / STEVENSONS

Midland Red (North) Ltd, Stevensons of Uttoxeter Ltd
Delta Way, Longford Road, Cannock, Staffordshire   WS11 3XB

2	82HBC	DAF MB200DKFL600	Plaxton Paramount 3200	C53F	1983	Ex Viking, Woodville, 1987
3	565LON	Volvo B10M-61	Plaxton Paramount 3200 II	C57F	1985	Ex Blue Bus Services, 1995
4	614WEH	Volvo B58-61	Plaxton P 3200 II (1986)	C53F	1976	Ex Coliseum, Southampton, 1985
5	XAF759	Volvo B10M-61	Plaxton Paramount 3500	C53F	1984	Ex Blue Bus Services, 1995
6	852YYC	Volvo B10M-61	Plaxton Paramount 3500 II	C53F	1985	Ex Blue Bus Services, 1995
7	HIL3652	Volvo B10M-61	Duple 340	C55F	1987	Ex Crosville Cymru, 1995
9	WYR562	Bova FHD12.290	Bova Futura	C36FT	1990	Ex Boyden, Castle Donington, 1991
10	803HOM	Volvo B10M-61	Plaxton Paramount 3200 III	C53F	1987	Ex Blue Bus Services, 1995
11	OGL518	Volvo B10M-61	Plaxton Paramount 3200 II	C53F	1985	Ex Blue Bus Services, 1995
12	AAL303A	Leyland Leopard PSU5D/4R (TL11)	Plaxton P3200 III (1987)	C53F	1980	Ex Rhondda, 1992
13	AAL404A	Leyland Leopard PSU5D/4R (TL11)	Plaxton P3200 III (1987)	C53F	1980	Ex Rhondda, 1992
14	LUY742	Volvo B10M-61	Plaxton Paramount 3500 III	C49F	1987	Ex Sealandair, West Bromwich, 1991
15	VOI6874	Volvo B10M-61	Plaxton Paramount 3500	C53F	1983	Ex Bagnall, Swadlincote, 1989
16	FSU661	Volvo B10M-60	Plaxton Paramount 3500 III	C49F	1991	Ex Clydeside, 1996
17	VLT166	Volvo B10M-61	Plaxton Paramount 3500 III	C49F	1991	Ex Clydeside, 1996
19	468KPX	Volvo B10M-61	Van Hool Alizée	C44DL	1982	Ex Cumberland, 1992
20	784RBF	Volvo B10M-61	Jonckheere Jubilee P50	C53F	1987	Ex Tellings-Golden Miller, 1993
21	YSU953	Volvo B10M-60	Van Hool Alizée	C53F	1989	
23	123TKM	Volvo B58-56	Plaxton Supreme IV	C53F	1979	Ex Blue Bus Services, 1995
24	124YTW	Volvo B58-61	Plaxton Supreme IV	C53F	1980	Ex G M Buses, 1986
25	422AKN	Volvo B10M-60	Plaxton Paramount 3200 III	C53F	1989	
26	XOR841	Volvo B10M-61	Van Hool Alizée	C53F	1983	Ex Sealandair, West Bromwich, 1991
27	TOU962	Volvo B10M-61	Van Hool Alizée	C53F	1983	Ex Sealandair, West Bromwich, 1991
28	PCW946	Volvo B10M-61	Plaxton Paramount 3500	C49FT	1984	Ex Bagnall, Swadlincote, 1989
29	YSU954	Volvo B10M-60	Van Hool Alizée	C49F	1990	
30	430UFM	Dennis Javelin 11SDA1905	Duple 320	C53F	1988	Ex The Shires, 1996
31	429UFM	Dennis Javelin 11SDA1905	Duple 320	C53F	1988	Ex The Shires, 1996
32	HIL7596	Dennis Javelin 11SDA1905	Duple 320	C53F	1988	Ex The Shires, 1996
33	GIL8487	Dennis Javelin 11SDA1905	Duple 320	C53F	1988	Ex The Shires, 1996
34	PSV323	MCW MetroRider MF154/2	MCW	C28F	1990	Ex Northumbria, 1994

51-61

		Mercedes-Benz Vario O810	Alexander ALX100	B27F	1997

51	P51HOJ	54	P54HOJ	56	P56HOJ	58	P58HOJ	60	P260HOJ
52	P52HOJ	55	P255HOJ	57	P57HOJ	59	P59HOJ	61	P61HOJ
53	P53HOJ								

Stevensons coaches are divided between the coaching unit which trades as Viking, and the red and yellow liveried vehicles which operate for the main fleet. A pair of re-bodied Leyland Leopards joined the fleet from Rhondda in 1992. The first of these, 13, AAL404A, illustrates the livery then in use. The Viking coach fleet is currently for sale and it is expected that it will be sold by January 1998.
Phillip Stephenson

The final Midland Red/Stevensons livery incorporates a 'Staffordshire' knot motif before the name, and in the case of Midland, the use of the Red which has been omitted since the days of the original BMMO. Illustrating the scheme on Ford Transit 188, H188EHA, one of the 1988 order for minibuses which first displaced the original Transits. *Phillip Stephenson*

88-107

		Ford Transit VE6		Dormobile		B16F		1986		
88	D88CFA	92	D92CFA	96	D96CFA	102	D102CFA	107	D107CFA
91	D91CFA	95	D95CFA	98	D98CFA	104	D104CFA		

112-119

		Mercedes-Benz L608D		Rootes		B20F		1986	Ex Maidstone & District, 1997
112w	D22KKP	114w	D24KKP	116w	D23KKP	118	D38KKP	119w	C201EKJ
113w	D32KKP	115w	C210EKJ	117w	D27KKP				

120	C822SDY	Mercedes-Benz L608D	Alexander	B20F	1986	Ex East Midland, 1993
121	C823SDY	Mercedes-Benz L608D	Alexander	B20F	1986	Ex East Midland, 1993
122	C78WRE	Mercedes-Benz L608D	PMT Hanbridge	DP19F	1986	
123	C802SDY	Mercedes-Benz L608D	Alexander	B20F	1986	Ex East Midland, 1993
125	F188REH	Mercedes-Benz 609D	PMT	B21F	1988	
126	D176LNA	Mercedes-Benz 609D	Dixon Lomas	B27F	1986	Ex Marriott, Clayworth, 1988
127	F77ERJ	Mercedes-Benz 609D	Reeve Burgess Beaver	B25F	1988	Ex Star Line, Knutsford, 1991
129	D135NUS	Mercedes-Benz L608D	Alexander	B21F	1986	Ex Kelvin Central, 1992
131	D534FAE	Mercedes-Benz L608D	Dormobile	B20F	1986	Ex Frontline, 1996
132	C202EKJ	Mercedes-Benz L608D	Rootes	B20F	1986	Ex Maidstone & District, 1997
133	F187REH	Mercedes-Benz 609D	Whittaker Europa	B20F	1988	
134	D538FAE	Mercedes-Benz L608D	Dormobile	B20F	1986	Ex Frontline, 1996
135	C218EKJ	Mercedes-Benz L608D	Rootes	B20F	1986	Ex Maidstone & District, 1997
136	K136ARE	Mercedes-Benz 709D	Wright NimBus	B29F	1992	
137	K137ARE	Mercedes-Benz 709D	Wright NimBus	B29F	1992	
140	F190RRF	Mercedes-Benz 709D	Robin Hood	B29F	1988	
141	F191SRF	Mercedes-Benz 709D	Robin Hood	B29F	1989	
142	F192VFA	Mercedes-Benz 709D	Robin Hood	B29F	1989	
143	J143SRF	Mercedes-Benz 709D	Wright NimBus	B29F	1992	
146	F189RRF	Mercedes-Benz 709D	Robin Hood	B29F	1988	
147	K947BRE	Mercedes-Benz 709D	Dormobile Routemaker	B29F	1993	
148	J208SRF	Mercedes-Benz 709D	Wright NimBus	B27F	1992	
149	J209SRF	Mercedes-Benz 709D	Wright NimBus	B27F	1992	
150	K150BRF	Mercedes-Benz 709D	Wright NimBus	B27F	1992	
152	G183DRF	Mercedes-Benz 709D	LHE Commuter	B29F	1990	

Ten Renault-Dodge S56 minibuses joined the Midland Red fleet in 1991 and these carried Northern Counties bodywork. From this batch 336, H336DHA is seen here. To these were added several similar, almost new, buses from North Western. Withdrawals have started, however, although a handful of the type still operate at each of Crewe and Tamworth. *Phillip Stephenson*

153	F703KFM	Mercedes-Benz 709D	Reeve Burgess Beaver	B25F	1989	Ex C-Line, 1992
154	E564YBU	Mercedes-Benz 709D	Reeve Burgess Beaver	B25F	1988	Ex Star Line, Knutsford, 1990
155	F705KFM	Mercedes-Benz 709D	Reeve Burgess Beaver	B25F	1989	Ex C-Line, 1992
156	F186PRE	Mercedes-Benz 709D	Reeve Burgess Beaver	B25F	1988	
157	G184DRF	Mercedes-Benz 709D	LHE Commuter	B29F	1990	
158	F326PPO	Mercedes-Benz 709D	Robin Hood	B29F	1989	Ex Robin Hood demonstrator, 1989
159	H880NFS	Mercedes-Benz 709D	PMT Ami	B29F	1991	Ex Gold Circle, Airdrie, 1994
160	F700LCA	Mercedes-Benz 709D	Reeve Burgess Beaver	B23F	1989	Ex C-Line, 1992

164-173		Mercedes-Benz 709D		LHE Commuter		B29F		1990	
164	G164YRE	**166**	G166YRE	**168**	G168YRE	**170**	G170YRE	**172**	G172YRE
165	G165YRE	**167**	G167YRE	**169**	G169YRE	**171**	G171YRE	**173**	G173YRE

175	F185PRE	Mercedes-Benz 709D	Robin Hood	B29F	1988	
178	E478NSC	Mercedes-Benz 709D	Alexander Sprint	DP25F	1988	Ex Oakley Buses, 1994
180	F39HOD	Ford Transit VE6	Dormobile	B18F	1988	Ex Panda Hire, Exeter, 1990

181-191		Ford Transit VE6		Dormobile		B18F		1990-91	
181	H181DHA	**183**	H183DHA	**185**	H185DHA	**187**	H187EHA	**189**	H189EHA
182	H182DHA	**184**	H184DHA	**186**	H186EHA	**188**	H188EHA	**191**	H191EHA

201-206		Ford Transit 190		Carlyle		B20F*		1985-86 Ex Stevensons, 1994	
								*205 is B18F	
201w	B732YUD	**203**w	B733YUD	**204**w	B734YUD	**205**w	C85AUB	**206**	C726JJO
202w	B875EOM								

218	H708LOL	Freight Rover Sherpa	Carlyle Citybus 2	B20F	1991	
219	H709LOL	Freight Rover Sherpa	Carlyle Citybus 2	B20F	1991	
220	H710LOL	Freight Rover Sherpa	Carlyle Citybus 2	B20F	1991	

221	H731LOL	Freight Rover Sherpa	Carlyle Citybus 2	B20F	1991	
222	H729LOL	Freight Rover Sherpa	Carlyle Citybus 2	B20F	1991	
229	L229HRF	Mercedes-Benz 709D	Dormobile Routemaker	B27F	1993	
230	L230HRF	Mercedes-Benz 709D	Dormobile Routemaker	B27F	1993	
252	L232HRF	Mercedes-Benz 709D	Dormobile Routemaker	B27F	1993	
253	L253NFA	Mercedes-Benz 709D	Wadham Stringer Wessex II	B29F	1994	
254	L254NFA	Mercedes-Benz 709D	Wadham Stringer Wessex II	B29F	1994	
255	L255NFA	Mercedes-Benz 709D	Wadham Stringer Wessex II	B29F	1994	
256	L226JFA	Mercedes-Benz 709D	Dormobile Routemaker	B29F	1993	
274	F44XVP	Iveco Daily 40.06	Carlyle Dailybus 2	B21F	1989	Ex Carlyle demonstrator, 1989
275	F275CEY	Iveco Daily 49.10	Robin Hood City Nippy	DP21F	1988	Ex Crosville Cymru, 1991
284	F484EJC	Iveco Daily 49.10	Carlyle Dailybus 2	DP25F	1989	Ex Crosville Cymru, 1991
285	F485EJC	Iveco Daily 49.10	Carlyle Dailybus 2	DP25F	1989	Ex Crosville Cymru, 1991
286	F486EJC	Iveco Daily 49.10	Carlyle Dailybus 2	DP25F	1989	Ex Crosville Cymru, 1991
296	F276CEY	Iveco Daily 49.10	Robin Hood City Nippy	DP25F	1988	Ex Crosville Cymru, 1991
300	G150GOL	Iveco Daily 49.10	Carlyle Dailybus 2	B25F	1990	Ex Carlyle, 1991

301-328 — Iveco Daily 49-10 — Carlyle Dailybus — B23F — 1989-90

301	F601EHA	306	F606EHA	311	F611EHA	316	F616EHA	325	F625EHA
302	F602EHA	307	F607EHA	312	F612EHA	319	F619EHA	326	F626EHA
303	F603EHA	308	F608EHA	313	F613EHA	322	F622EHA	327	G327PHA
304	F604EHA	309	F609EHA	314	F614EHA	323	F623EHA	328	G328PHA
305	F605EHA	310	F610EHA	315	F615EHA	324	F624EHA		

329-338 — Renault-Dodge S56 — Northern Counties — B23F — 1990-91

329	H329DHA	331	H331DHA	333	H433DHA	335	H335DHA	337	H337DHA
330	H330DHA	332	H332DHA	334	H334DHA	336	H336DHA	338	H338DHA

340-350 — Renault-Dodge S56 — Northern Counties — B23F — 1988 — Ex North Western, 1991

340w	E90WCM	343w	E93WCM	345w	E95WCM	349	E99WCM	350	E611LFV
341w	E91WCM	344w	E94WCM	346	E96WCM				

359	D319DEF	Renault-Dodge S56	Northern Counties	B22F	1987	Ex Cleveland Transit, 1992

371-381 — Mercedes-Benz 709D — Alexander Sprint — B29F* — 1995-96 *376-81 are B27F

371	M371EFD	374	M374EFD	376	M376EFD	378	M378EFD	380	M380EFD
372	M372EFD	375	M375EFD	377	M377EFD	379	M379EFD	381	M381EFD
373	M373EFD								

382-401 — Mercedes-Benz 709D — Alexander Sprint — B25F — 1996

382	P382FEA	386	P386FEA	390	P390FEA	394	P394FEA	398	P398FEA
383	P383FEA	387	P387FEA	391	P391FEA	395	P395FEA	399	P399FEA
384	P384FEA	388	P388FEA	392	P392FEA	396	P396FEA	401	P401FEA
385	P385FEA	389	P389FEA	393	P393FEA	397	P397FEA		

402	K142BFA	Mercedes-Benz 811D	Dormobile Routemaker	B31F	1993	
403	F822GDT	Mercedes-Benz 811D	Reeve Burgess Beaver	C25F	1989	Ex Gordons, Rotherham, 1993
404	IDZ8561	Mercedes-Benz 811D	Wright NimBus	B26F	1990	Ex Wright demonstrator, 1992
405	F985EDS	Mercedes-Benz 811D	Alexander Sprint	DP33F	1988	Ex Rhondda, 1994
406	H176JVT	Mercedes-Benz 811D	Wright NimBus	B29F	1990	
407	H177JVT	Mercedes-Benz 811D	Wright NimBus	B29F	1990	
410	G807FJX	Mercedes-Benz 811D	PMT Ami	B33F	1990	Ex Abbeyways, Halifax, 1993
411	G111TND	Mercedes-Benz 811D	Carlyle	B31F	1989	Ex C-Line, 1991
413	G901MNS	Mercedes-Benz 811D	Reeve Burgess Beaver	B33F	1989	Ex Edinburgh Transport, 1994

414-428 — Mercedes-Benz 811D — Carlyle — B33F — 1989-90 Ex C-Line, 1991-92 / 414 ex Bee Line Buzz, 1993

414	G114TND	417	G117TND	422	G122TJA	427	G127TJA	428	G128TJA
415	G115TND	421	G121TJA	426	G126TJA				

431-436 — Mercedes-Benz 811D — LHE Commuter — B31F — 1990 — Ex C-Line, 1992

431	H131CDB	433	H133CDB	434	H134CDB	435	H135CDB	436	H136CDB
432	H132CDB								

438	K138BRF	Mercedes-Benz 811D	Dormobile Routemaker	B31F	1993	
439	K139BRF	Mercedes-Benz 811D	Dormobile Routemaker	B31F	1993	
440	K140BFA	Mercedes-Benz 811D	Dormobile Routemaker	B31F	1993	
441	K141BFA	Mercedes-Benz 811D	Dormobile Routemaker	B31F	1993	
442	H112DDS	Mercedes-Benz 811D	Carlyle	B33F	1990	Ex Harte Coaches, Greenock, 1995
447	G897TGG	Mercedes-Benz 811D	Reeve Burgess Beaver	B33F	1990	Ex Stevensons, 1995
448	904AXY	Mercedes-Benz 811D	Alexander AM	DP33F	1988	Ex Happy Days, Woodseaves, 1991
449	G399FSF	Mercedes-Benz 811D	PMT Ami	B33F	1990	Ex Stevensons, 1994
450	G900TJA	Mercedes-Benz 811D	Mellor	B32F	1990	Ex Stevensons, 1994

451-462

Mercedes-Benz 811D — Marshall C16 — B31F — 1995

451	M451EDH	454	M454EDH	457	M457EDH	459	M459EDH	461	M461EDH
452	M452EDH	455	M455EDH	458	M458EDH	460	M460EDH	462	M462EDH
453	M453EDH	456	M456EDH						

463-472

Mercedes-Benz 811D — Alexander Sprint — B31F — 1995

| 463 | N463EHA | 465 | N465EHA | 467 | N467EHA | 469 | N469EHA | 471 | N471EHA |
| 464 | N464EHA | 466 | N466EHA | 468 | N468EHA | 470 | N470EHA | 472 | N472EHA |

481-498

Mercedes-Benz 814D — Wright NimBus — B31F* — 1991 — *481/2/97/8 are B33F

| 481 | H201LRF | 483 | J203REH | 486 | J206REH | 495 | J205REH | 497 | H197JVT |
| 482 | H202LRF | 484 | J204REH | 487 | J207REH | 496 | H196JVT | 498 | H198JVT |

| 499 | H199KEH | Mercedes-Benz 814D | Phoenix | DP31F | 1990 |
| 501 | H501GHA | Dennis Dart 8.5SDL3003 | East Lancashire EL2000 | B35F | 1991 |

502-523

Dennis Dart 9SDL3034 — East Lancashire EL2000 — B33F — 1994

502	L502BNX	507	L507BNX	512	L512BNX	516	L516BNX	520	L620BNX
503	L503BNX	508	L508BNX	513	L513BNX	517	L517BNX	521	L521BNX
504	L504BNX	509	L509BNX	514	L514BNX	518	L618BNX	522	L522BNX
505	L605BNX	510	L510BNX	515	L515BNX	519	L519BNX	523	L523BNX
506	L506BNX	511	L511BNX						

524	J556GTP	Dennis Dart 9SDL3002	Wadham Stringer Portsdown	B35F	1991	Ex Irwell Valley, Boothstown, 1992
525	H192JNF	Dennis Dart 9SDL3002	Wadham Stringer Portsdown	B35F	1990	Ex Jim Stones, Glazebury, 1993
541	G141GOL	Dennis Dart 9SDL3002	Duple Dartline	B39F	1990	Ex Arrowline, Knutsford, 1992
551	H851NOC	Dennis Dart 9.8SDL3004	Carlyle Dartline	B43F	1991	Ex Thanet Bus, Ramsgate, 1992
580	JOX480P	Leyland National 11351/1R		B49F	1976	

647-699

Leyland National 11351A/1R — B49F — 1977-78 647 ex Midland Red East, 1982

| 647 | PUK647R | 685 | TOF685S | 687 | TOF687S | 698 | TOF698S | 699 | TOF699S |
| 684 | TOF684S | | | | | | | | |

702-767

Leyland National 11351A/1R — B49F — 1977-80 Ex Midland Red, 1981

| 702 | TOF702S | 705 | TOF705S | 719 | TOF719S | 764 | BVP764V | 767 | BVP767V |
| 703 | TOF703S | 718w | TOF718S | 763 | BVP763V | 765 | BVP765V | | |

790	L300SBS	Dennis Dart 9.8SDL3035	Plaxton Pointer	B40F	1994	
791	L301NFA	Dennis Dart 9.8SDL3035	Plaxton Pointer	B40F	1994	
792	L302NFA	Dennis Dart 9.8SDL3035	Plaxton Pointer	B40F	1994	
793	L303NFA	Dennis Dart 9.8SDL3035	Plaxton Pointer	B40F	1994	
794	L304NFA	Dennis Dart 9.8SDL3035	Plaxton Pointer	B40F	1994	
795	L305NFA	Dennis Dart 9.8SDL3035	Plaxton Pointer	B40F	1994	
801	J701NHA	Dennis Dart 9.8SDL3004	East Lancashire EL2000	B40F	1991	
802	M802MOJ	Dennis Dart 9.8SDL3040	Marshall C37	B40F	1994	
803	M803MOJ	Dennis Dart 9.8SDL3040	Marshall C37	B40F	1994	
804	M804MOJ	Dennis Dart 9.8SDL3054	Marshall C37	B40F	1994	
805	M805MOJ	Dennis Dart 9.8SDL3054	Marshall C37	B40F	1994	
806	N806EHA	Dennis Dart 9.8SDL3054	East Lancashire	B40F	1995	
807	N807EHA	Dennis Dart 9.8SDL3054	East Lancashire	B40F	1995	
808	N808EHA	Dennis Dart 9.8SDL3054	East Lancashire	B40F	1995	
826	DOC26V	Leyland National 2 NL116L11/1R		B50F	1980	Ex West Midlands Travel, 1996
829	DOC29V	Leyland National 2 NL116L11/1R		B50F	1980	Ex West Midlands Travel, 1996
837	DOC37V	Leyland National 2 NL116L11/1R		B50F	1980	Ex West Midlands Travel, 1996

The Dennis Dart has become the principal midibus for Midland Red. Early examples were bodied by East Lancashire to the EL2000 design and were principally allocated to services in Stafford and Telford. Photographed arriving in Wolverhampton is 505, L605BNX, one of several where the 5xx series number was not available.

859	TPE159S	Leyland National 11351A/1R (6HLXB)		B49F	1978	Ex Alder Valley, 1990
863	TPE163S	Leyland National 11351A/1R (6HLXB)		B49F	1978	Ex Alder Valley, 1990
866	TPE166S	Leyland National 11351A/1R (6HLXB)		B49F	1978	Ex Alder Valley, 1990
872	GMB372T	Leyland National 11351A/1R (6HLXB)		B49F	1978	Ex C-Line, 1992
873	GMB373T	Leyland National 11351A/1R (6HLXB)		B49F	1978	Ex Crosville, 1989
874	GMB374T	Leyland National 11351A/1R (6HLXB)		B49F	1978	Ex Bee Line Buzz, 1990
875	LFR875X	Leyland National 2 NL106L11/1R East Lancs Greenway (1995)		B41F	1981	Ex North Western, 1995
876	GMB376T	Leyland National 11351A/1R (6HLXB)		B49F	1978	Ex Crosville, 1989
878	GMB378T	Leyland National 11351A/1R (6HLXB)		B49F	1979	Ex Crosville, 1989
883	GMB383T	Leyland National 11351A/1R (6HLXB)		B49F	1978	Ex C-Line, 1992
890	GMB390T	Leyland National 11351A/1R (6HLXB)		B49F	1978	Ex Crosville, 1989
891	KMA401T	Leyland National 11351A/1R (6HLXB)		B49F	1979	Ex C-Line, 1992
892	KMA402T	Leyland National 11351A/1R (6HLXB)		B49F	1979	Ex C-Line, 1992
901	TOF701S	Leyland National 11351A/1R		B49F	1978	
904	TOF704S	Leyland National 11351A/1R (Cummins)		B49F	1978	
917	JOX717P	Leyland National 11351A/1R (Volvo)		B49F	1976	
937	PUK637R	Leyland National 11351A/1R	East Lancs Greenway (1994)	B49F	1977	Ex Midland Red, 1981
939	PUK639R	Leyland National 11351A/1R (Cummins)		B49F	1977	
952	PUK652R	Leyland National 11351A/1R	East Lancs Greenway (1994)	B49F	1977	Ex Midland Red East, 1983
968w	BVP768V	Leyland National 11351A/1R		B41F	1980	
1001	TR6147	Bristol LH6L	Hants & Dorset(1982)	Ch25F	1974	Ex Shamrock & Rambler, 1988
1006	HXI3006	Leyland Lynx LX5636LXCTFR	Alexander N	B53F	1985	Ex Citybus, Belfast, 1992
1007	HXI3007	Leyland Lynx LX5636LXBFR	Alexander N	B49F	1986	Ex Citybus, Belfast, 1992
1008	HXI3008	Leyland Lynx LX5636LXBFR	Alexander N	B53F	1986	Ex Citybus, Belfast, 1992
1009	HXI3009	Leyland Lynx LX5636LXBFR	Alexander N	B49F	1986	Ex Citybus, Belfast, 1992
1010	HXI3010	Leyland Lynx LX563TL11FR	Alexander N	B49F	1986	Ex Citybus, Belfast, 1992
1011	HXI3011	Leyland Lynx LX563TL11FR	Alexander N	B53F	1986	Ex Citybus, Belfast, 1992
1012	HXI3012	Leyland Lynx LX563TL11FR	Alexander N	B53F	1986	Ex Citybus, Belfast, 1992
1013	H408YMA	Leyland Lynx LX2R11C15Z4R	Leyland Lynx	B51F	1990	Ex The Wright Company, Wrexham, 1994
1014	F258GWJ	Leyland Lynx LX112L10ZR1R	Leyland Lynx	B51F	1989	Ex The Wright Company, Wrexham, 1993
1015	E72KBF	Leyland Lynx LX112L10ZR1	Leyland Lynx	B51F	1988	
1016	D401MHS	Leyland Lynx LX5636LXCTFR1	Leyland Lynx	B47F	1986	Ex Kelvin Central, 1991
1017	F61PRE	Leyland Lynx LX112L10ZR1R	Leyland Lynx	B48F	1989	

One of the requirements for the replacement Leyland National was the option to have bodywork supplied by other builders, as a result the Lynx has a separate chassis to the body. Early examples were bodied by Alexanders, using their N-type body which was only assembled in Belfast. All these are now back on the mainland, many with Midland Red. Seen leaving Manchester for Macclesfield is 1010, HXI3010 with, as all Lynx at present, Stevensons names. *Tony Wilson*

1100	L100SBS	Mercedes-Benz 0405	Wright Cityranger	B51F	1993	
1102	L102MEH	MAN 11.190 HOCLR	Optare Vecta	B42F	1994	
1103	K140RYS	MAN 11.190 HOCLR	Optare Vecta	B37F	1993	Ex Express Travel, Perth, 1994
1104	UOI772	MAN 11.190 HOCLR	Optare Vecta	B40F	1993	Ex Express Travel, Perth, 1994
1106	G785PWL	DAF SB220LC550	Optare Delta	B49F	1989	Ex Edinburgh Transport, 1994
1107	F792DWT	DAF SB220LC550	Optare Delta	B49F	1989	Ex Edinburgh Transport, 1994
1131	J31SFA	Leyland Swift ST2R44C97A4	Wright Handybus	B39F	1992	
1132	J32SFA	Leyland Swift ST2R44C97A4	Wright Handybus	B39F	1992	
1133	H313WUA	Leyland Swift ST2R44C97A4	Reeve Burgess Harrier	DP39F	1991	Ex Pennine, Gargrave, 1992
1134	J34SRF	Leyland Swift ST2R44C97A4	Wright Handybus	B39F	1992	
1135	H314WUA	Leyland Swift ST2R44C97A4	Reeve Burgess Harrier	DP39F	1991	Ex Pennine, Gargrave, 1992
1136	J36SRF	Leyland Swift ST2R44C97A4	Wright Handybus	B39F	1992	
1137	G616WGS	Leyland Swift LBM6T/2RA	Reeve Burgess Harrier	B39F	1989	Ex Chambers, Stevenage, 1992
1138	F907PFH	Leyland Swift LBM6T/2RA	G C Smith Whippet	B36F	1988	Ex Gloucestershire CC, 1993
1139	G727RGA	Leyland Swift LBM6T/2RA	Reeve Burgess Harrier	B39F	1990	Ex Kelvin Central, 1993
1140	H166MFA	Leyland Swift ST2R44C97A4	Wadham Stringer Vanguard II	B39F	1991	
1141	F956XCK	Leyland Swift LBM6N/2RAO	Wadham Stringer Vanguard II	B39F	1989	Ex Jim Stones, Glazebury, 1991
1142	F155DKU	Leyland Swift LBM6T/2RA	Reeve Burgess Harrier	B41F	1989	Ex K-Line, Kirkburton, 1993
1143	J169REH	Leyland Swift ST2R44C97A4	Wadham Stringer Vanguard II	B39F	1991	
1144	J162REH	Leyland Swift ST2R44C97A4	Wadham Stringer Vanguard II	B39F	1991	
1145	G98VMM	Leyland Swift LBM6T/2RA	Wadham Stringer Vanguard II	B39F	1989	Ex Green, Kirkintilloch, 1991
1146	E990NMK	Leyland Swift LBM6T/2RS	Wadham Stringer Vanguard II	B37F	1988	Ex Armchair, Brentford, 1993
1147	E992NMK	Leyland Swift LBM6T/2RS	Wadham Stringer Vanguard II	B37F	1988	Ex Armchair, Brentford, 1993
1148	E993NMK	Leyland Swift LBM6T/2RS	Wadham Stringer Vanguard II	B37F	1988	Ex Armchair, Brentford, 1993

Opposite, top:- Two Leyland-bodied examples of the Lynx were supplied new to Stevensons, though a further three have subsequently been acquired. Four are currently allocated to Lichfield while the fifth is at the Midland Red depot in Stafford. When photographed, 1014 was operating the Tamworth service. *Tony Wilson*

Opposite, bottom:- The 1996 intake of East Lancashire-bodied Dennis Darts are now based in Tamworth where 1313, P313FEA was photographed on route-branded service 7. The *xf* logo was mised understood by many people who were looking for route 11. *Tony Wilson*

The 1998 Cowie Bus Handbbook

1201-1210
Dennis Falcon HC SDA421 · East Lancashire EL2000 · B48F · 1990 · Ex London & Country, 1991

1201	G301DPA	1207	G307DPA	1208	G308DPA	1209	G309DPA	1210	G310DPA
1206	G306DPA								

1211-1219
Dennis Falcon HC SDA423 · East Lancashire EL2000 · B48F · 1992-93

1211	K211UHA	1213	K213UHA	1215	K215UHA	1217	K217UHA	1219	K219UHA
1212	K212UHA	1214	K214UHA	1216	K216UHA	1218	K218UHA		

1301-1305
Dennis Dart SLF · Plaxton Pointer · B37F · 1996 · *1301 is B43F

1301	N301ENX	1302	N302ENX	1303	N303ENX	1304	N304ENX	1305	N305ENX

1306-1310
Dennis Dart SLF · Plaxton Pointer · DP37F · 1996

1306	P306FEA	1307	P307FEA	1308	P308FEA	1309	P309FEA	1310	P310FEA

1311-1315
Dennis Dart SLF · East Lancashire Spryte · B41F · 1996

1311	P311FEA	1312	P312FEA	1313	P313FEA	1314	P314FEA	1315	P315FEA

1316-1327
Dennis Dart SLF · Plaxton Pointer · DP39F · 1997

1316	P316FEA	1319	P319HOJ	1322	P322HOJ	1324	P324HOJ	1326	P326HOJ
1317	P317FEA	1320	P320HOJ	1323	P323HOJ	1325	P325HOJ	1327	P327HOJ
1318	P318FEA	1321	P321HOJ						

1329-1344
Dennis Dart SLF · Plaxton Pointer 2 · DP39F · 1997-98

1329	R329TJW	1332	R332TJW	1336	R336TJW	1339	R339TJW	1332	R332TJW
1330	R330TJW	1334	R334TJW	1337	R337TJW	1340	R340TJW	1333	R333TJW
1331	R331TJW	1335	R335TJW	1338	R338TJW	1341	R341TJW	1334	R334TJW

1401	M401EFD	Scania N113CRL	East Lancashire European	B42F	1995	
1402	M402EFD	Scania N113CRL	East Lancashire European	B42F	1995	
1403	M403EFD	Scania N113CRL	East Lancashire European	B42F	1995	
1404	M404EFD	Scania N113CRL	East Lancashire European	B42F	1995	
1407	F170DET	Scania K93CRB	Plaxton Derwent II	B57F	1989	Ex Capital Citybus, 1993
1409	G109YRE	Scania K93CRB	Alexander PS	B51F	1989	
1410	F110SRF	Scania K93CRB	Alexander PS	B51F	1989	
1411	G611CFA	Scania K93CRB	Plaxton Derwent	B57F	1990	Ex North Western (Liverline), 1996
1412	G612CFA	Scania K93CRB	Plaxton Derwent	B57F	1990	Ex North Western (Liverline), 1996
1413	G41HKY	Scania K93CRB	Plaxton Derwent	B57F	1990	Ex North Western (Liverline), 1996
1414	G610CFA	Scania K93CRB	Plaxton Derwent	B57F	1990	Ex North Western (Liverline), 1996

1415-1429
Scania L113CRL · Plaxton Prestige · B47F · On order 1416-25 as DP45F

1415	R415TJW	1418	R418TJW	1421	R421TJW	1424	R424TJW	1427	R427TJW
1416	R416TJW	1419	R419TJW	1422	R422TJW	1425	R425TJW	1428	R428TJW
1417	R417TJW	1420	R420TJW	1423	R423TJW	1426	R426TJW	1429	R429TJW

1500	OKY822X	Leyland Leopard PSU5C/4R	Plaxton Supreme VI Exp	C57F	1982	Ex Frontline, 1996
1504w	ROP835R	Leyland Leopard PSU3C/4R	Willowbrook Warrior(1989)	B53F	1978	Ex Loch Lomond Coaches, 1994
1508	KUB671V	Leyland Leopard PSU3E/4R	Plaxton Supreme IV Express	C49F	1980	Ex Frontline, 1996
1510	VOV926S	Leyland Leopard PSU3E/4R	Plaxton Supreme III	C53F	1978	
1512	AVT345S	Leyland Leopard PSU3E/4R	Plaxton Supreme III Express	C49F	1977	Ex Rhondda, 1993
1513	BOK364T	Leyland Leopard PSU3E/4R	Plaxton Supreme III Express	C53F	1978	Ex Greater Manchester PTE, 1984
1514	479BOC	Leyland Leopard PSU3B/4R (TL11)	Duple 320 (1987)	C53F	1973	Ex Blue Bus, Rugeley, 1985
1516	B516OEH	Leyland Tiger TRCTL11/3RH	Duple Laser 2	C53F	1985	
1522	BPR102Y	Leyland Tiger TRCTL11/3R	Duple Laser	C50F	1983	Ex London & Country, 1991
1526w	BPR106Y	Leyland Tiger TRCTL11/3R	Duple Laser	C50F	1983	Ex London & Country, 1991
1527	BPR107Y	Leyland Tiger TRCTL11/3R	Duple Laser	C50F	1983	Ex London & Country, 1991

Opposite, top:- **Four Marshall-bodied Dennis Darts were placed into stock in 1994 all four were allocated to Shrewsbury where three were liveried for the town's Park & Ride service. Seen in fleet colours is 804, M804MOJ, which is seen on lay-over after arriving in Wellington.** *Tony Wilson*
Opposite, bottom:- **Scania double-deck buses were added the varied selection of double-deck types operated by Midland Red during 1995 and these are used on the Birmingham commuter services that target the city from the north. Three of the five East Lancashire-bodied vehicles have high-back seating, while 1834, M834SDA, and 1835 are fitted with standard bus seating.** *Tony Wilson*

1604	B604OEH	Leyland Tiger TRCTL11/3RH	Duple Laser 2	C55F	1984	
1605	B605OEH	Leyland Tiger TRCTL11/3RH	Duple Laser 2	C55F	1984	
1606	B606OEH	Leyland Tiger TRCTL11/3RH	Duple Laser 2	C55F	1984	
1607	B607OEH	Leyland Tiger TRCTL11/3RH	Duple Laser 2	C55F	1984	
1615	A215PEV	Leyland Tiger TRCTL11/2R	Duple Dominant IV Express	DP53F	1983	Ex Southdown, 1990
1616	A115EPA	Leyland Tiger TRCTL11/2RH	Plaxton Paramount 3200 E	C53F	1984	Ex The Shires, 1996
1618	A118EPA	Leyland Tiger TRCTL11/2RH	Plaxton Paramount 3200 E	C53F	1984	Ex London & Country, 1997
1619	GDZ795	Leyland Tiger TRCTL11/3RH	Duple 320	C53F	1986	Ex Crosville Cymru, 1996
1620	YYJ955	Leyland Tiger TRCTL11/3RH	Duple 320	C53F	1986	Ex Crosville Cymru, 1996
1621	A121EPA	Leyland Tiger TRCTL11/2R	Plaxton Paramount 3200 E	C53F	1983	Ex London & Country, 1997
1628	A101EPA	Leyland Tiger TRCTL11/2RH	Plaxton Paramount 3200 E	C53F	1983	Ex The Shires, 1996
1635	A195KKF	Leyland Tiger TRCTL11/2R	Duple Laser	DP49F	1983	Ex North Western, 1995
1636	A136EPA	Leyland Tiger TRCTL11/2RH	Plaxton Paramount 3200 E	C53F	1984	Ex The Shires, 1996
1639	A139EPA	Leyland Tiger TRCTL11/2R	Plaxton Paramount 3200 E	C53F	1984	Ex C-Line, 1992
1641	A41SMA	Leyland Tiger TRCTL11/2RH	Duple Laser	C49F	1983	Ex North Western, 1995
1642	A39SMA	Leyland Tiger TRCTL11/2R	Duple Laser	C49F	1983	Ex North Western, 1995
1643	A858YOX	Leyland Tiger TRCTL11/3RH	Plaxton Paramount 3200 E	C53F	1983	Ex Frontline, 1996
1645	B145ALG	Leyland Tiger TRCTL11/2RH	Duple Laser 2	C49F	1984	Ex North Western, 1995
1646	488BDN	Leyland Tiger TRCTL11/3R	Duple 320	C53F	1986	Ex Crosville Cymru, 1996
1647	B147ALG	Leyland Tiger TRCTL11/2RH	Duple Laser 2	C49F	1984	Ex North Western, 1995
1648	B148ALG	Leyland Tiger TRCTL11/2RH	Duple Laser 2	C49F	1984	Ex North Western, 1995
1649	B149ALG	Leyland Tiger TRCTL11/2RH	Duple Laser 2	C49F	1984	Ex North Western, 1995
1650	B150ALG	Leyland Tiger TRCTL11/2RH	Duple Laser 2	C49F	1984	Ex North Western, 1995
1653	A859YOX	Leyland Tiger TRCTL11/3RH	Plaxton Paramount 3200 E	C53F	1983	Ex Frontline, 1996
1654	TDC854X	Leyland Tiger TRCTL11/3R	Duple Dominant IV Express	C53F	1982	Ex Shamrock & Rambler, 1998
1660	A160EPA	Leyland Tiger TRCTL11/3R	Plaxton Paramount 3200 E	C53F	1984	Ex C-Line, 1992
1679	FAZ5279	Leyland Tiger TRCTL11/3R	Plaxton Paramount 3200 E	C53F	1984	Ex Crosville Cymru, 1995
1681	FAZ5181	Leyland Tiger TRCTL11/3R	Plaxton Paramount 3200 E	C53F	1984	Ex Crosville Cymru, 1996
1689	SIB7689	Leyland Tiger TRCTL11/3RH	Duple 320	C53F	1986	Ex Crosville Cymru, 1997
1694	FAZ3194	Leyland Tiger TRCTL11/2RH	Duple 320	C53F	1986	Ex Crosville Cymru, 1997
1695	FAZ3195	Leyland Tiger TRCTL11/2RH	Plaxton Paramount 3200 II	C53F	1985	Ex Crosville Cymru, 1995
1698	A898KAH	Leyland Tiger TRCTL11/3RH	Plaxton Paramount 3200 E	C53F	1983	Ex C-Line, 1992

1701-1709

Leyland Tiger TRCTL11/2R — Duple Dominant — B51F — 1984

1701	A701HVT	1703	A703HVT	1705	A705HVT	1707	A707HVT	1709	A709HVT
1702	A702HVT	1704	A704HVT	1706	A706HVT	1708	A708HVT		

1710-1720

Leyland Tiger TRCTL11/2R — East Lancashire (1989) — B51F* — 1982 — Ex London & Country, 1989
*1710/3/4/8 are DP49F; 1712 is B55F

1710	TPC101X	1713	TPC103X	1715	WPH125Y	1717	TPC107X	1719	WPH139Y
1711	WPH121Y	1714	TPC104X	1716	WPH126Y	1718	TPC114X	1720	WPH122Y
1712	TPC102X								

1721-1729

Leyland Tiger TRCTL11/3RH — East Lancashire (1991) — B59F — 1984-86 Ex London & Country, 1991

1721	C141SPB	1723	B103KPF	1725	B105KPF	1728	B108KPF	1729	B109KPF
1722	B102KPF	1724	B104KPF	1726	C262SPC				

1730	YPJ207Y	Leyland Tiger TRCTL11/3R	East Lancashire (1992)	B59F	1982	Ex County, 1991
1733	OOV761X	Leyland Tiger TRCTL11/3R	East Lancashire (1992)	B59F	1982	Ex Tame Valley, Birmingham, 1992
1735	DJN25X	Leyland Tiger TRCTL11/2R	East Lancashire (1992)	B53F	1982	Ex County, 1992
1737	UJN430Y	Leyland Tiger TRCTL11/2R	East Lancashire (1991)	B53F	1982	Ex County, 1991
1738	WPH118Y	Leyland Tiger TRCTL11/2R	East Lancashire (1992)	B53F	1983	Ex County, 1991
1739	E829AWA	Leyland Tiger TRBTL11/2RP	Plaxton Derwent II	B54F	1988	Ex Liverline, 1993
1740	AAX590A	Leyland Tiger TRCTL11/3R	East Lancashire (1993)	B61F	1984	Ex Rhondda, 1992
1742	A42SMA	Leyland Tiger TRCTL11/2R	East Lancashire (1992)	B53F	1984	Ex North Western, 1991
1743	WPH123Y	Leyland Tiger TRCTL11/2R	East Lancashire (1992)	B53F	1983	Ex County, 1991

1745-1752

Leyland Tiger TRBTL11/3ARZA — Alexander N — B53F — 1988 — Ex Timeline, 1993-95

1745	E25UNE	1747	E27UNE	1749	E29UNE	1751	E31UNE	1752	E32UNE
1746	E26UNE	1748	E28UNE	1750	E30UNE				

1753-1772

Leyland Tiger TRBL10/3ARZA — Alexander N — B53F* — 1988-89 Ex Timeline, 1994-95
*1759/60/71/2 are B55F

1753	F33ENF	1755	F35ENF	1759	F39ENF	1771	F51ENF	1772	F52ENF
1754	F34ENF	1756	F36ENF	1760	F40ENF				

1778	F278HOD	Leyland Tiger TRBTL11/2RP	Plaxton Derwent 2	B54F	1988	Ex Thames Transit, 1994

Two Scania buses are illustrated here. The upper picture shows 1411, G611CFA, which has returned to the Midland Red/Stevensons fleet after a time with Bee Line, and North Western's Liverline operation. One of a trio new to Happy Days of Woodseaves, it has recently been joined by a fourth which it met at Liverpool, this being new to Trans City of Sidcup. The lower picture shows the second batch of buses purchased for the Meole Brace park and ride service, the first being Dennis Darts. These Scania N113s carry East Lancashire European bodywork and are liveried in blue and yellow for the service. Seen here is 1403, M403EFD. *Phillip Stephenson*

1801-1806

1801-1806	Dennis Dominator DDA1032*	East Lancashire	H47/29F	1990	*1803-6 are DDA1031

1801	G801THA	1803	H803AHA	1804	H804AHA	1805	H805AHA	1806	H806AHA
1802	G802THA								

Fleet	Reg	Chassis	Body	Details	Year	Notes
1823	BMA523W	Bristol VRT/SL3/6LXB	Eastern Coach Works	H43/31F	1981	Ex Crosville Cymru, 1991
1831	M831SDA	Scania N113DRB	East Lancashire	DPH43/29F	1995	
1832	M832SDA	Scania N113DRB	East Lancashire	DPH43/29F	1995	
1833	M833SDA	Scania N113DRB	East Lancashire	DPH43/29F	1995	
1834	M834SDA	Scania N113DRB	East Lancashire	H45/33F	1995	
1835	M835SDA	Scania N113DRB	East Lancashire	H45/33F	1995	
1858	VCA458W	Bristol VRT/SL3/6LXB	Eastern Coach Works	H43/31F	1981	Ex Crosville Cymru, 1991
1860	VCA460W	Bristol VRT/SL3/6LXB	Eastern Coach Works	H43/31F	1981	Ex Crosville Cymru, 1991
1870	WTU470W	Bristol VRT/SL3/6LXB	Eastern Coach Works	H43/31F	1981	Ex Crosville Cymru, 1991
1887	AHW206V	Bristol VRT/SL3/6LXB	Eastern Coach Works	H43/27F	1980	Ex Frontline, 1996

1902-1910

1902-1910	Leyland Olympian ONLXB/1R	Eastern Coach Works	H45/32F	1983

1902	EEH902Y	1904w	EEH904Y	1906	EEH906Y	1909	EEH909Y	1910	EEH910Y
1903	EEH903Y	1905	EEH905Y	1907	EEH907Y				

Fleet	Reg	Chassis	Body	Details	Year	Notes
1911	B911NBF	Leyland Olympian ONLXB/1R	Eastern Coach Works	DPH42/28F	1984	
1912	B912NBF	Leyland Olympian ONLXB/1R	Eastern Coach Works	DPH42/28F	1984	
1913	B913NBF	Leyland Olympian ONLXB/1R	Eastern Coach Works	DPH42/28F	1984	
1914	B197DTU	Leyland Olympian ONLXB/1R	Eastern Coach Works	H45/32F	1985	Ex Crosville, 1989
1915	B198DTU	Leyland Olympian ONLXB/1R	Eastern Coach Works	H45/32F	1985	Ex Crosville, 1989
1916	G916LHA	Leyland Olympian ON2R50G16ZA	East Lancashire	H45/29F	1989	
1917	G917LHA	Leyland Olympian ON2R50G16ZA	East Lancashire	H45/29F	1989	
1918	G918LHA	Leyland Olympian ON2R50G16ZA	East Lancashire	H45/29F	1989	
1919	G919LHA	Leyland Olympian ON2R50G16ZA	East Lancashire	H45/29F	1989	
1923	B203DTU	Leyland Olympian ONLXB/1R	Eastern Coach Works	DPH42/27F	1985	Ex Crosville Cymru, 1990
1924	B204DTU	Leyland Olympian ONLXB/1R	Eastern Coach Works	DPH42/27F	1985	Ex Crosville Cymru, 1990
1937	GFM107X	Leyland Olympian ONLXB/1R	Eastern Coach Works	H45/32F	1982	Ex Crosville, 1989
1938	PFM130Y	Leyland Olympian ONLXB/1R	Eastern Coach Works	H45/32F	1983	Ex Crosville, 1989
1950	A150UDM	Leyland Olympian ONLXB/1R	Eastern Coach Works	H45/32F	1983	Ex Stevensons, 1995
1952	A152UDM	Leyland Olympian ONLXB/1R	Eastern Coach Works	H45/32F	1984	Ex Midland, 1994
1954	A154UDM	Leyland Olympian ONLXB/1R	Eastern Coach Works	H45/32F	1984	Ex Crosville, 1989
1955	A155UDM	Leyland Olympian ONLXB/1R	Eastern Coach Works	H45/32F	1984	Ex Crosville, 1989
1972	A172VFM	Leyland Olympian ONLXB/1R	Eastern Coach Works	H45/32F	1984	Ex C-Line, 1992
1994	L94HRF	DAF DB250RS200505	Optare Spectra	H48/29F	1993	to Midland Fox, 1998
1995	L95HRF	DAF DB250RS200505	Optare Spectra	H48/29F	1993	to Midland Fox, 1998
1996	F96PRE	Leyland Olympian ONCL10/1RZ	Alexander RL	H47/32F	1988	
1997	F97PRE	Leyland Olympian ONCL10/1RZ	Alexander RL	H47/32F	1988	
2005	G505SFT	Leyland Olympian ONCL10/1RZ	Northern Counties Palatine	H47/30F	1989	Ex Bee Line Buzz, 1993
2007	G507SFT	Leyland Olympian ONCL10/1RZ	Northern Counties Palatine	H47/30F	1989	Ex Bee Line Buzz, 1993
2010	G510SFT	Leyland Olympian ONCL10/1RZ	Northern Counties Palatine	H47/30F	1989	Ex Bee Line Buzz, 1993
2011	G511SFT	Leyland Olympian ONCL10/1RZ	Northern Counties Palatine	H47/30F	1989	Ex Bee Line Buzz, 1993
2044	G644BPH	Volvo Citybus B10M-50	Northern Counties Palatine	H45/35F	1989	Ex Bee Line Buzz, 1993
2045	G645BPH	Volvo Citybus B10M-50	Northern Counties Palatine	H45/35F	1989	Ex Bee Line Buzz, 1993
2046	G646BPH	Volvo Citybus B10M-50	Northern Counties Palatine	H45/35F	1989	Ex Bee Line Buzz, 1993
2047	G647BPH	Volvo Citybus B10M-50	Northern Counties Palatine	H45/35F	1989	Ex Bee Line Buzz, 1993
2050	GOG272W	MCW Metrobus DR102/18	MCW	H43/30F	1981	Ex West Midlands Travel, 1990

2051-2071

2051-2071	MCW Metrobus DR102/22	MCW	H43/30F	1981	Ex West Midlands Travel, 1990

2051	KJW296W	2053	KJW305W	2055	KJW310W	2070	KJW318W	2071	KJW320W
2052	KJW301W	2054	KJW306W	2056	KJW322W				

Fleet	Reg	Chassis	Body	Details	Year	Notes
2073	UWW512X	MCW Metrobus DR101/15	Alexander RH	H43/32F	1982	Ex Yorkshire Rider, 1987
2074	UWW513X	MCW Metrobus DR101/15	Alexander RH	H43/32F	1982	Ex Yorkshire Rider, 1987
2075	UWW515X	MCW Metrobus DR101/15	Alexander RH	H43/32F	1982	Ex Yorkshire Rider, 1987
2076	UWW517X	MCW Metrobus DR101/15	Alexander RH	H43/32F	1982	Ex Yorkshire Rider, 1987
2079	BSN878V	MCW Metrobus DR102/5	MCW	H45/30F	1979	Ex Enterprise & Silver Dawn, 1988
2080	TOJ592S	MCW Metrobus DR101/2	MCW	H43/30F	1977	Ex MCW demonstrator, 1989
2081	F181YDA	MCW Metrobus DR132/12	MCW	H43/30F	1988	Ex MCW demonstrator, 1989

Between 1993 and 1996 Timeline reduced the number of Leyland Tiger buses they inherited from Shearings and several are now to be found in the Midland Red fleet. These form two batches separated by their different engine types. From the second batch is 1759, F39ENF, which is based at Crewe where it is seen in this picture. *Phillip Stephenson*

2089	D676MHS	MCW Metrobus DR102/52	Alexander RL	DPH45/33F	1986	Ex Kelvin Central, 1994
2090	D678MHS	MCW Metrobus DR102/52	Alexander RL	DPH45/33F	1986	Ex Kelvin Central, 1994
2091	D680MHS	MCW Metrobus DR102/52	Alexander RL	DPH45/33F	1986	Ex Kelvin Central, 1994
2092	D682MHS	MCW Metrobus DR102/52	Alexander RL	H45/33F	1986	Ex Kelvin Central, 1994
2093	D683MHS	MCW Metrobus DR102/52	Alexander RL	DPH45/33F	1986	Ex Kelvin Central, 1994

Ancilliary vehicles

AV14	B504PRF	Ford Transit 190D	Dormobile	B6F	1985	publicity vehicle
AV20	CBF21Y	Daimler Fleetline CRL6	MCW	H44/29F	1974	
AV37	C37WBF	Ford Transit 190D	Dormobile	B16F	1986	
RV23	SBF233	Leyland Titan PD2/28	Northern Counties	RV	1962	Ex Midland Red, 1981
RV24	Q124VOE	Leyland Leopard PSU4/4R	Plaxton Panorama	RV	1966	Ex Midland Red, 1981
RV25	Q125VOE	Leyland Leopard PSU4/4R	Plaxton Panorama	RV	1966	Ex Midland Red, 1981
RV26	Q126VOE	Leyland Leopard PSU4/4R	Plaxton Panorama	RV	1966	Ex Midland Red, 1981
TV51	RUJ351R	Ford R1114	Plaxton Supreme III	C49F	1977	Ex Grimsby Cleethorpes, 1991
TV53	MRO993P	Ford R1114	Plaxton Supreme III	C53F	1977	Ex Grimsby Cleethorpes, 1991
TV55	GSU854T	Leyland Leopard PSU3E/4R	Alexander AT	DP49F	1979	Ex Kelvin Central, 1994
TV81	NGR681P	Bristol LH6L	Eastern Coach Works	B43F	1976	Ex City Rider, 1995
TV86	XPT686R	Bristol LH6L	Eastern Coach Works	B43F	1977	Ex Northumbria, 1996
TV93	TOF693S	Leyland National 11351A/1R		B49F	1978	

82HBC	DFP707Y	GIL8487	E32SBO
123TKM	DVO1T, ERC247T	GIL8487	E32SBO
124YTW	DEN247W	HIJ3652	E472BTN
422AKN	G25YVT	HIL7596	E31SBO
429UFM	E614AEY	HXI3006	From new
430UFM	E615AEY	HXI3007	From new
468KPX	VRR447, UHH575X	HXI3008	From new
479BOC	AJA360L	HXI3009	From new
488BDN	C252SPC	HXI3010	From new
565LON	B549BMH, MSU432, B413LRA	HXI3011	From new
614WEH	LOT777R	HXI3012	From new
784RBF	D319VVV	LUY742	E562UHS
803HOM	D264HFX	OGL518	B912SPR
852YYC	B666XVO	OOV761X	VSS1X, WLT610, LTS93X
904AXY	F148USX	PCW946	A703OWY, HIJ3652, A788MEH
A858YOX	A622ATV, YSU954	PSV323	G298SKP, HKR11, G118NUP
A859YOX	A618ATV, YSU953	Q124VOE	GHA326D
AAL303A	BUH226V	Q125VOE	GHA338D
AAL404A	BUH222V	Q126VOE	GHA336D
AAX590A	A217VWO	ROP835R	VCA995R, 2154K, WGD792R, UOI772
AVT345S	SOA676S, 488BDN	SIB7689	C251SPC
BOK364T	TWH687T, WYR562	TOU962	MSU573Y
CBF31Y	THM689M	TR6147	NLJ516M
DJN25X	TPC106X, OIB3510	UJN430Y	WPH124Y, FBZ2514
FAZ3194	C250SPC	UOI772	K141RYS
FAZ3195	B269KPF	VLT166	G58RGG
FAZ5181	A147EPA	VOI6874	YNN29Y
FAZ5279	A145EPA	VOV926S	XRE305S, 422AKN
FSU661	H908AHS	WYR562	G417WFP
GDZ795	C299SPC	XAF759	B555HAL

Allocations and liveries

Livery: Red and yellow; yellow and blue ⚓ (Shrewsbury Park & Ride); green ❣ (Budget Bus); grey ⚓ (Viking)

Abermule (Station Yard, Kerry Road)

Tiger	1722	1730	1737	1742

Bridgnorth (Chartwell Business Park, Stourbridge Road)

Iveco	300			
Tiger	1701	1705	1706	1709

Burslem (Nevada Lane)

Mercedes-Benz	148	149	150	156	164	165	168	403
	405	413	449	486	499			
Swift	1133	1135	1141					

Burton-on-Trent (Wetmore Road)

Mercedes-Benz	230	253	481	482	483			
Dart	790	791	792	793	794	795		
Vecta	1102	1103	1104					
Leopard	1513							
National	826	829	837					
Tiger	1516	1639	1642	1647	1654	1689	1694	
Olympian	1911	1912	1923	1924	2007	2010		
Spectra	1994	1995						
Scania	1415	1416	1417	1418				
Metrobus	2050	2051	2052	2055	2075	2076	2079	2080
	2081							

Cannock (Delta Way)

Mercedes-Benz	136	137	153	155	159	166	382	383
	384	385	386	387	388	389	390	391
	411	415	417	442	447	450	496	
Sherpa	218	219	220	221	222			
Dart	516	519	522	523	524	525	541	551
Tiger	1718	1740	1749	1752	1753	1754	1756	1760
	1778							
Olympian	1903	1907	1909	1910	1913	1915	1938	1950

Crewe (Bus Station, Delamere Street)

Mercedes-Benz	51	52	53	54	55	56	57	160
	394	395	432	433	434	435	436	
Renault-Dodge	330	331	334	335	336			
Tiger	1702	1704	1708	1755	1759	1771	1772	
Dominator	1801	1802	1803	1804	1805	1806		
Olympian	1914	1937	1954	1972				

Lichfield (Freeford Bridge, Common Road)

Mercedes-Benz	58	59	60	61	118♥	167	229	255
	402	406	407	439	440	484	487	497
Lynx	1013	1014	1015	1017				
Cityranger	1100							
Scania	1407	1409	1410	1411	1412	1413	1414	
Tiger	1616	1618	1643	1653	1660	1681	1739	

The latest park & ride vehicles for Shrewsbury are a further batch of Dennis Darts. Seen on the Harlescott service is 1309, P309FEA, which carries a low floor body from Plaxton with thirty-seven seats and access for prams and wheel-chairs. *Phillip Stephenson*

Macclesfield (Bus station, Sunderland Street)

Mercedes-Benz	126	141	142	143	154	157	158	171
	252	396	397	398	399	401	404	441
Lynx	1007	1009	1010	1012				
Delta	1106	1107						
Swift	1131	1132	1138	1139	1143	1144	1147	1148
Olympian	1902	1904	1952	1996	1997			
Metrobus	2089	2090	2091	2092	2093			

Oswestry (Oswald Road)

Renault-Dodge	333	337	338			
Mercedes-Benz	422	453				
National	859	890				
Greenway	875					
Falcon	1201	1206	1207	1208	1209	1210
Bristol VR	1823					
Olympian	1905	1906	1917	1919	1955	

Shrewsbury (Spring Gardens, Ditherington)

Volvo	10							
Mercedes-Benz	7	421	426	428	451	452		
Iveco	296	301	302	303	304	305	306	307
	308	309	310	311	312	313	314	315
	316	319	327	328				
National	687	698	702	705	763	765	767	872
	883	901	904	939				
Greenway	937	952						
Tiger	1735							
Dart	802	803	804	805				
Falcon	1214	1219	1302	1303	1304	1305	1306	1307
	1308	1309	1310					
Scania	1401Ⓜ	1402Ⓜ	1403Ⓜ	1404Ⓜ				

Stafford (Dorrington Park Industrial Estate, Common Road)

Mercedes-Benz	88	91	92	95	96	98	102	
	104	107	114	120	121	122	123	125
	129	131♥	133	134	135	140	175	392
	393	410	431	438	454	456	457	459
Transit	180	181	182	183	184	185	186	187
	188	189	191					
Renault-Dodge	332	359						
Dart	514	515	517	520	521	807	808	
National	647	699	703	764	917			
Lynx	1008	1011	1016					
Tiger	1635	1641	1710	1711	1712	1715	1716	1717
	1720	1721	1725	1726	1727	1728	1733	1738
	1743							

Swadlincote (Midland Road)

Mercedes-Benz	146	170	172	173	254	256	495	498
Swift	1134	1136	1140	1142	1145	1146		
Dart	1321	1322	1323	1324	1325	1326	1327	
Leopard	1508	1514						
Tiger	1615	1645	1698	1723				
Lynx	1006							
Bristol VR	1887							
Metrobus	2054	2071						

Swadlincote (Ryder Close, Cadley Hill) - Viking - *(to be disposed of by 1/98)*

DAF	2♠						
Volvo	5♠	6♠	11♠	14♠	15♠	16♠	171
	29♠						
	19♠	20♠	28♠				
Bova	9♠						
Javelin	30♠	31♠	32♠	33♠			
MetroRider	34♠						

Tamworth (Aldergate)

Mercedes-Benz	132♥	152	169	371	372	373	374	375
	376	377	378	379	380	381	455	458
	460	461	462					
Renault-Dodge	329	346	349	350				
Dart	1311	1312	1313	1314	1315			
Tiger	1522	1527	1604	1605	1606	1607	1714	1745
	1746	1747	1748	1750	1751			
Scania	1831	1832	1833	1834	1835	1420	1421	1422
	1423	1424	1425	1426	1427	1428		
Olympian	1916	1918	2005	2011	2044	2045	2046	2047

Uttoxeter (The Garage, Spath)

Volvo Coach	3	4	20	21	23	24	25	26
	27							
Mercedes-Benz	127	147	178	448				
Swift	1137							
Leopard	12	13	1500	1510	1512			
Tiger	1619	1620	1621	1628	1646	1648	1649	1650
	1679	1695						
Metrobus	2053	2070	2073	2074				

Wellington (Charlton Street, Telford)

Iveco	274	284	285	286	320	322	323	324
	325	326						
Mercedes-Benz	414	427	463	464	465	466	467	468
	469	470	471	472				
Dart	501	502	503	504	505	506	507	508
	509	510	511	512	513	518	801	1301
	1316	1317	1318	1319	1320			
Charabanc	1001							
National	580	684	685	719	863	866	873	874
	876	878	891	892				
Falcon	1211	1212	1213	1215	1216	1217	1218	
Tiger	1703	1707						
Bristol VR	1858	1860	1870					

Woodseaves (c/o Happy Days Ltd)

Dart	806				
Tiger	1713	1719	1720	1724	1729

Reserve/disposal

Mercedes-Benz	112♥	113	114	115	116♥	117	119
Transit	201	202	203	204	205	206	
Iveco	320						
Renault-Dodge	340	341	343	344	345		
Leopard	1504	1526					
National	718	968					

NORTHUMBRIA

Northumbria Motor Services Ltd, Portland Terrace, Jesmond,
Newcastle upon Tyne, NE2 1QS

131	K131FKW	Bova FHD12.290	Bova Futura	C44FT	1992	
132	K132FKW	Bova FHD12.290	Bova Futura	C44FT	1992	
133	L33NMS	Bova FHD12.340	Bova Futura	C44FT	1993	
134	NMS700	Bova FHD12.290	Bova Futura	C44FT	1990	Ex Boyden, Castle Donington, 1991
135	J20NMS	Bova FHD12.290	Bova Futura	C44FT	1992	
136	WSV570	Bova FHD12.340	Bova Futura	C44FT	1994	
137	WSV571	Bova FHD12.340	Bova Futura	C44FT	1994	
138	WSV572	Bova FHD12.340	Bova Futura	C44FT	1994	
139	WLT859	Bova FHD12.290	Bova Futura	C46FT	1993	
140	M122UUB	Bova FHD12.340	Bova Futura	C46FT	1994	
202	XSV689	Leyland Tiger TRCTL11/3RH	Duple 320	C53F	1986	Ex Kentish Bus, 1997

203-207

		Leyland Leopard PSU3E/4RT	Duple 320(1987)	C55F	1977-78	Ex United, 1986

203	WSV565	204	WSV566	205	WSV567	206	WSV568

211	JUP115T	Leyland Leopard PSU5C/4R	Plaxton Supreme III	C51F	1979	Ex United, 1986
219	TSU636	Leyland Tiger TRCTL11/3R	Duple Laser	C53F	1983	Ex Maidstone & District, 1997
220	869SVX	Leyland Tiger TRCTL11/3R	Duple Laser	C53F	1983	Ex Maidstone & District, 1997
221	YOT607	Leyland Tiger TRCTL11/3R	Duple Laser	C53F	1983	Ex Maidstone & District, 1997
222	VAY879	Leyland Tiger TRCTL11/3R	Duple Laser	C53F	1983	Ex Maidstone & District, 1997
223	NDC238W	Leyland Leopard PSU3F/4R	Plaxton Supreme IV Express	C49F	1980	Ex United, 1986
229	NDC501W	Leyland Leopard PSU3F/4R	Plaxton Supreme IV Express	C49F	1980	Ex United, 1986
230	NDC502W	Leyland Leopard PSU3F/4R	Plaxton Supreme IV Express	C49F	1980	Ex United, 1986
231	NDC503W	Leyland Leopard PSU3F/4R	Plaxton Supreme IV Express	C49F	1980	Ex United, 1986
232	NDC504W	Leyland Leopard PSU3F/4R	Plaxton Supreme IV Express	C49F	1980	Ex United, 1986
235	PPT823T	Leyland Leopard PSU5C/4R	Plaxton Supreme IV	C51F	1979	Ex United, 1986
239	SND296X	Leyland Leopard PSU5D/4R	Plaxton Supreme V	C53F	1981	Ex Kentish Bus, 1991
241	YEL98Y	Leyland Leopard PSU5E/4R	Eastern Coach Works B51	C50F	1983	Ex Kentish Bus, 1991
242	B262KPF	Leyland Tiger TRCTL11/2RH	Plaxton Paramount 3200 IIE	C51F	1985	Ex Kentish Bus, 1992
243	B265KPF	Leyland Tiger TRCTL11/2RH	Plaxton Paramount 3200 IIE	C51F	1985	Ex Kentish Bus, 1992
244	B273KPF	Leyland Tiger TRCTL11/3RH	Plaxton Paramount 3200 IIE	C51F	1985	Ex Kentish Bus, 1992
245	B279KPF	Leyland Tiger TRCTL11/3RH	Plaxton Paramount 3200 IIE	C51F	1985	Ex Kentish Bus, 1992
246	B276KPF	Leyland Tiger TRCTL11/3RH	Plaxton Paramount 3200 IIE	C51F	1985	Ex Kentish Bus, 1992
247	B277KPF	Leyland Tiger TRCTL11/3RH	Plaxton Paramount 3200 IIE	C51F	1985	Ex Kentish Bus, 1992
248	B284KPF	Leyland Tiger TRCTL11/3RH	Plaxton Paramount 3200 IIE	C53F	1985	Ex The Shires, 1996
250	EDZ215	Leyland Tiger TRCTL11/2R	Plaxton Paramount 3200 E	C53F	1983	Ex Hunters, 1994

251-267

		DAF SB220LC550	Optare Delta	DP48F	1989-90	

251	G251SRG	255	G255UVK	258	G258UVK	261	H261CFT	264	H264CFT
252	G252SRG	256	G256UVK	259	H259CFT	262	H262CFT	266	H266CFT
253	G253SRG	257	G257UVK	260	H598CNL	263	H263CFT	267	H267CFT
254	G254SRG								

268	F701ECC	DAF SB220LC550	Optare Delta	DP48F	1989	Ex Crosville Cymru, 1997
269	F702ECC	DAF SB220LC550	Optare Delta	DP48F	1989	Ex Crosville Cymru, 1997

271-280

		Scania L113CRL	East Lancashire European	DP45F	1996

271	P271VRG	273	P273VRG	275	P275VRG	277	P277VRG	279	P279VRG
272	P272VRG	274	P274VRG	276	P276VRG	278	P278VRG	280	P814YTY

281-290

		Scania L113CRL	East Lancashire European	DP45F	1995

281	N281NCN	283	N283NCN	285	N285NCN	287	N287NCN	289	N289NCN
282	N282NCN	284	N284NCN	286	N286NCN	288	N288NCN	290	N290NCN

291	R291KRG	DAF DE33WSSB3000	Plaxton Prima	C48F	1997
292	R292KRG	DAF DE33WSSB3000	Plaxton Prima	C48F	1997
293	R293KRG	DAF DE33WSSB3000	Plaxton Prima	C48F	1997
294	R294KRG	DAF DE33WSSB3000	Plaxton Prima	C48F	1997

For National Express operations, Northumbria have for some time selected the Bova Futura. These coaches can be found on services running between the North East and London. Numbered 136, WSV570 is seen in Leicester, outside the St Margaret's bus station when en-route for Newcastle. *Phillip Stephenson*

The East Lancashire European body has now been superceded by the Spryte. An example of the former on the Scania L113CRL chassis is Northumbria 284, N284NCN. In common with most recent deliveries to the company, high-backed seating is fitted to this bus. *Richard Godfrey*

| 301 | C263XEF | Leyland Olympian ONLXB/1R | Eastern Coach Works | DPH43/29F | 1986 | Ex United, 1986 |
| 302 | C264XEF | Leyland Olympian ONLXB/1R | Eastern Coach Works | DPH43/29F | 1986 | Ex United, 1986 |

303-312
Leyland Olympian ONCL10/2RZ Alexander RH — DPH47/33F* 1988 — *305 is DPH43/33F

| 303 | F303JTY | 305 | F305JTY | 307 | F307JTY | 309 | F309JTY | 311 | F311JTY |
| 304 | F304JTY | 306 | F306JTY | 308 | F308JTY | 310 | F310JTY | 312 | F312JTY |

313	C616ANW	Leyland Olympian ONLXB/1R(TL11)	Eastern Coach Works	DPH42/32F	1985	Ex West Riding, 1993
314	C617ANW	Leyland Olympian ONLXB/1R(TL11)	Eastern Coach Works	DPH42/32F	1985	Ex West Riding, 1993
315	C613ANW	Leyland Olympian ONLXB/1R(TL11)	Eastern Coach Works	DPH42/32F	1985	Ex West Riding, 1993
316	C614ANW	Leyland Olympian ONLXB/1R(TL11)	Eastern Coach Works	DPH42/32F	1985	Ex West Riding, 1993
317	EEH901Y	Leyland Olympian ONLXB/1R	Eastern Coach Works	DPH41/32F	1983	Ex Kentish Bus, 1990
318	EEH908Y	Leyland Olympian ONLXB/1R	Eastern Coach Works	DPH41/32F	1983	Ex Kentish Bus, 1990
319	SPY205X	Leyland Olympian ONLXB/1R	Eastern Coach Works	DPH41/32F	1982	Ex United, 1986
320	SPY210X	Leyland Olympian ONLXB/1R	Eastern Coach Works	DPH41/32F	1982	Ex United, 1986
321	WDC212Y	Leyland Olympian ONLXB/1R	Eastern Coach Works	DPH41/32F	1982	Ex United, 1986
322	SPY204X	Leyland Olympian ONLXB/1R	Eastern Coach Works	DPH41/32F	1982	Ex United, 1986
323w	OSK774	Leyland Olympian ONTL11/2R(LG1200) N Counties(1992)		DPH47/30F	1984	Ex Kentish Bus, 1988

370-377
Volvo Olympian YN2RV18Z4 Northern Counties Palatine II DPH45/27F 1994

| 370 | M370FTY | 372 | M372FTY | 374 | M374FTY | 376 | M376FTY | 377 | M377FTY |
| 371 | M371FTY | 373 | M373FTY | 375 | M375FTY | | | | |

381-393
Scania N113DRB — East Lancashire Cityzen — DPH43/31F 1996

381	N381OTY	384	N384OTY	387	N387OTY	390	N390OTY	392	N392OTY
382	N382OTY	385	N385OTY	388	N388OTY	391	N391OTY	393	N393OTY
383	N383OTY	386	N386OTY	389	N389OTY				

The East Lancashire Cityzen body is only fitted to Scania chassis. In 1995, Northumbria purchased a batch of thirteen based on the N113DRB chassis type. All these vehicles have high-backed seats suitable for longer distance services such as X1 to Blyth on which is seen 389, N389OTY.
Richard Godfrey

401-405

Leyland Olympian ONLXB/1R — Eastern Coach Works — H44/32F — 1982 — Ex United, 1986

401	SPY201X	402	SPY202X	403	SPY203X	404	WDC211Y	405	WDC213Y

406	C259UAJ	Leyland Olympian ONLXB/1R	Eastern Coach Works	H45/32F	1985	Ex United, 1986
407	C260UAJ	Leyland Olympian ONLXB/1R	Eastern Coach Works	H45/32F	1985	Ex United, 1986
408	C261UAJ	Leyland Olympian ONLXB/1R	Eastern Coach Works	H45/32F	1985	Ex United, 1986
409	C262UAJ	Leyland Olympian ONLXB/1R	Eastern Coach Works	H45/32F	1985	Ex United, 1986

410-420

Volvo Olympian — Northern Counties Palatine II — H43/29F — 1997

410	P410CCU	413	P413CCU	415	P415CCU	417	P417CCU	419	P419CCU
411	P411CCU	414	P414CCU	416	P416CCU	418	P418CCU	420	P420CCU
412	P412CCU								

504	OCU809R	Leyland Fleetline FE30AGR	Alexander AL	H44/29F	1977	Ex Busways, 1994
505	OCU810R	Leyland Fleetline FE30AGR	Alexander AL	H44/29F	1977	Ex Busways, 1994
506	OCU812R	Leyland Fleetline FE30AGR	Alexander AL	H44/29F	1977	Ex Busways, 1994
526w	BPT917S	Bristol VRT/SL3/6LXB	Eastern Coach Works	H43/31F	1977	Ex United, 1986
527	BPT919S	Bristol VRT/SL3/6LXB	Eastern Coach Works	H43/31F	1977	Ex United, 1986
530	BPT923S	Bristol VRT/SL3/6LXB	Eastern Coach Works	H42/31F	1977	Ex United, 1986

536-553

Bristol VRT/SL3/6LXB — Eastern Coach Works — H43/31F — 1978-79 Ex United, 1986

536	CPT734S	541	CPT739S	544	DUP747S	547	HUP757T	549	HUP759T
538	CPT736S	543	DUP745S	546	DUP753S	548	HUP758T	553	OBR769T
540	CPT738S								

558-572

Bristol VRT/SL3/6LXB — Eastern Coach Works — H43/31F — 1980 — Ex United, 1986

558	SGR777V	563	SGR784V	566	SGR789V	570	SGR795V	572	SGR797V
562	SGR783V	565	SGR788V						

In 1986, Northumbria was formed out of the Northumberland operations of United. The new company inherited a number of Eastern Coach Works-bodied Bristol LH lightweight single deckers. One of the surviving members of this type is 638, AFB593V which had previously been in the Provincial fleet, but new to Bristol Omnibus. *Phillip Stephenson*

576-584

576-584		Bristol VRT/SL3/6LXB	Eastern Coach Works	H43/31F	1980-81 Ex United, 1986; 577 rebodied 1980		
576	XPT802V	**580**	APT810W	**581**	APT811W	**583**	APT816W	**584**	APT817W
577	XPT803V						

590	PAJ827X	Bristol VRT/SL3/6LXB	Eastern Coach Works	H43/31F	1981
591	PAJ829X	Bristol VRT/SL3/6LXB	Eastern Coach Works	H43/31F	1981

592-597

592-597		Daimler Fleetline CRG6LXB	Northern Counties	H43/32F	1976-77 Ex GM Buses, 1987		
592	PRJ486R	**594**	PRJ489R	**595**	PRJ490R	**596**	PRJ492R	**597**	PRJ494R
593	PRJ488R						

598	OBN505R	Leyland Fleetline FE30AGR	Northern Counties	H43/34F	1977	Ex GM Buses, 1987
599	PTD639S	Leyland Fleetline FE30AGR	Northern Counties	H43/34F	1977	Ex GM Buses, 1987
624	NGR685P	Bristol LH6L	Eastern Coach Works	B43F	1976	Ex United, 1986
627w	SNU384R	Bristol LH6L	Eastern Coach Works	B43F	1977	Ex United, 1986
631	VDV125S	Bristol LH6L	Eastern Coach Works	DP37F	1978	Ex Moor-Dale, 1994

633-638

633-638		Bristol LH6L	Eastern Coach Works	B43F	1979-80 Ex United, 1986		
633	LPT701T	**634**	LPT707T	**636**	MUP712T	**637**	MUP714T	**638**	AFB593V

701	R701KCU	DAF DE0ZSB220GS	Northern Counties Paladin	B39F	1997	
736	JTH763P	Leyland National 11351A/1R (Volvo)		B52F	1975	Ex South Wales, 1989
776	UBR113V	Leyland National 2 NL116AL11/1R		B49F	1980	Ex United 1986
777	APT120W	Leyland National 2 NL116AL11/1R		B49F	1980	Ex United 1986
798	L532EHD	DAF SB220LC550	Ikarus CitiBus	B48F	1994	Ex North Western (Starline), 1997
799	L533EHD	DAF SB220LC550	Ikarus CitiBus	B48F	1994	Ex North Western (Starline), 1997

801-827

801-827		MCW MetroRider MF150/27*	MCW	DP25F*	1987	*801-6/9 are MF150/21	
						*804 is B23F; 813/5 are B21F	
801	E801BTN	**806**	E806BTN	**814**	E814BTN	**819**	E819BTN	**824**	E824BTN
802	E802BTN	**809**	E809BTN	**815**	E815BTN	**820**	E820BTN	**825**	E825BTN
803	E803BTN	**810**	E810BTN	**816**	E816BTN	**821**	E821BTN	**826**	E826BTN
804	E804BTN	**812**	E812BTN	**817**	E817BTN	**822**	E822BTN	**827**	E827BTN
805	E805BTN	**813**	E813BTN	**818**	E818BTN	**823**	E823BTN		

828	E676DCU	MCW MetroRider MF150/63	MCW	DP21F	1987	Ex Rochester & Marshall, 1994

829-845

829-845		MCW MetroRider MF150/27	MCW	DP25F*	1987	*845 is B23F	
829	E829BTN	**832**	E832BTN	**836**	E836BTN	**841**	E841BTN	**844**	E844BTN
830	E830BTN	**833**	E833BTN	**840**	E840BTN	**842**	E842BTN	**845**	E845BTN
831	E831BTN	**834**	E834BTN						

846	H840UUA	Optare MetroRider	Optare	B25F	1990	Ex Lancaster, 1993
847	J363BNW	Optare MetroRider	Optare	B23F	1991	Ex Lancaster, 1993
850	J366BNW	Optare MetroRider	Optare	B29F	1992	Ex Lancaster, 1993

851-858

851-858		Optare MetroRider	Optare	DP28F*	1992-93 *855-8 are DP29F		
851	K851RBB	**853**	K853RBB	**855**	L855WRG	**857**	L857WRG	**858**	L858WRG
852	K852RBB	**854**	K854RBB	**856**	L856WRG				

Opposite, top:- **Belford is the location of this picture of Northumbria 419, P419CCU, a Volvo Olympian with Northern Counties Palatine II bodywork. While two of the type are working from Ashington, the remainder are based at Newcastle, including 419.** *Derek Akrigg*
Opposite, bottom:- **Ashington depot is the location of this view of Northumbria Delta 264, H264CFT. The batch of Delta buses has been joined during 1997 by the pair previously with Crosville Cymru. Readers will also note that since the last edition of the North East Bus Handbook, the Hunter's has been disbanded.** *Derek Akrigg*

The standard Northumbria minibus is the now the Optare MetroRider. This type has been used to replace the smaller Freight Rover Sherpa. The wide 'Fastflow' entrance can be seen in this view of 855, L855WRG. *Richard Godfrey*

859-871

| | | | | | | Optare MetroRider | | Optare | | DP29F | | 1995 | | | |

859	M859KCU	862	M862KCU	865	M865KCU	868	M868KCU	870	M870KCU
860	M860KCU	863	M863KCU	866	M866KCU	869	M869KCU	871	M871KCU
861	M861KCU	864	M864KCU	867	M867KCU				

872-876

Optare MetroRider   Optare   B31F   1995

872	M872LBB	873	M873LBB	874	M874LBB	875	M875LBB	876	M876LBB

877-896

Optare MetroRider   Optare   B31F   1996-97

877	N877RTN	881	N881RTN	885	N885RTN	889	N889RTN	893	P893XCU
878	N878RTN	882	N882RTN	886	N886RTN	890	N890RTN	894	P894XCU
879	N879RTN	883	N883RTN	887	N887RTN	891	N891RTN	895	P895XCU
880	N880RTN	884	N884RTN	888	N192RVK	892	P892XCU	896	P896XCU

897-901

Optare MetroRider   Optare   B31F   1997

897	P56XTN	898	P57XTN	899	P58XTN	900	P59XTN	901	P61XTN

902-914

Optare MetroRider MR15   Optare   B31F   1997

902	P902DRG	905	R905JNL	908	R908JNL	911	R251JNL	913	R913JNL
903	P903DRG	906	R906JNL	909	R909JNL	912	R912JNL	914	R914JNL
904	P904DRG	907	R907JNL	910	R910JNL				

In 1995, Northumbria acquired a number of Mercedes-Benz minibuses from Stevensons and these have displaced many of the Sherpas from the fleet. Number 963, H802SKY is one of a trio of 709D types which carry Reeve Burgess Beaver 25-seat bodies, though this example has just been taken out of service. *Tony Wilson*

960	D960EOW	Freight Rover Sherpa	Dormobile	B16F	1986	
961	E329EJR	Iveco Daily 49.10	Robin Hood City Nippy	B19F	1988	Ex R & M, 1994
962	H801SKY	Mercedes-Benz 709D	Reeve Burgess Beaver	B25F	1990	Ex Stevensons, 1994
964	H803SKY	Mercedes-Benz 709D	Reeve Burgess Beaver	B25F	1990	Ex Stevensons, 1994
965	G174YRE	Mercedes-Benz 811D	Carlyle	B33F	1990	Ex Stevensons, 1994
966	G175DRF	Mercedes-Benz 811D	LHE	B33F	1990	Ex Stevensons, 1994
967	F835BCW	Mercedes-Benz 811D	Reeve Burgess Beaver	B33F	1989	Ex Stevensons, 1994
968	F836BCW	Mercedes-Benz 811D	Reeve Burgess Beaver	B33F	1989	Ex Stevensons, 1994
971	D916VCN	Freight Rover Sherpa	Rootes	B16F	1986	
973	D973VCN	Freight Rover Sherpa	Dormobile	DP16F	1987	
975	D975VCN	Freight Rover Sherpa	Dormobile	DP16F	1987	

Ancilliary vehicles:-

9990	GSU347	Leyland National 11351/1R		B49F	1975	Ex Midland Red North, 1987
9991	RDC736X	Leyland National 2 NL116L11/1R		B49F	1981	Ex United, 1986
9992	UBR110V	Leyland National 2 NL116AL11/1R		B49F	1980	Ex United, 1986

Previous Registrations:

869SVX	A179MKE	WSV567	ABR867S
EDZ215	RMO203Y	WSV568	CUP706S
J20NMS	J849MCN	WSV569	CUP707S
NMS700	G418WFP	WSV570	E692JUT
OSK774	A103FPL	WSV571	C160UHN, NMS700
TSU636	A183MKE	WSV572	B337WFJ
VAY879	A182MKE	XSV238	A141FDC
WLT859	D193ESC	XSV689	C256SPC
WSV565	ABR865S	YOT607	A180MKE
WSV566	ABR866S		

Allocations and liveries

Livery: Grey, red and white; white ✈ (National Express)

Alnwick (Lisburn Street)

Leopard	203	204	205	230	232		
Tiger	219	220	222	242	244	248	250
MetroRider	890	891					
Bristol LH	637						
Bristol VR	536	546	547	558			
Olympian	301	313	315	317			

Ashington (Lintonville Terrace)

MetroRider	813	815	817	827	846	847	848	849
	850	851	893	894	895	896	897	898
	899	900	908	909	910	911		
Mercedes-Benz	962	964	967	968				
National	733	736	776	777	781			
Delta	253	257	258	263	264	266	267	
Bristol VR	530	562						
Olympian	305	306	308	309	310	311	401	402

Berwick (Tweedmouth Industrial Park)

MetroRider	801	805	806	809	810	818	819	823
	832							
Bristol LH	624	638						
Leopard	221	223						
Tiger	245	246						
Olympian	304	318						

Blyth (Bridge Street)

MetroRider	812	820	821	822	824	825	826	829
	830	831	833	834	840	841	844	845
	854	866	867	868	869	870	871	881
	882	883	884	901	902	903		
Scania L	275	276	277	278	279	280	281	282
	283	284	285	286	287	288	289	290
Bristol VR	565	566	570	572	577	580	581	584
Olympian	314	319	320					
Scania N	381	382	383	384	385	386	387	388
	389	390	391	392	393			

Hexham (Burn Lane)

Mercedes-Benz	965	966						
MetroRider	803	804	814	828	877	878	885	886
Leopard	241							
Tiger	247							
DAF	291	292	293	294				
Bristol VR	527	553						
Olympian	370	371	372	373	374	375	376	377

The number of Leyland Nationals remaining with Northumbria is quickly deminishing. One of the interesting ones that remains is 736, JTH763P which has received a revised front end treatment and Volvo engine. The removal of the heating pod will also be noticed. *Richard Godfrey*

Morpeth (Park Lane)

Sherpa	971	973	975				
MetroRider	802	816	836	842	852	872	873	874
	875	876	889	892			
Leopard	206	211	229	231	235	239	
Tiger	202	243					
Bristol LH	633	634	636				
Bristol VR	538	544	548	563	576		
Olympian	302	307	316				

Newcastle (Jesmond Road)

MetroRider	853	855	856	857	858	859	860	861
	861	862	863	864	865	879	880	887
	888	904	905	906	907	912	913	914
Bova	131⅄	132⅄	133⅄	134⅄	135⅄	136⅄	137⅄	138⅄
	139⅄	140⅄					
Delta	251	252	254	255	256	259	260	261
	262						
Scania	271	272	273	274			
DAF	701						
Bristol VR	540	541	543	549	583	590	591	
Fleetline	504	505	506	592	593	594	595	596
	597	598	599				
Olympian	303	321	322	403	404	405	406	407
	408	409	410	411	412	413	414	415
	416	417	418	419	420		

Withdrawn and unallocated:-

Sherpa	960
Bristol LH	627
Bristol VR	526
Olympian	323

NORTH WESTERN

North Western Road Car Co Ltd, Liverline Travel Services Ltd,
73 Ormskirk Road, Aintree, Liverpool, Merseyside, L9 5AE
The Bee Line Buzz Company, Hulme Hall Road, Manchester, M15 4LY
South Lancashire Transport Co Ltd, Unit B Beaufort Street, Peasley Cross,
St Helens, Merseyside, WA9 3BQ
Arrowline (Travel) Ltd, Grebba Road, Wythenshawe, Manchester M23 9ET

48	D257NCS	Renault-Dodge S56	Alexander AM	B25F	1987	Ex South Lancashire, 1997
49	D249NCS	Renault-Dodge S56	Alexander AM	B25F	1987	Ex South Lancashire, 1997
50	J78MHF	Mercedes-Benz 709D	Wright NimBus	B29F	1992	Ex Amberline, 1993
51	J734MFY	Mercedes-Benz 709D	Wright NimBus	B29F	1992	Ex Amberline, 1993
52	J735MFY	Mercedes-Benz 709D	Wright NimBus	B29F	1992	Ex Amberline, 1993

53-67

			Mercedes-Benz 709D	Alexander Sprint	B25F	1994			
53	L153UEM	56	L156UEM	59	M59WKA	62	M62WKA	65	M65WKA
54	L154UEM	57	M157WWM	60	M160WTJ	63	M63WKA	66	M166WTJ
55	L155UEM	58u	M158WWM	61	M61WKA	64	M64WKA	67	M67WKA

| 68w | H407BVR | Mercedes-Benz 609D | Reeve Burgess Beaver | B20F | 1990 | Ex Star Line, 1995 |
| 69 | L647DNA | Mercedes-Benz 709D | Plaxton Beaver | B23F | 1994 | Ex Star Line, 1995 |

70-95

			Mercedes-Benz 811D	Carlyle	B33F	1989-90			
70	G100TND	75	G105TND	79	G109TND	86	G116TND	93	G123TJA
72w	G102TND	76	G106TND	80w	G110TND	88w	G118TND	94w	G124TJA
73	G103TND	77	G107TND	82	G112TND	89w	G119TND	95	G125TJA
74	G104TND	78w	G108TND						

96	J291NNB	Mercedes-Benz 709D	Carlyle	B29F	1991	Ex Star Line, 1995
97	J292NNB	Mercedes-Benz 709D	Carlyle	B29F	1991	Ex Star Line, 1995
98	J293NNB	Mercedes-Benz 709D	Carlyle	B29F	1991	Ex Star Line, 1995
99	H129CDB	Mercedes-Benz 811D	LHE Commuter	B31F	1990	Ex C-Line, 1993
100	H130CDB	Mercedes-Benz 811D	LHE Commuter	B31F	1990	Ex C-Line, 1992

Star Line moved from Altrincham into a new base on the Wythenshawe industrial estate to the south of Manchester from where services are operated to parts of north Cheshire as well as Greater Manchester. Seen entering Altrincham Interchange is Mercedes-Benz 107, L646DNA which which came into the company with Star Line in 1995. Early in 1998 Starline bus services will change to Bee Line identity, while the airport coach operations will retain that of Starline.
Richard Godfrey

101-105 Mercedes-Benz 709D, Alexander Sprint, DP23F, 1994

101	M101WKA	102	M102WKA	103	M103WKA	104	M104WKA	105	M105WKA

106	K880UDB	Mercedes-Benz 709D	Dormobile Routemaker	DP29F	1993	Ex Star Line, 1995
107	L646DNA	Mercedes-Benz 709D	Dormobile Routemaker	B27F	1994	Ex Star Line, 1995
108	L648DNA	Mercedes-Benz 709D	Marshall C19	B29F	1994	Ex Star Line, 1995
109	L649DNA	Mercedes-Benz 709D	Marshall C19	B29F	1994	Ex Star Line, 1995
110	H404BVR	Mercedes-Benz 814D	Carlyle	C29F	1991	Ex Star Line, 1995
111	J10SLT	Mercedes-Benz 811D	Reeve Burgess Beaver	B31F	1991	Ex South Lancashire, 1997
113	G113PGT	Mercedes-Benz 811D	Alexander Sprint	B28F	1990	Ex South Lancashire, 1997
114	K3SLT	Mercedes-Benz 811D	Plaxton Beaver	B31F	1992	Ex South Lancashire, 1997
115	K1SLT	Mercedes-Benz 811D	Plaxton Beaver	B31F	1993	Ex South Lancashire, 1997
116	K2SLT	Mercedes-Benz 811D	Plaxton Beaver	B31F	1993	Ex South Lancashire, 1997
119	J4SLT	Mercedes-Benz 709D	Plaxton Beaver	B23F	1992	Ex South Lancashire, 1997

120-129 Mercedes-Benz 709D, Alexander Sprint, B29F, 1995

120	M120YCM	122	M122YCM	125	M125YCM	127	M127YCM	129	M129YCM
121	M121YCM	124	M124YCM	126	M126YCM	128	M128YCM		

130-134 Mercedes-Benz 709D, Reeve Burgess Beaver, B27F, 1992 Ex Star Line, 1995

130	J296NNB	131	J297NNB	132	J298NNB	133	J299NNB	134	K876UDB

135-142 Mercedes-Benz 709D, Plaxton Beaver, B27F*, 1993-94 Ex Star Line, 1995
*139 is B29F

135	K878UDB	137	K882UDB	139	K887UDB	141	L642DNA	142	L643DNA
136	K879UDB	138	K884UDB	140	L641DNA				

143-149 Mercedes-Benz 709D, Alexander Sprint, B27F, 1994-95 Ex Star Line, 1995

143	M363KVR	145	M365KVR	147	M367KVR	148	M368KVR	149	M369KVR
144	M364KVR	146	M366KVR						

150	J3SLT	Mercedes-Benz 709D	Plaxton Beaver	B29F	1997	Ex South Lancashire, 1997
151	F997EKM	MCW MetroRider MF154	MCW	B26F	1988	Ex Kentish Bus, 1997
152	F847EKP	MCW MetroRider MF154	MCW	B26F	1988	Ex Kentish Bus, 1997
160	E673DCU	MCW MetroRider MF154	MCW	B23F	1987	Ex Kentish Bus, 1997
161	E31NEF	MCW MetroRider MF154/9	MCW	DP33F	1988	Ex Kentish Bus, 1997
162	E32NEF	MCW MetroRider MF154/9	MCW	DP33F	1988	Ex Kentish Bus, 1997
163	E33NEF	MCW MetroRider MF154/9	MCW	DP33F	1988	Ex Kentish Bus, 1997

Three minibuses from the Amberline operations in Speke, which are referred to in the history, remain in the North Western fleet. Lettered for the Warrington Gold Line service is 51, J734MFY, which is seen in this picture working the Skelmersdale service at Wigan.
Phillip Stephenson

The Welsh operator, Parfitt's, was the source of ten short Leyland Nationals in 1995. These had originally been dual-doored examples for London Transport, though once purchased by Parfitt's they were re-built to single door layout. Riding over the temporary road surface in Bootle is 203, BYW402V. *Richard Godfrey*

175-184

| | | | | | | | | | | | Mercedes-Benz 811D | Plaxton Beaver | B31F | 1996 |

175	N175DWM	**177**	N177DWM	**179**	N179DWM	**181**	P181GND	**183**	P183GND
176	N176DWM	**178**	N178DWM	**180**	P180GND	**182**	P182GND	**184**	P184GND

189u	M239XLV	Iveco TurboDaily 59.10	Marshall C31	B27F	1995	Ex Little White Buses, 1995
190u	M240XLV	Iveco TurboDaily 59.10	Marshall C31	B27F	1995	Ex Little White Buses, 1995
191	K457EVC	Mercedes-Benz 811D	Wright NimBus	B31F	1993	Ex Little White Buses, 1995
192	K787VNR	Mercedes-Benz 811D	Dormobile Routemaker	B33F	1993	Ex Little White Buses, 1995
193	L193DBC	Mercedes-Benz 811D	Marshall C16	B31F	1994	Ex Little White Buses, 1995
194	L529XNR	Mercedes-Benz 811D	Dormobile Routemaker	B31F	1993	Ex Little White Buses, 1995
195	M689FJF	Mercedes-Benz 811D	Marshall C16	B31F	1994	Ex Little White Buses, 1995
196	M615XLG	Mercedes-Benz 811D	Marshall C16	B31F	1994	Ex Little White Buses, 1995
197	M998XRF	Mercedes-Benz 811D	Marshall C16	B31F	1995	Ex Little White Buses, 1995

200-210

| | | | | | | | | | Leyland National 10351A/2R | | | B44F | 1979-80 Ex Parfitt's, 1995 |

200	BYW359V	**202**w	BYW379V	**204**	BYW406V	**206**	BYW413V	**209**	BYW432V
201	BYW367V	**203**	BYW402V	**205**	BYW412V	**208**	BYW430V	**210**	BYW437V

211	MIL5581	Leyland National 10351A/1R(Volvo)		B41F	1976	Ex London & Country, 1989
214	MAR781P	Leyland National 11351A/1R		B49F	1976	Ex Maidstone & District, 1995

215-253

| | | | | | | | | | Leyland National 11351A/1R | | B49F | 1976-78 Ex Ribble, 1986 |

215	SCK688P	**219**	SCK693P	**229**	UHG724R	**250**	CBV791S	**253**	CBV794S
218	SCK692P	**220**	SCK698P	**241**	ACW764R	**251**	CBV792S		

256	JOX515P	Leyland National 11351A/1R		B49F	1976	Ex Midland Red North, 1988
260w	JOX522P	Leyland National 11351A/1R		B49F	1976	Ex Midland, 1995
261	LRB202W	Leyland National 2 NL116L11/2R		B52F	1980	Ex West Riding, 1995

The latest minibus arrivals with North Western are a batch of ten Mercedes-Benz 811s with Plaxton Beaver bodywork. All are allocated to the Wigan Bus base at Haydock and seen here in Wigan bus station is 177, N177DWM. *Phillip Stephenson*

262	AFM2W	Leyland National 2 NL116AL11/2R	B52F	1981	Ex Crosville, 1989
263	AFM3W	Leyland National 2 NL116AL11/2R	B52F	1981	Ex Crosville, 1989
264	AFM4W	Leyland National 2 NL116AL11/2R	B52F	1981	Ex Crosville, 1989
267	FCA7X	Leyland National 2 NL116AL11/2R	B52F	1982	Ex Crosville, 1989
271	VBG89V	Leyland National 2 NL116L11/2R(6HLXB)	B49F	1980	Ex Yorkshire Bus (YB), 1997
275	BVP811V	Leyland National 2 NL116L11/1R	B49F	1980	Ex Midland Red North, 1988
277	CCY817V	Leyland National 2 NL116L11/2R	B52F	1980	Ex West Riding, 1995
278	EON823V	Leyland National 2 NL116L11/1R	B49F	1980	Ex Midland Red North, 1988
280	FCA10X	Leyland National 2 NL116AL11/2R(6HLXB)	B52F	1982	Ex Crosville, 1989
281	NTU11Y	Leyland National 2 NL116HLXB/2R	B52F	1983	Ex Crosville, 1989
282	NTU12Y	Leyland National 2 NL116HLXB/2R	B52F	1983	Ex Crosville, 1989
283	NTU13Y	Leyland National 2 NL116HLXB/2R	B52F	1983	Ex Crosville, 1989
284	NTU15Y	Leyland National 2 NL116HLXB/2R	B52F	1983	Ex Crosville, 1989
291	PUP505T	Leyland National 11351A/1R	B49F	1979	Ex Maidstone & District, 1995
294	KNV514P	Leyland National 11351/1R	B49F	1976	Ex Midland Fox, 1994
301	DBV845W	Leyland National 2 NL106L11/1R	B44F	1980	Ex Ribble, 1986
303	JCK851W	Leyland National 2 NL106AL11/1R	B44F	1981	Ex Ribble, 1986
306	LFR854X	Leyland National 2 NL106AL11/1R	B44F	1981	Ex Ribble, 1986
309	LFR867X	Leyland National 2 NL106AL11/1R	B44F	1981	Ex Ribble, 1986
310	LFR869X	Leyland National 2 NL106AL11/1R	B44F	1981	Ex Ribble, 1986
311	NPK250R	Leyland National 10351A/1R	B41F	1976	Ex Northumbria, 1994
312	NPK263R	Leyland National 10351A/1R	B41F	1977	Ex Northumbria, 1995
320	GHU643N	Leyland National 10351/1R	B44F	1975	Ex Crosville, 1989
326	NPK259R	Leyland National 10351A/1R	B41F	1976	Ex Northumbria, 1995
329	LPB219P	Leyland National 10351/1R	B41F	1976	Ex London & Country, 1989
331	NPK242P	Leyland National 10351A/1R	B41F	1976	Ex London & Country, 1989
332	NPK245P	Leyland National 10351A/1R	B41F	1976	Ex London & Country, 1989
334	SPC279R	Leyland National 10351A/1R	B41F	1977	Ex London & Country, 1989
340	UPB335S	Leyland National 10351A/1R	B41F	1977	Ex London & Country, 1989
347w	GMB657T	Leyland National 10351B/1R	B44F	1978	Ex Crosville, 1989
348w	GMB663T	Leyland National 10351B/1R	B44F	1978	Ex Crosville, 1989

Following a period on hire some 100 West Midlands Metrobuses were returned with Leyland Nationals heading north as replacements. While the early arrivals gained date-less index marks the later ones retained their Birmingham numbers. Photographed in Liverline's final colours is 427, OOX803R.
Richard Godfrey

356-373

				Leyland National 11351A/1R (6HLX)		B49F	1977-79	Ex Crosville, 1990	
356	CFM350S	361	EMB367S	364	GMB380T	368	KMA395T	371	KMA403T
357	CFM351S	362	GMB375T	365	GMB384T	369	KMA396T	372	LMA412T
359	EMB360S	363	GMB379T	367	GMB386T	370	KMA400T	373	YTU986S
360	EMB366S								

374	GMB392T	Leyland National 11351A/1R(6HLX)	B49F	1978	
375	KMA397T	Leyland National 11351A/1R(6HLX)	B49F	1979	Ex C-Line, 1993
376w	GMB666T	Leyland National 10351B/1R	B44F	1978	Ex Midland, 1995
378w	BPL495T	Leyland National 10351B/1R	B41F	1979	Ex Midland, 1995
379w	HMA559T	Leyland National 10351B/1R	B44F	1978	Ex Midland, 1995

Line 374: Ex C-Line, 1993

381-388

				Dennis Falcon SDA421		East Lancashire EL2000	B48F	1990	
381	G381EKA	383	G383EKA	385	G385EKA	387	G387EKA	388	G388EKA
382	G382EKA	384	G384EKA	386	G386EKA				

389	A50LHG	Dennis Falcon H SDA413	East Lancashire	DP43F	1984	Ex South Lancashire, 1997
390	B51XFV	Dennis Falcon H SDA413	East Lancashire	DP40F	1985	Ex South Lancashire, 1997

400-409

				Leyland National 11351/1R (DAF)		B50F	1974	Ex West Midlands Travel, 1995-96	
400	MIL5580	402	MIL5582	404	MIL5574	406	MIL6676	408	MIL6678
401w	LRN664N	403	MIL5573	405	MIL5575	407	MIL6677	409	MIL6679

410-424

				Leyland National 11351/1R (DAF)		B50F	1974-75 Ex West Midlands Travel, 1996	
410	MIL6680	413	MIL7613	416	MIL7616	419	MIL7619	422	MIL7622
411	MIL6681	414	MIL7614	417	MIL7617	420	MIL7620	423	MIL7623
412	MIL7612	415	MIL7615	418	MIL7618	421	MIL7621	424	MIL7624

1995 was a busy year for North Western with the acquisition of two operations inthe Wigan area, Little White Bus and Wigan Bus Company. One of three Dennis Darts that came with the Wigan Bus operation is now 1271, M843RCP, photographed in Castle Street, Liverpool while working the local service to Netherton. *Tony Wilson*

426-437 — Leyland National 11351A/1R (DAF) — B50F — 1977-79 — Ex West Midlands Travel, 1996

426	OOX801R	429	OOX805R	432	OOX810R	434	OOX813R	436	TVP837S
427	OOX802R	430	OOX807R	433	OOX811R	435	OOX818R	437w	AOL11T
428	OOX803R	431	OOX809R						

450-459 — Leyland National 2 NL116L11/1R(DAF) — B50F — 1980 — Ex West Midlands Travel, 1996

450	DOC20V	452	DOC32V	454	DOC38V	456	DOC45V	458	DOC21V
451	DOC30V	453	DOC36V	455	DOC43V	457	DOC47V	459	DOC22V

461	OAH552M	Leyland National 1151/1R/0401	B52F	1973	On loan from Volvo
462	KHT121P	Leyland National 11351/1R	B52F	1976	On loan from Volvo
463	UHG741R	Leyland National 11351A/1R	B49F	1976	On loan from Volvo
464	RAU597R	Leyland National 11351A/1R	B49F	1976	On loan from Volvo
465	VKE566S	Leyland National 11351A/1R	B49F	1977	On loan from Volvo
466	URA605S	Leyland National 11351A/1R	B49F	1977	On loan from Volvo

545-563 — Bristol VRT/SL3/501 — Eastern Coach Works — H43/31F* — 1978-81 Ex Crosville, 1989-90
*545/7/50/63 are H43/30F

545	PCA423V	547w	PCA425V	550w	BTU374S	562w	WTU496W	563w	WTU497W
546	PCA424V	548w	RLG427V	551w	FTU382T				

564	VCA453W	Bristol VRT/SL3/6LXB	Eastern Coach Works	H43/31F	1980	Ex Crosville, 1989
565w	VCA454W	Bristol VRT/SL3/6LXB	Eastern Coach Works	H43/31F	1980	Ex Crosville, 1989
568	VCA463W	Bristol VRT/SL3/6LXB	Eastern Coach Works	H43/30F	1980	Ex Crosville, 1989
569	WTU479W	Bristol VRT/SL3/6LXC	Eastern Coach Works	H43/30F	1981	Ex Crosville, 1990
570	WTU480W	Bristol VRT/SL3/6LXC	Eastern Coach Works	H43/30F	1981	Ex Crosville, 1990

The number of double-deck buses working with North Western is reducing as new deliveries of Scania single-deck buses have ousted the Leyland Atlanteans and only six Bristol VRs remain. Photographed in Manchester's Piccadilly is Olympian 606, A144OFR, which is seen with Bee Line titles. *Richard Godfrey*

600-625   Leyland Olympian ONLXB/1R   Eastern Coach Works   H45/32F   1983-85 Ex Ribble, 1986

600	DBV133Y	605	A141MRN	610	B149TRN	615u	B155TRN	621	B965WRN
601	DBV135Y	606u	A144OFR	611	B150TRN	616	B960WRN	622	B966WRN
602	DBV136Y	607	A146OFR	612	B151TRN	618	B962WRN	623	B967WRN
603	A139MRN	608	A147OFR	613	B153TRN	619u	B963WRN	624	B968WRN
604	A140MRN	609	B148TRN	614	B154TRN	620	B964WRN	625	B969WRN

629w	G629EKA	Dennis Dominator DDA1031	East Lancashire	H47/29F	1990

630-635   Dennis Dominator DDA1026   East Lancashire   H43/25F   1989

630w	F630BKD	632w	F632BKD	633w	F633BKD	634w	F634BKD	635w	F635BKD

636w	F636BKD	Dennis Dominator DDA1025	East Lancashire	H45/31F	1989
637w	F637BKD	Dennis Dominator DDA1025	East Lancashire	H45/31F	1989
650	G650EKA	Volvo Citybus B10M-50	East Lancashire	H49/39F	1990
651	G651EKA	Volvo Citybus B10M-50	East Lancashire	H49/39F	1990
652	G652EKA	Volvo Citybus B10M-50	East Lancashire	H49/39F	1990
653	G653EKA	Volvo Citybus B10M-50	East Lancashire	H49/39F	1990

654-662   Leyland Olympian ONLXB/1R   Eastern Coach Works   H45/32F   1983-84 Ex Crosville, 1989

654	PFM126Y	656	PFM129Y	658	A140SMA	660	A149UDM	662	A153UDM
655	PFM128Y	657	A139SMA	659	A141SMA	661	A151UDM		

The North Western fleet has been noted for the variety of colour it has used since its formation. Here are shown two variations, both based on Scania chassis. The upper picture shows the latest scheme which is now used on the main fleet and those operations of Warrington Gold Line, Bee Line and Wigan Bus. The vehicle is 1033, N133DWM, one of the Wright-bodied Scania low floor saloons while the lower picture shows the last blue-based livery for Liverbus before it, too, started to used the standard colours. Pictured in Liverpool's Paradise Street is 679, H804RWJ, with Northern Counties bodywork. *Tony Wilson*

666w	G667FKA	Dennis Dominator DDA1031	East Lancashire	H47/29F	1990	
667	GFM110X	Leyland Olympian ONLXB/1R	Eastern Coach Works	H45/32F	1982	Ex Crosville, 1989
668	A142SMA	Leyland Olympian ONLXB/1R	Eastern Coach Works	H45/32F	1983	Ex Crosville, 1989
669u	A148UDM	Leyland Olympian ONLXB/1R	Eastern Coach Works	H45/32F	1983	Ex Crosville, 1989
670	A147UDM	Leyland Olympian ONLXB/1R	Eastern Coach Works	H45/32F	1983	Ex Crosville, 1989

671-680

Scania N113DRB   Northern Counties   H47/33F   1990-91 Ex Liverline, 1993

671	G34HKY	673	G36HKY	675	G38HKY	677	G714LKW	679	H804RWJ
672	G35HKY	674	G37HKY	676	G711LKW	678	H803RWJ	680	H805RWJ

700	B212JTY	Volvo B57	East Lancashire	B53F	1985	Ex South Lancashire, 1997
701	B26ADW	Leyland Tiger TRBTL11/2RP	East Lancashire	DP47F	1984	Ex South Lancashire, 1997
702	B27ADW	Leyland Tiger TRBTL11/2RP	East Lancashire	DP47F	1984	Ex South Lancashire, 1997
703	D154THG	Leyland Tiger TRBTL11/2RP	East Lancashire	B55F	1986	Ex South Lancashire, 1997
704	49XBF	Leyland Tiger TRBTL11/2RP	Plaxton Derwent 2	B54F	1988	Ex South Lancashire, 1997
844	K100SLT	Dennis Javelin 10SDA2119	Berkhof Excellence 1000 L	C32FT	1993	Ex Star Line, 1995
854	TOS799X	Leyland Leopard PSU3F/5R	Plaxton Supreme V	C53F	1982	Ex Clydeside, 1995
855	TSU646	Leyland Tiger TRCTL11/3R	Plaxton Paramount 3200 E	C53F	1983	Ex Maidstone & District, 1997
858	K523RJX	DAF SB3000WS601	Van Hool Alizée	C49FT	1993	Ex Hughes-DAF, 1997
859	K546RJX	DAF SB3000WS601	Van Hool Alizée	C49FT	1993	Ex East Midland (Chesterfield), 1997
860	L544EHD	DAF SB3000WS601	Van Hool Alizée	C49FT	1994	Ex Bennetts Silverline, Chieveley, 1997
861	P861PWW	DAF DE33WSSB3000	Van Hool Alizée	C49FT	1997	
890	K890UDB	Toyota Coaster HDB30R	Caetano Optimo II	C18F	1992	Ex Star Line, 1995
891	K200SLT	Toyota Coaster HDB30R	Caetano Optimo II	C18F	1993	
893	L3SLT	Toyota Coaster HDB30R	Caetano Optimo III	C21F	1994	

1001-1005

Scania L113CRL   Wright Axcess-ultralow   B42F   1996

1001	N101YVU	1002	M2SLT	1003	N103YVU	1004	N104YVU	1005	N105YVU

1006-1034

Scania L113CRL   Wright Axcess-ultralow   B43F   1996

1006	N106DWM	1012	N112DWM	1018	N118DWM	1024	N124DWM	1030	N130DWM
1007	N107DWM	1013	N113DWM	1019	N119DWM	1025	N125DWM	1031	N131DWM
1008	N108DWM	1014	N114DWM	1020	N120DWM	1026	N126DWM	1032	N132DWM
1009	N109DWM	1015	N115DWM	1021	N121DWM	1027	N127DWM	1033	N133DWM
1010	N110DWM	1016	N116DWM	1022	N122DWM	1028	N128DWM	1034	N134DWM
1011	N211DWM	1017	N117DWM	1023	N123DWM	1029	N129DWM		

1035-1040

Scania L113CRL   East Lancashire Flyte   B47F   1996

1035	P135GND	1037	P137GND	1038	P138GND	1039	P139GND	1040	P140GND
1036	P136GND								

1041-1061

Scania L113CRL   Northern Counties Paladin   B42F   1997

1041	P41MVU	1046	P46MVU	1050	P250NBA	1054	R54XVM	1058	P58MVU
1042	P42MVU	1047	R47XVM	1051	R51XVM	1055	R255WRJ	1059	R59XVM
1043	P43MVU	1048	R48XVM	1052	P52MVU	1056	P56MVU	1060	P260NBA
1044	P244NBA	1049	P49MVU	1053	P53MVU	1057	R57XVM	1061	P61MVU
1045	P45MVU								

1150	L150SBG	Dennis Dart 9SDL3034	East Lancashire	B32F	1993
1151	L151SBG	Dennis Dart 9SDL3034	East Lancashire	B32F	1993
1152	L152SBG	Dennis Dart 9SDL3034	East Lancashire	B32F	1993
1153	L153UKB	Dennis Dart 9SDL3034	Plaxton Pointer	B20F	1994
1154	L154UKB	Dennis Dart 9SDL3034	Plaxton Pointer	B20F	1994
1155	L155UKB	Dennis Dart 9SDL3034	Plaxton Pointer	B20F	1994
1156	L156UKB	Dennis Dart 9SDL3034	Plaxton Pointer	B20F	1994

1157-1170

Dennis Dart 9.8SDL3040*   East Lancashire   B40F   1994-95 1170 is 9.8SDL3054

1157	M157WKA	1160	M160WKA	1163	M163WKA	1166	M166WKA	1169	M169WKA
1158	M158WKA	1161	M161WKA	1164	M164WKA	1167	M167WKA	1170	M170WKA
1159	M159WKA	1162	M162WKA	1165	M165WKA	1168	M168WKA		

The West Lancashire operation of North Western is based at Skelmersdale where the whole of the East Lancashire Flyte-bodied Scania buses are based. Seen here is 1036, P136GND. The latest deliveries of saloons are similar chassis but with almost the last Northern Counties bodies built at the plant in Wigan. This is now part of the same company as Plaxton, and that name is expected to be affixed to all future double-decks built at the factory, while single-deck production has now moved to Scarborough with the Paladin replaced with the Prestige. *Tony Wilson/Terry Wightman*

The 1998 Cowie Bus Handbook

The dormant Mexborough and Swinton Traction Company was renamed North Western to take over the Merseyside, West Lancashire, and Wigan operations of Ribble in September 1986. Since then the geographical spread has extended into Greater Manchester and Cheshire. Pictured with the Star Line operation is Scania 1005, N105YVU which carries route-branding for service 19 which links Altrincham with Manchester International Airport.

1171-1187
Dennis Dart 9.8SDL3040   Plaxton Pointer   B40F   1995

1171	M171YKA	1175	M175YKA	1179	M179YKA	1182	M182YKA	1185	M185YKA
1172	M172YKA	1176	M176YKA	1180	M180YKA	1183	M183YKA	1186	M186YKA
1173	M173YKA	1177	M177YKA	1181	M181YKA	1184	M184YKA	1187	M187YKA
1174	M174YKA	1178	M178YKA						

1188-1199
Dennis Dart 9.8SDL3054   Plaxton Pointer   B40F   1995

1188	M188YKA	1191	M191YKA	1194	M194YKA	1196	M196YKA	1198	M198YKA
1189	M189YKA	1192	M192YKA	1195	M195YKA	1197	M197YKA	1199	M199YKA
1190	M190YKA	1193	M193YKA						

1201-1210
Dennis Lance 11SDA3113   Plaxton Verde   B49F   1995

1201	M201YKA	1203	M203YKA	1205	M205YKA	1207	M207YKA	1209	M209YKA
1202	M202YKA	1204	M204YKA	1206	M206YKA	1208	M208YKA	1210	M210YKA

1211	M211YKD	Dennis Dart 9.8SDL3040	Plaxton Pointer	B40F	1995
1212	M212YKD	Dennis Dart 9.8SDL3040	Plaxton Pointer	B40F	1995
1213	M213YKD	Dennis Dart 9.8SDL3040	Plaxton Pointer	B40F	1995
1214	M214YKD	Dennis Dart 9.8SDL3054	Plaxton Pointer	B40F	1995
1215	M215YKD	Dennis Dart 9.8SDL3054	Plaxton Pointer	B40F	1995
1216	M216YKD	Dennis Dart 9.8SDL3054	Plaxton Pointer	B40F	1995

One of the largest deliveries of buses to North Western was the supply of East Lancashire-bodied Dennis Darts which were fitted with EL2000-style bodies. These are now used extensivly on the services to the north of Liverpool and use the City Plus branding. Representing the type is 1220, **M220AKB.** *Phillip Stephenson*

1217-1264   Dennis Dart 9.8SDL3054   East Lancashire   B40F   1995

1217	M217AKB	1227	M227AKB	1237	N237CKA	1247	N247CKA	1256	N256CKA
1218	M218AKB	1228	M228AKB	1238	N238CKA	1248	N248CKA	1257	N257CKA
1219	M219AKB	1229	M229AKB	1239	N239CKA	1249	N249CKA	1258	N258CKA
1220	M220AKB	1230	M230AKB	1240	N240CKA	1250	N250CKA	1259	N259CKA
1221	M221AKB	1231	M231AKB	1241	N241CKA	1251	N251CKA	1260	N260CKA
1222	M322AKB	1232	M232AKB	1242	N242CKA	1252	N252CKA	1261	N261CKA
1223	M223AKB	1233	N233CKA	1243	N243CKA	1253	N253CKA	1262	N262CKA
1224	M224AKB	1234	N234CKA	1244	N244CKA	1254	N254CKA	1263	N263CKA
1225	M225AKB	1235	N235CKA	1245	N245CKA	1255	N255CKA	1264	N264CKA
1226	M226AKB	1236	N236CKA	1246	N246CKA				

1265	K877UDB	Dennis Dart 9.8SDL3017	Plaxton Pointer	B40F	1992	Ex Star Line, 1995
1266	M370KVR	Dennis Dart 9.8SDL3035	Northern Counties Paladin	B40F	1994	Ex Star Line, 1995
1267	M371KVR	Dennis Dart 9.8SDL3035	Northern Counties Paladin	B40F	1994	Ex Star Line, 1995
1268	M372KVR	Dennis Dart 9.8SDL3035	Northern Counties Paladin	B40F	1995	Ex Star Line, 1995
1269	M841RCP	Dennis Dart 9.8SDL3054	Northern Counties Paladin	B39F	1995	Ex Wigan Bus Company, 1995
1270	M842RCP	Dennis Dart 9.8SDL3054	Northern Counties Paladin	B39F	1995	Ex Wigan Bus Company, 1995
1271	M843RCP	Dennis Dart 9.8SDL3054	Northern Counties Paladin	B39F	1995	Ex Wigan Bus Company, 1995
1272	M5SLT	Dennis Dart 9.8SDL3040	Plaxton Pointer	B40F	1994	Ex South Lancashire, 1997
1273	K73SRG	Dennis Dart 9.8SDL3017	Plaxton Pointer	B43F	1993	Ex Northumbria (Hunters), 1997
1274	K74SRG	Dennis Dart 9.8SDL3017	Plaxton Pointer	B43F	1993	Ex Northumbria (Hunters), 1997
1275u	K75SRG	Dennis Dart 9.8SDL3017	Plaxton Pointer	B43F	1993	Ex Northumbria (Hunters), 1997
1276u	J8SLT	Dennis Dart 9.8SDL3017	Plaxton Pointer	B38F	1992	Ex South Lancashire, 1997
1277u	J9SLT	Dennis Dart 9.8SDL3017	Plaxton Pointer	B38F	1992	Ex South Lancashire, 1997
1278	L1SLT	Dennis Dart 9SDL3011	Plaxton Pointer	B35F	1993	Ex South Lancashire, 1997
1279	L2SLT	Dennis Dart 9SDL3011	Plaxton Pointer	B35F	1993	Ex South Lancashire, 1997
1280	L11SLT	Dennis Dart 9.8SDL3025	Plaxton Pointer	B38F	1993	Ex South Lancashire, 1997
1281	J7SLT	Dennis Dart 9.8SDL3040	Plaxton Pointer	B38F	1996	Ex South Lancashire, 1997
1282	J6SLT	Dennis Dart 9.8SDL3040	Plaxton Pointer	B40F	1996	Ex South Lancashire, 1997
1283	P3SLT	Dennis Dart	Plaxton Pointer	B40F	1996	Ex South Lancashire, 1997

1290-1299 — Dennis Lance 11SDA3113 — Plaxton Verde — B49F — 1994 — Ex Clydeside, 1996

1290	M930EYS	1292	M932EYS	1294	M934EYS	1296	M936EYS	1298	M928EYS
1291	M931EYS	1293	M933EYS	1295	M935EYS	1297	M927EYS	1299	M929EYS

Heritage fleet:-

881	838AFM	Bristol Lodekka LD6G	Eastern Coach Works	H33/27R	1957	Ex Crosville, 1990
918	AJA118	Bristol L5G	Burlingham (1950)	B35R	1938	Ex preservation, 1994

Ancilliary vehicles:-

6	D406NNA	Renault-Dodge S46	Northern Counties	B22F	1987	Ex Ribble, 1989
13	D413NNA	Renault-Dodge S46	Northern Counties	B22F	1987	Ex Ribble, 1989
27	D427NNA	Renault-Dodge S46	Northern Counties	B22F	1987	Ex Ribble, 1989
857	G644EVN	CVE Omni	CVE	B15FL	1990	Ex Greater Manchester PTE, 1994
914	GGR406N	Leyland Leopard PSU3/3R	Plaxton Elite III/UAS	RV	1974	Ex Northumbria,
916t	VDB916	Leyland Leopard PSU3/3RT	Alexander Highlander	DP49F	1962	Ex preservation, 1994
918	AJA142B	Leyland Leopard PSU3/3RT	Alexander AY/CMS	RV	1964	Tow vehicles
938t	WSU442S	Leyland Leopard PSU3/3R	Alexander AYS	B53F	1977	Ex Clydeside, 1996
940t	FBV506W	Leyland Atlantean AN68A/1R	Eastern Coach Works	H43/31F	1981	Ex Ribble, 1998
941t	HFM186N	Leyland National 11351/1R		DP48F	1975	Ex Crosville, 1989
950t	WSU450S	Leyland Leopard PSU3/3R	Alexander AYS	B53F	1977	Ex Clydeside, 1996
952t	WSU441S	Leyland Leopard PSU3/3R	Alexander AYS	B53F	1977	Ex Clydeside, 1996
953t	AFB597V	Bristol LH6L	Eastern Coach Works	B43F	1980	Ex South Lancashire, 1997
t	LRB201W	Leyland National 2 NL116L11/1R		B52F	1980	Ex Yorkshire Bus (WR), 1997

Previous Registrations:

49XBF	F603CET, A19RBL, F603CET	MIL6679	TOE498N
J4SLT	J61MHF	MIL6680	TOE499N
J10SLT	J470XHL	MIL6681	TOE492N
K3SLT	K445EDT, 30938 (GBG), K455EDT	MIL7612	TOE495N
K200SLT	K380NHU	MIL7613	TOE496N
L3SLT	IIB847, L748EAY	MIL7614	TOE505N
LRN664N	TOE469N, MIL5581	MIL7615	TOE510N
M2SLT	N102YVU	MIL7616	TOE511N
M5SLT	M20CLA	MIL7617	TOE513N
MIL5573	TOE487N	MIL7618	TOE522N
MIL5574	TOE488N	MIL7619	TOE508N
MIL5575	TOE489N	MIL7620	TOE512N
MIL5580	ROK468N	MIL7621	TOE523N
MIL5581	LPB209P	MIL7622	ROK469M
MIL5582	TOE486N	MIL7623	ROK470M
MIL6676	TOE490N	MIL7624	GOK618N
MIL6677	TOE491N	TOS799X	LTY559X, MNX305
MIL6678	TOE497N	TSU646	FKL175Y

Allocations and liveries:-

Livery:Yellow, blue and red; white, blue and red (Star Line); white and blue (Liverline and Little White Buses); yellow, blue and white (South Lancashire); grey, red and white (Easylink)

Bootle (Hawthorne Road) - North Western

National	214	215	218	219	220	229	241	250
	251	253	256	291	294	311	312	320
	326	329	331	332	334	340		
Dart	1150	1151	1152	1178	1217	1218	1219	1220
	1221	1222	1223	1224	1225	1226	1227	1228
	1229	1230	1231	1232	1233	1234	1235	1236
	1237	1238	1239	1240	1241	1242	1243	1244
	1245	1246	1247	1248	1249	1250	1251	1252
	1253	1254	1255	1256	1257	1258	1259	1260
	1261	1262	1263	1264	1269	1270	1271	
Lance	1294	1295	1298	1299				
Heritage	881	918						

Dennis Dart 1154, L154UKB, is seen working service 674 to Beach Hill in Easylink colours. These four Darts are fitted with special facilities for the less-mobile and carry a grey, red and white livery. All are based at Haydock. *Phillip Stephenson*

Bootle (Hawthorne Road) - Liverline

Mercedes-Benz	59	60	64	65	66	67		
National	203	204	205	211	359	375	419	420
	421	422	423	424	425	426	427	428
	429	430	431	432	433	434	435	436
	461	462	463	464	465	466		
Scania	671	672	673	674	675	676	677	678
	679	680						

Haydock (Yew Tree Trading Estate, Kilbuck Lane) - Wigan Bus Company - Easylink♦

Mercedes-Benz	175	176	177	178	179	180	181	182
	183	184						
Scania	1006	1008	1009	1010	1011	1012	1013	1014
	1015	1016	1017	1018	1019	1021	1022	1023
	1024	1025	1026	1027	1028	1029	1030	1031
	1032	1033	1034					
Dart	1153♦	1154♦	1155♦	1156♦				

Manchester (Hulme Hall Road) - Bee Line

Mercedes-Benz	70	73	74	75	76	82		
National	271	400	402	403	404	405	406	407
	408	409	410	411	412	413	414	415
	416	417	418					
Falcon	381	382	383	384	385	386	387	388
Scania	1041	1042	1043	1044	1045	1046	1047	1048
	1049							
Olympian	603	604	605	607	608	613	614	615
	619	620	621	622	623	625	658	659
	660	661	662	668				

Runcorn (Beechwood) - North Western, Runcorn Busway♣

Mercedes-Benz	120	121	122	124	125	127	129	130
	131	132	133					
MetroRider	161	162						
National	261	262	263	264	267	277	278	280
	281	282	284	301	303	306	309	310
	450	451	452	453	454	455	456	457
	458	459						
Dart	1158♣	1159♣	1160♣	1161♣	1162♣	1163♣D	1164♣	1165♣
	1166♣	1167♣	1168♣	1169♣	1170♣	1178	1215	1273
	1274							
Lance	1201♣	1202♣	1203♣	1204♣	1205♣	1206♣	1207♣	1208♣
	1209♣	1210						

Skelmersdale (Neverstich Road) - North Western, Little White Buses♥

Mercedes-Benz	51	52	77	79	80	97♥	98♥	108
	126	128	191♥	192♥	193♥	194♥	195♥	196♥
	197♥							
MetroRider	151♥	152♥						
National	200	201	206	208	209	210		
Volvo Citybus	650	651	652	653				
Scania	1035	1036	1037	1038	1039	1040	1050	1051
	1052	1053	1054	1055	1056	1057	1058	1059
	1060	1061						
Olympian	609	611	616	670				

Warrington (Athlone Road) - Warrington Gold Line

Dart	1171	1172	1173	1174	1175	1176	1177	1179
	1180	1181	1182	1183	1184	1186	1188	1189
	1190	1191	1192	1194	1195	1196	1197	1198
	1199	1212	1213	1214	1216			
Lance	1290	1291	1292	1293				

1993 saw North Western acquire Liverline of Liverpool, by then a 51 vehicle company, which it was ran as a separate subsidary until 1997, since when the blue Liverline livery has been changed to standard colours on repaint. One of those remaining blue is Olympian 619, B963WRN.
Tony Wilson

Winsford (Winsford Industrial Estate) - North Western

Mercedes-Benz	50	53	54	55	56	57	61	62
	63	69	96	101	102	103	104	105
Dart	1265							
Tiger	855							
National	356	357	360	361	362	363	364	365
	367	368	369	370	371	372	373	374
Bristol VR	545	546	564	568	569	570		
Olympian	600	601	602	610	612	618	624	654
	655	656	657	667				
Heritage	881							

Wythenshawe (Grebba Road) - Star Line

Mercedes-Benz	86	93	95	99	100	106	107	109
	110	134	135	136	137	138	139	140
	141	142	143	144	145	146	147	148
	149							
Optimo	890	891	893					
Leopard	854							
Javelin	844							
DAF Coach (hire)	858	859						
Dart	1185	1187	1193	1211	1266	1267	1268	
Scania	1001	1002	1003	1004	1005	1007	1020	

St Helens (Beaufort Street, Peasley Cross) - South Lancashire

Renault-Dodge	48	49						
Mercedes-Benz	111	113	114	115	116	119	150	
Dart	1272	1276	1277	1278	1279	1280	1281	1282
	1283							
Falcon	389	390						
Tiger	701	702	703	704				
Volvo B57	700							

Disposal/Stored

Mercedes-Benz	58	68	72	78	80	88	89	94
	110	123						
Iveco	189	190						
Dart	1275							
Lance	1296	1297						
National	202	260	347	348	376	378	379	437
Dominator	629	630	632	633	634	635	637	
Bristol VR	547	548	550	551	562	563	565	
Olympians	606	615	619	669				

Deliveries of Scania buses included a batch delivered to the Wigan Bus operation during 1996. Representing this batch of twenty-nine vehicles is 1010, N110DWM, seen here working the 362 service between Wigan and Chorley.
Richard Godfrey

157

THE SHIRES

LDT Ltd, Castle Street, Luton, Bedfordshire, LU1 3AJ

Minibuses

2001-2011 MCW MetroRider MF150/81 MCW B23F 1988 Ex London Country NW, 1990

2001w	E971DNK	2003	E973DNK	2006	E976DNK	2008w	E978DNK	2009	E979DNK
2002	E972DNK	2005	E975DNK	2007	E977DNK				

2012	LIL2288	Mercedes-Benz 307D	Reeve Burgess	M12	1984	Ex Lucky Bus, Watford, 1997
2013w	D203RGH	Volkswagen LT55	Optare City Pacer	B25F	1987	Ex Lucky Bus, Watford, 1997
2014w	D989JYG	Volkswagen LT55	Optare City Pacer	DP20FL	1986	Ex Lucky Bus, Watford, 1997

2015-2030 MCW MetroRider MF150/83* MCW B23F 1988 Ex London Country NW, 1990
*2015-18 are MF150/81

2015	E985DNK	2020	E990DNK	2022	E992DNK	2024	E994DNK	2027	E997DNK
2016	E986DNK	2021	E991DNK	2023	E993DNK	2025	E995DNK	2029w	E999DNK
2018	E988DNK								

2031	D23RPP	Iveco Daily 49.10	Robin Hood City Nippy	B21F	1987	Ex London Country NW, 1991
2032w	E479CNM	MCW MetroRider MF150/72	MCW	B23F	1988	Ex London Country NW, 1991
2033	E486CNM	MCW MetroRider MF150/74	MCW	B23F	1987	Ex Sovereign, 1990
2037	F122TRU	Mercedes-Benz 709D	Reeve Burgess Beaver	B25F	1988	Ex Kentish Bus, 1991
2038	F123TRU	Mercedes-Benz 709D	Reeve Burgess Beaver	B25F	1988	Ex Metrobus, Orpington, 1991
2039	F124TRU	Mercedes-Benz 709D	Reeve Burgess Beaver	B25F	1988	Ex Kentish Bus, 1991
2040	F125TRU	Mercedes-Benz 709D	Reeve Burgess Beaver	B25F	1988	Ex Metrobus, Orpington, 1991

In late 1997 Lucketts Garages (Watford) Ltd was acquired. in addition to local bus services in Watford there are substantial dial-a-ride operations and a commercial workshop. Pictured in Lucketts livery is The Shires 2104, L800BUS, an Optare MetroRider. *Richard Godfrey*

Re-numbering of the LDT fleet has dispensed with letter classification of vehicles inherited from the former London Country (North West) garages. Number 2019, E989DNK, sports its new four figure fleet number as it approaches central Watford before heading south into the northern reaches of Greater London. *Phillip Stephenson*

2041	E341DRO	Iveco Daily 49.10	Dormobile	B25F	1988	
2043	F128TRU	Mercedes-Benz 709D	Reeve Burgess Beaver	B25F	1988	Ex Metrobus, Orpington, 1991
2045	E335DRO	Iveco Daily 49.10	Dormobile	B25F	1988	
2048	F598CET	Mercedes-Benz 709D	Reeve Burgess Beaver	B25F	1988	Ex Argyll Bus & Coach, 1992
2049	F287FGL	Iveco Daily 49.10	Carlyle Dailybus 2	B23F	1988	Ex Buffalo, Flitwick, 1994
2050	G58BEL	Mercedes-Benz 811D	Wadham Stringer Wessex	DP31F	1989	Ex Buffalo, Flitwick, 1995
2051	F985GKJ	Iveco Daily 49.10	Robin Hood City Nippy	B21F	1990	Ex Buffalo, Flitwick, 1995
2052	MBZ6455	Iveco Daily 49.10	Carlyle Dailybus	B25F	1988	Ex Buffalo, Flitwick, 1995
2053	F969GKJ	Iveco Daily 49.10	Robin Hood City Nippy	B21F	1989	Ex Buffalo, Flitwick, 1995
2054	G360FOP	Mercedes-Benz 709D	Carlyle	B25F	1989	Ex Yellow Bus, Stoke Mandeville, 1995
2055	G896TGG	Mercedes-Benz 811D	Reeve Burgess Beaver	B33F	1990	Ex Stevensons, 1995
2056	H523SWE	Mercedes-Benz 709D	Whittaker Europa	B29F	1990	Ex Rhondda, 1995
2057	H407FGS	Mercedes-Benz 811D	Reeve Burgess Beaver	B31F	1991	Ex Sovereign, 1996
2058	H408FGS	Mercedes-Benz 811D	Reeve Burgess Beaver	B31F	1991	Ex Sovereign, 1996
2059	H406FGS	Mercedes-Benz 811D	Reeve Burgess Beaver	B31F	1990	Ex Sovereign, 1996
2060	H848AUS	Mercedes-Benz 709D	Reeve Burgess Beaver	B25F	1990	Ex Argyll Bus & Coach, 1992
2061	H641UWE	Mercedes-Benz 814D	Europa Enterprise	B31F	1991	Ex Buffalo, Flitwick, 1995
2062	H642UWE	Mercedes-Benz 814D	Europa Enterprise	B31F	1991	Ex Buffalo, Flitwick, 1995
2063	H35DGD	Mercedes-Benz 811D	Dormobile Routemaker	B33F	1991	Ex Pathfinder, Newark, 1995
2064	H614CGG	Mercedes-Benz 709D	Dormobile Routemaker	B33F	1991	Ex Pathfinder, Newark, 1995
2065	F121TRU	Mercedes-Benz 709D	Reeve Burgess Beaver	B25F	1988	Ex Kentish Bus, 1991
2066	J917HGD	Mercedes-Benz 709D	Reeve Burgess Beaver	B25F	1991	Ex Argyll Bus & Coach, 1992
2067	H231KBH	Mercedes-Benz 709D	Carlyle	B27F	1992	Ex Buffalo, Flitwick, 1995
2068	H408BVR	Mercedes-Benz 709D	Reeve Burgess Beaver	B25F	1990	Ex Star Line, Knutsford, 1995
2069	H409BVR	Mercedes-Benz 709D	Reeve Burgess Beaver	B25F	1990	Ex Star Line, Knutsford, 1995
2070	J65UNA	Mercedes-Benz 709D	Plaxton Beaver	B23F	1992	Ex South Lancashire, St Helens, 1996
2071	K8BUS	Mercedes-Benz 811D	Wright NimBus	B33F	1993	Ex Patterson, Birmingham, 1995
2072	K578YOJ	Mercedes-Benz 709D	Dormobile Routemaker	B29F	1993	Ex Patterson, Birmingham, 1995
2073	K543OGA	Mercedes-Benz 811D	Dormobile Routemaker	B29F	1992	Ex Pathfinder, Newark, 1995
2074	K579YOJ	Mercedes-Benz 709D	Dormobile Routemaker	B29F	1993	Ex Patterson, Birmingham, 1995

2075-2079
Mercedes-Benz 709D | Made-to-Measure | B24F | 1992 | Ex Birmingham Omnibus, Tividale, 1995

2075	K25WND	2076	K26WND	2077	K27WND	2078	K28WND	2079	K29WND

2080	K580YOJ	Mercedes-Benz 811D	Wright NimBus	B33F	1993	Ex Patterson, Birmingham, 1995
2081	K31WND	Mercedes-Benz 709D	Made-to-Measure	B24F	1992	Ex Birmingham Omnibus, Tividale, 1995
2082	K32WND	Mercedes-Benz 709D	Made-to-Measure	B24F	1992	Ex Birmingham Omnibus, Tividale, 1995
2083	K203FEH	Mercedes-Benz 709D	Dormobile Routemaker	B27F	1993	Ex Stevensons, 1995
2084	L864BEA	Iveco Daily 49.10	Marshall	B23F	1993	Ex Buffalo, Flitwick, 1994
2085	L863BEA	Iveco Daily 49.10	Marshall	B23F	1993	Ex Buffalo, Flitwick, 1994
2086	L326AUT	Mercedes-Benz 709D	Leicester Carriage Builders	B25F	1994	Ex Midland Fox, 1994
2087	L327AUT	Mercedes-Benz 709D	Leicester Carriage Builders	B25F	1994	Ex Midland Fox, 1994
2088	L328AUT	Mercedes-Benz 709D	Leicester Carriage Builders	B25F	1994	Ex Midland Fox, 1994
2089	K202FEH	Mercedes-Benz 709D	Dormobile Routemaker	B27F	1993	Ex Stevensons, 1995

2090-2094
Iveco TurboDaily 59-12 | Marshall C31 | B27F | 1994

2090	M150RBH	2091	M151RBH	2092	M152RBH	2093	M153RBH	2094	M154RBH

2095	K184GDU	Mercedes-Benz 811D	Wright	B31F	1993	Ex Yellow Bus, Stoke Mandeville, 1995

2096-2100
Iveco TurboDaily 59-12 | Marshall C31 | B27F | 1994

2096	M156RBH	2097	M157RBH	2098	M158RBH	2099	M159RBH	2100	M160RBH

2101	J171GGG	Mercedes-Benz 709D	Dormobile Routemaker	B29F	1991	Ex Yellow Bus, Stoke Mandeville, 1995
2102	L600BUS	Optare MetroRider MR11	Optare	B31F	1995	Ex Lucky Bus, Watford, 1997
2103	L700BUS	Optare MetroRider MR11	Optare	B32F	1996	Ex Lucky Bus, Watford, 1997
2104	L800BUS	Optare MetroRider MR11	Optare	B31F	1996	Ex Lucky Bus, Watford, 1997
2105	M45WUR	Mercedes-Benz 709D	Plaxton Beaver	B25F	1995	
2106	M46WUR	Mercedes-Benz 709D	Plaxton Beaver	B25F	1995	
2107	M47WUR	Mercedes-Benz 709D	Plaxton Beaver	B25F	1995	
2108	M38WUR	Mercedes-Benz 811D	Plaxton Beaver	B25F	1995	
2109	M39WUR	Mercedes-Benz 811D	Plaxton Beaver	B25F	1995	
2110	N906ETM	Mercedes-Benz 709D	Plaxton Beaver	B27F	1995	
2111	M41WUR	Mercedes-Benz 811D	Plaxton Beaver	DP31F	1995	
2112	M42WUR	Mercedes-Benz 811D	Plaxton Beaver	DP31F	1995	
2113	M43WUR	Mercedes-Benz 709D	Plaxton Beaver	B25F	1995	
2114	N918ETM	Mercedes-Benz 709D	Plaxton Beaver	B27F	1995	
2115	N919ETM	Mercedes-Benz 709D	Plaxton Beaver	DP27F	1995	

2116-2137
Mercedes-Benz 709D | Plaxton Beaver | B27F | 1995

2116	N186EMJ	2121	N191EMJ	2126	N196EMJ	2130	N910ETM	2134	N914ETM
2117	N187EMJ	2122	N192EMJ	2127	N907ETM	2131	N911ETM	2135	N915ETM
2118	N188EMJ	2123	N193EMJ	2128	N908ETM	2132	N912ETM	2136	N916ETM
2119	N189EMJ	2124	N194EMJ	2129	N909ETM	2133	N913ETM	2137	N917ETM
2120	N190EMJ	2125	N195EMJ						

2138-2162
Mercedes-Benz 709D | Plaxton Beaver | B25F | 1996

2138	N368JGS	2143	N373JGS	2148	N378JGS	2153	N383JGS	2158	N366JGS
2139	N369JGS	2144	N374JGS	2149	N379JGS	2154	N384JGS	2159	N367JGS
2140	N370JGS	2145	N375JGS	2150	N380JGS	2155	N385JGS	2160	P670PNM
2141	N371JGS	2146	N376JGS	2151	N381JGS	2156	N386JGS	2161	P671PNM
2142	N372JGS	2147	N377JGS	2152	N382JGS	2157	N387JGS	2162	P669PNM

2165	WIB1114	Mercedes-Benz 609D	PMT	C26F	1987	Ex Checker, Garston, 1997
2166	J465UFS	Mercedes-Benz 609D	Crystals	C24F	1992	Ex Checker, Garston, 1997
2167	SLU261	Ford Transit VE6	Deansgate	M12	1987	Ex Checker, Garston, 1997
2168	G40OHS	Ford Transit VE6	Dormobile	B16F	1989	Ex Checker, Garston, 1997
2169	G715PGA	Ford Transit VE6	Deansgate	M14	1989	Ex Checker, Garston, 1997
2170	J964NLL	Ford Transit VE6	Crystals	M13	1992	Ex Checker, Garston, 1997

Opposite, top: - **The 1997 single deck bus requirement for The Shires was met with a batch a fourteen Northern Counties-bodied Scania low floor L113s. Pictured here is 3190, P190SRO, which carries route branding for service 373 at Watford. The bus was caught on camera while passing through Leavesden.** *Tony Wilson*

Opposite, bottom:- **Luton & Dunstable names are carried on Leyland Olympian 5090, F640LMJ. In this picture, the Alexander-bodied bus still displays is former number.** *Gerald Mead*

2171-2184 Mercedes-Benz Vario O810 Plaxton Beaver 2 B27F 1997

2171	R171VBM	2174	R174VBM	2177	R177VBM	2180	R180VBM	2183	R183VBM
2172	R172VBM	2175	R175VBM	2178	R178VBM	2181	R181VBM	2184	R184VBM
2173	R173VBM	2176	R176VBM	2179	R179VBM	2182	R182VBM		

2801	LAZ5765	Mercedes-Benz L608D	Reeve Burgess	B20F	1986	Ex Clydeside, 1997
2802	LAZ5785	Mercedes-Benz L608D	Alexander AM	B20F	1985	Ex Clydeside, 1997
2803	LAZ5929	Mercedes-Benz L608D	Rootes	B20F	1986	Ex Clydeside, 1997
2804	LAZ5962	Mercedes-Benz L608D	Rootes	B20F	1986	Ex Clydeside, 1997
2805	LAZ5964	Mercedes-Benz L608D	Reeve Burgess	B20F	1986	Ex Clydeside, 1997
2806	LAZ6771	Mercedes-Benz L608D	Rootes	B20F	1986	Ex Clydeside, 1997
2807	C206EKJ	Mercedes-Benz L608D	Rootes	B20F	1986	Ex Clydeside, 1997
2808	HIL8438	Mercedes-Benz L608D	Rootes	B20F	1986	Ex Clydeside, 1997
2809	HIL8439	Mercedes-Benz L608D	Rootes	B20F	1986	Ex Clydeside, 1997
2810	D36KKP	Mercedes-Benz L608D	Rootes	B20F	1986	Ex Clydeside, 1997
2811	D203SKD	Mercedes-Benz L608D	Reeve Burgess	DP19F	1986	Ex Clydeside, 1997
2812	D206SKD	Mercedes-Benz L608D	Reeve Burgess	DP19F	1986	Ex Clydeside, 1997

3010	KNV513P	Leyland National 11351/1R	B49F	1976	Ex United Counties, 1986
3011	VRP531S	Leyland National 11351A/1R	B49F	1977	Ex Milton Keynes City Bus, 1987
3014	SBD524R	Leyland National 11351A/1R	B49F	1977	Ex United Counties, 1986
3015	BVV545T	Leyland National 11351A/1R	B49F	1978	Ex United Counties, 1986
3016w	BVV542T	Leyland National 11351A/1R	B49F	1978	Ex United Counties, 1986
3017	XVV537S	Leyland National 11351A/1R	B49F	1978	Ex United Counties, 1986
3018	XVV538S	Leyland National 11351A/1R	B49F	1978	Ex United Counties, 1986
3020w	BVV547T	Leyland National 11351A/1R	B49F	1978	Ex United Counties, 1986
3025w	EPD523V	Leyland National 10351B/1R	B41F	1979	Ex London Country NW, 1991
3026	MNH569V	Leyland National 11351A/1R	B49F	1979	Ex United Counties, 1986
3027	MNH577V	Leyland National 11351A/1R	B49F	1979	Ex United Counties, 1986
3030w	KRP560V	Leyland National 11351A/1R	B49F	1979	Ex United Counties, 1986
3031	NRP581V	Leyland National 2 NL116L11/1R	B49F	1980	Ex United Counties, 1986
3033	SVV588W	Leyland National 2 NL116L11/1R	B49F	1980	Ex United Counties, 1986

3035-3043 Leyland National 2 NL106AL11/2R B44F 1981 Ex Parfitt's, Rhymney Bridge, 1995

3035	GUW465W	3037	GUW457W	3039	GUW447W	3041	GUW461W	3043	GUW475W
3036	GUW456W	3038	GUW441W	3040	GUW494W	3042	GUW462W		

3044	IIL4821	Leyland 10351/1R/SC(6HLX)	East Lancs Greenway (1993)	B41F	1974	Ex Crosville Cymru, 1995
3045	IIL4822	Leyland 10351/1R/SC(6HLX)	East Lancs Greenway (1993)	B41F	1976	Ex Crosville Cymru, 1995
3046	TIB4873	Leyland 10351B/1R(6HLX)	East Lancs Greenway (1993)	B41F	1979	Ex Crosville Cymru, 1995
3047	IIL4824	Leyland 10351/1R(6HLX)	East Lancs Greenway (1994)	B41F	1975	Ex Crosville Cymru, 1995
3048	BAZ6869	Leyland 10351B/1R(6HLX)	East Lancs Greenway (1994)	B41F	1979	Ex Crosville Cymru, 1995
3049	RJI6861	Leyland 10351B/1R(6HLX)	East Lancs Greenway (1994)	B41F	1979	Ex Crosville Cymru, 1995
3050	BTX152T	Leyland 10351A/2R(6HLX)	East Lancs Greenway (1994)	B44F	1979	Ex Parfitts, Rhymney Bridge, 1995
3051	IAZ3457	Leyland National 11351A/1R(Volvo)		DP47FL	1978	Ex United Counties, 1986
3052	IAZ4037	Leyland National 11351A/1R(Volvo)		B49F	1977	Ex United Counties, 1986
3053	CAZ6852	Leyland 10351B/1R(6HLX)	East Lancs Greenway (1994)	B41F	1978	Ex Crosville Cymru, 1995
3054	TIB7835	Leyland 10351B/1R(6HLX)	East Lancs Greenway (1994)	B41F	1979	Ex Crosville Cymru, 1995
3055	RJI6862	Leyland 10351B/1R(6HLX)	East Lancs Greenway (1994)	B41F	1979	Ex Crosville Cymru, 1995
3056	IIL4823	Leyland 10351B/1R(6HLX)	East Lancs Greenway (1993)	B41F	1978	Ex Crosville Cymru, 1995
3057	TIB4886	Leyland 10351B/1R(6HLX)	East Lancs Greenway (1993)	B41F	1975	Ex Crosville Cymru, 1995
3058	GHB574V	Volvo B58-61	East Lancs EL2000(1994)	B53F	1980	Ex Parfitt's, Rhymney Bridge, 1995
3059u	HIL7467	Volvo B10M-61	East Lancs EL2000(1991)	B55F	1983	Ex Buffalo, Flitwick, 1995
3060u	MBZ6454	Volvo B10M-61	East Lancs EL2000(1991)	B55F	1985	Ex Buffalo, Flitwick, 1995
3061	D603ACW	Leyland Lynx LX112L10ZR1R	Leyland Lynx	B51F	1987	Ex Sovereign, 1990
3062	E970NMK	Leyland Lynx LX112TL11ZR1S	Leyland Lynx	B49F	1987	Ex Sovereign, 1990
3063	E420EBH	Leyland Lynx LX112TL11ZR1R	Leyland Lynx	B51F	1988	Ex Sovereign, 1996
3064	E969PME	Leyland Lynx LX112L10ZR1R	Leyland Lynx	B49F	1988	Ex Atlas Bus, Harlesden, 1994
3065	E965PME	Leyland Lynx LX112TL11ZR1R	Leyland Lynx	B49F	1988	Ex Yellow Bus, Stoke Mandeville, 1995
3066	E966PME	Leyland Lynx LX112TL11ZR1R	Leyland Lynx	B49F	1988	Ex Yellow Bus, Stoke Mandeville, 1995
3067	H407ERO	Leyland Lynx LX2R11C15Z4S	Leyland Lynx	DP45F	1990	
3068	H408ERO	Leyland Lynx LX2R11C15Z4S	Leyland Lynx	DP45F	1990	
3069	H409ERO	Leyland Lynx LX2R11C15Z4S	Leyland Lynx	DP45F	1990	
3070	H410ERO	Leyland Lynx LX2R11C15Z4S	Leyland Lynx	DP45F	1990	

3071-3075 Leyland Lynx LX112L10ZR1R Leyland Lynx B51F 1989

3071	F401PUR	3072	F402PUR	3073	F403PUR	3074	F404PUR	3075	F400PUR

The fleet of Leyland Lynx with The Shires ranges in age from 1987-90, and features both bus and high-back seating. 3069, H409ERO, here in Dunstable, is one of the latter, coming into the fleet from new. Other second-hand versions have come from various sources. *Phillip Stephenson*

3076	E970PME	Leyland Lynx LX112L10ZR1R	Leyland Lynx	B49F	1988	Ex Atlas Bus, Harlesden, 1994
3077	NIB8459	Volvo B10M-61	East Lancs EL2000(1991)	B55F	1988	Ex Buffalo, Flitwick, 1995
3078	F314RMH	Volvo B10M-56	Plaxton Derwent II	B54F	1988	Ex Buffalo, Flitwick, 1995
3079	F151KGS	Volvo B10M-56	Plaxton Derwent II	B54F	1988	Ex Buffalo, Flitwick, 1995
3080	F152KGS	Volvo B10M-56	Plaxton Derwent II	B54F	1988	Ex Buffalo, Flitwick, 1995
3081	F153KGS	Volvo B10M-56	Plaxton Derwent II	B54F	1988	Ex Buffalo, Flitwick, 1995
3082w	F302MNK	Leyland Swift LBM6T/2RA	Wadham Stringer Vanguard II	B35F	1989	
3083w	F303MNK	Leyland Swift LBM6T/2RA	Wadham Stringer Vanguard II	B35F	1989	
3084w	F154KGS	Leyland Swift LBM6T/2RA	Wadham Stringer Vanguard II	B39F	1988	Ex Buffalo, Flitwick, 1995
3085w	F155KGS	Leyland Swift LBM6T/2RA	Wadham Stringer Vanguard II	B39F	1988	Ex Buffalo, Flitwick, 1995
3086w	F300MNK	Leyland Swift LBM6T/2RA	Wadham Stringer Vanguard II	B35F	1989	
3088w	F301MNK	Leyland Swift LBM6T/2RA	Wadham Stringer Vanguard II	B35F	1989	
3089	L133HVS	Volvo B10B-58	Alexander Strider	B51F	1993	Ex Buffalo, Flitwick, 1995
3090	M247SPP	Dennis Dart 9.8SDL3054	Wright Handybus	B40F	1994	

3091-3098

			Dennis Dart 9.8SDL3004	Carlyle Dartline	B40F	1991	Ex London Country NW, 1991
3091	H922LOX	3093	H925LOX	3095	H242MUK	3097	H244MUK	3098	H245MUK
3092	H923LOX	3094	H926LOX	3096	H243MUK				

3099	K447XPA	Dennis Dart 9.8SDL3017	Plaxton Pointer	B40F	1992	Ex Buffalo, Flitwick, 1995
3100	K448XPA	Dennis Dart 9.8SDL3017	Plaxton Pointer	B40F	1992	Ex Buffalo, Flitwick, 1995
3101	L100BUS	Dennis Dart 9.8SDL3035	Plaxton Pointer	B39F	1994	Ex Lucky Bus, Watford, 1997
3102	L200BUS	Dennis Dart 9.8SDL3035	Plaxton Pointer	B39F	1994	Ex Lucky Bus, Watford, 1997
3103	L300BUS	Dennis Dart 9SDL3031	Marshall C36	B34F	1994	Ex Lucky Bus, Watford, 1997
3104	L400BUS	Dennis Dart 9SDL3031	Marshall C36	B34F	1994	Ex Lucky Bus, Watford, 1997

3105-3136   Volvo B6-9.9M   Northern Counties Paladin   B40F   1994

3105	L305HPP	3112	L312HPP	3119	M719OMJ	3125	M725OMJ	3131	M711OMJ
3106	L306HPP	3113	L313HPP	3120	M720OMJ	3126	M726OMJ	3132	M712OMJ
3107	L307HPP	3114	L314HPP	3121	M721OMJ	3127	M727OMJ	3133	M713OMJ
3108	L308HPP	3115	L315HPP	3122	M722OMJ	3128	M728OMJ	3134	M714OMJ
3109	L309HPP	3116	L316HPP	3123	M723OMJ	3129	M729OMJ	3135	M715OMJ
3110	L310HPP	3117	M717OMJ	3124	M724OMJ	3130	M710OMJ	3136	M716OMJ
3111	L311HPP	3118	M718OMJ						

3137	L43MEH	Volvo B6-9.9M	Plaxton Pointer	B40F	1994	Ex Stevensons, 1994
3138	L922LJO	Volvo B6-9.9M	Northern Counties Paladin	B40F	1994	Ex Yellow Bus, Stoke Mandeville, 1995
3139	L923LJO	Volvo B6-9.9M	Northern Counties Paladin	B40F	1994	Ex Yellow Bus, Stoke Mandeville, 1995
3140	M248SPP	Dennis Dart 9.8SDL3054	Wright Handybus	B40F	1994	
3141	M251SPP	Dennis Dart 9.8SDL3054	Wright Handybus	B40F	1994	
3142	M249SPP	Dennis Dart 9.8SDL3054	Wright Handybus	B40F	1994	

3143-3149   Scania L113CRL   East Lancashire European   B51F   1995

3143	N693EUR	3145	N695EUR	3147	N697EUR	3148	N698EUR	3149	N699EUR
3144	N694EUR	3146	N696EUR						

3150	M250SPP	Dennis Dart 9.8SDL3054	Wright Handybus	B40F	1994

3151-3166   Scania L113CRL   East Lancashire European   DP49F   1995

3151	N701EUR	3155	N705EUR	3158	N708EUR	3161	N711EUR	3164	N714EUR
3152	N702EUR	3156	N706EUR	3159	N709EUR	3162	N712EUR	3165	N715EUR
3153	N703EUR	3157	N707EUR	3160	N710EUR	3163	N713EUR	3166	N716EUR
3154	N704EUR								

3167	N28KGS	Scania L113CRL	East Lancashire European	B51F	1996
3168	N29KGS	Scania L113CRL	East Lancashire European	B51F	1996
3169	N31KGS	Scania L113CRL	East Lancashire European	B51F	1996
3170	N32KGS	Scania L113CRL	East Lancashire European	B51F	1996
3171	P671OPP	Dennis Dart SLF	East Lancashire Flyte	B41F	1996
3172	P672OPP	Dennis Dart SLF	East Lancashire Flyte	B41F	1996
3173	P673OPP	Dennis Dart SLF	East Lancashire Flyte	B41F	1996
3174	P674OPP	Dennis Dart SLF	East Lancashire Flyte	B41F	1996

3175-3190   Dennis Dart SLF   Plaxton Pointer 2   B39F*   1997   *3175-8 are B41F

3175	P175SRO	3179	P179SRO	3182	P182SRO	3185	P185SRO	3188	P188SRO
3176	P176SRO	3180	P180SRO	3183	P183SRO	3186	P186SRO	3189	P189SRO
3177	P177SRO	3181	P181SRO	3184	P184SRO	3187	P187SRO	3190	P190SRO
3178	P178SRO								

3191-3205   Scania L113CRL   Northern Counties Paladin   B49F   1997

3191	R191RBM	3194	R194RBM	3197	R197RBM	3201	R201RBM	3204	R204RBM
3192	R192RBM	3195	R195RBM	3198	R198RBM	3202	R202RBM	3205	R205RBM
3193	R193RBM	3196	R196RBM	3199	R199RBM	3203	R203RBM		

3206-3215   Dennis Dart SLF   Plaxton Pointer 2   B--F   On order

3206	R206GMJ	3208	R208GMJ	3210	R210GMJ	3212	R212GMJ	3214	R214GMJ
3207	R207GMJ	3209	R209GMJ	3211	R211GMJ	3213	R213GMJ	3215	R215GMJ

4001	A151EPA	Leyland Tiger TRCTL11/3R	Plaxton Paramount 3200 E	C57F	1984	Ex London Country NW, 1990
4002	A152EPA	Leyland Tiger TRCTL11/3R	Plaxton Paramount 3200 E	C57F	1984	Ex London Country NW, 1990
4003	A153EPA	Leyland Tiger TRCTL11/3R	Plaxton Paramount 3200 E	C57F	1984	Ex London Country NW, 1990
4004	HIL2358	Bedford YNT	Plaxton Supreme V	C49FL	1982	Ex Lucky Bus, Watford, 1997
4005	A155EPA	Leyland Tiger TRCTL11/3R	Plaxton Paramount 3200 E	C57F	1984	Ex London Country NW, 1990
4006	A113EPA	Leyland Tiger TRCTL11/2RH	Plaxton Paramount 3200 E	C53F	1983	Ex London Country NW, 1990
4007	A157EPA	Leyland Tiger TRCTL11/3R	Plaxton Paramount 3200 E	C57F	1984	Ex London Country NW, 1990
4008	A143EPA	Leyland Tiger TRCTL11/2RH	Plaxton Paramount 3200 E	C57F	1984	Ex London Country NW, 1990
4009	FIL4919	Volvo B10M-61	Duple 320	C49FT	1987	Ex Lucky Bus, Watford, 1997
4010	A150EPA	Leyland Tiger TRCTL11/3R	Plaxton Paramount 3200 E	C51F	1984	Ex London Country SW, 1989
4011	DIL7916	Bedford YNV	Duple 320	C51F	1987	Ex Lucky Bus, Watford, 1997
4012	B292KPF	Leyland Tiger TRCTL11/3RH	Plaxton Paramount 3200 IIE	C51F	1985	Ex London Country NW, 1990
4013	B293KPF	Leyland Tiger TRCTL11/3RH	Plaxton Paramount 3200 IIE	C51F	1985	Ex London Country NW, 1990

There are a number of vehicles wearing a most pleasant all-over livery for the West Herts College. When not being used as such, the vehicles operate normal stage service routes. The Shires 3160, N710EUR, an East Lancashire-bodied Scania, passes between the Watford Junction station and the town centre. *Phillip Stephenson*

Four East Lancashire Spryte-bodied 10-metre Dennis Darts appeared in 1996, bringing low-floor easy access types to Hemel Hempstead. Thus with Gade Valley local lettering, 3173, P673OPP, operates on route 4A through Marlowes in the centre of this Hertfordshire new town. *Phillip Stephenson*

4014	HIL7594	Volvo B10M-61	Plaxton Paramount 3500 III	C53F	1988	Ex Moor-Dale, 1994	
4015	HIL7595	Volvo B10M-61	Plaxton Paramount 3500 III	C53F	1988	Ex Moor-Dale, 1994	
4016	SIB4846	Leyland Tiger TRCTL11/3ARZA	Plaxton Paramount 3200 III	C53F	1988	Ex London Country NW, 1990	
4017	C147SPB	Leyland Tiger TRCTL11/3RH	Berkhof Everest 370	C53F	1986	Ex London Country NW, 1990	
4018	C148SPB	Leyland Tiger TRCTL11/3RH	Berkhof Everest 370	C53F	1986	Ex London Country NW, 1990	
4019	C149SPB	Leyland Tiger TRCTL11/3RH	Berkhof Everest 370	C53F	1986	Ex London Country NW, 1990	
4020	SIB7480	Leyland Tiger TRCTL11/3ARZA	Plaxton Paramount 3200 III	C51F	1988	Ex London Country NW, 1990	
4021	E881YKY	Leyland Tiger TRCTL11/3ARZ	Plaxton Paramount 3200 III	C53F	1988		
4022	E882YKY	Leyland Tiger TRCTL11/3ARZ	Plaxton Paramount 3200 III	C53F	1988		
4023	E323OMG	Leyland Tiger TRCTL11/3ARZA	Plaxton Paramount 3200 III	C53F	1988	Ex London Country NW, 1990	
4024	GIL6253	Volvo B10M-61	Plaxton Paramount 3200 III	C50F	1987	Ex Moor-Dale, 1994	
4025	SIB8529	Leyland Tiger TRCTL11/3ARZA	Plaxton Paramount 3500 III	C51FT	1988	Ex London Country NW, 1990	
4026	SIB7481	Leyland Tiger TRCTL11/3ARZA	Plaxton Paramount 3500 III	C51FT	1988	Ex London Country NW, 1990	
4027	HIL7597	Volvo B10M-61	Plaxton Paramount 3500 III	C53F	1988	Ex Moor-Dale, 1994	
4028	MIL2350	Dennis Javelin 12SDA1919	Duple 320	C57F	1990	Ex Lucky Bus, Watford, 1997	
4029	GIL6949	Volvo B10M-61	Plaxton Paramount 3200 III	C50F	1987	Ex Moor-Dale, 1994	
4031	E661AWJ	Leyland Tiger TRCTL11/3ARZ	Plaxton Paramount 3200 III	C53F	1988		
4032	E662AWJ	Leyland Tiger TRCTL11/3ARZ	Plaxton Paramount 3200 III	C53F	1988		
4033	E663AWJ	Leyland Tiger TRCTL11/3ARZ	Plaxton Paramount 3200 III	C53F	1988		
4034	H198AOD	Volvo B10M-60	Plaxton Expressliner	C50FT	1996	Ex Trathens, Plymouth, 1996	
4035	H199AOD	Volvo B10M-60	Plaxton Expressliner	C50FT	1996	Ex Trathens, Plymouth, 1996	
4036	L500BUS	Iveco Country Rider 48-10-21	WS Coachbuilders Vanguard	B47F	1995	Ex Lucky Bus, Watford, 1997	
4037	P100LOW	Dennis Javelin	UVG Unistar	C55FTL	1996	Ex Lucky Bus, Watford, 1997	
4038	ADZ4731	Volvo B10M-56	Plaxton Viewmaster IV Exp	C51F	1982	Ex Checker, Garston, 1997	
4039	WIB1113	Volvo B10M-61	Plaxton Paramount 3200 II	C53F	1985	Ex Checker, Garston, 1997	
4040	YIB2396	Volvo B10M-61	Plaxton Paramount 3200 II	C53F	1986	Ex Checker, Garston, 1997	
4042	WIB1118	Leyland Tiger TRCTL11/2R	Duple Dominant IV Express	C53F	1983	Ex Checker, Garston, 1997	
4043	YIB2397	Leyland Tiger TRCTL11/3RZ	Duple 320	C57F	1987	Ex Checker, Garston, 1997	
4044	WIB1115	DAF MB200DKTL600	Plaxton Supreme V	C53F	1983	Ex Checker, Garston, 1997	
4045w	B118KPF	Leyland Tiger TRCTL11/3RH	Berkhof Everest 370	C49FT	1984	Ex Kentish Bus, 1997	
4046	TIB5906	Leyland Tiger TRCTL11/3RH	Duple 320	C51F	1986	Ex Kentish Bus, 1997	

4047-4056

				DAF DE33WSSB3000	Plaxton Prima	C53F	1997

4047	R447SKX	**4049**	R449SKX	**4051**	R451SKX	**4053**	R453SKX	**4055**	R455SKX
4048	R448SKX	**4050**	R450SKX	**4052**	R452SKX	**4054**	R454SKX	**4056**	R456SKX

5000	BKE847T	Bristol VRT/SL3/6LXB	Eastern Coach Works	H43/31F	1979	Ex Maidstone & District, 1997	
5009w	CBD779K	Bristol VRT/SL2/6LX	Eastern Coach Works	H39/31F	1972	Ex United Counties, 1986	
5011	PRP802M	Bristol VRT/SL2/6LX	Eastern Coach Works	H43/31F	1974	Ex United Counties, 1986	
5013	LBD837P	Bristol VRT/SL3/6LX	Eastern Coach Works	H43/31F	1975	Ex United Counties, 1986	
5014	OVV851R	Bristol VRT/SL3/501(6LXB)	Eastern Coach Works	H43/31F	1976	Ex United Counties, 1986	
5015	TNH865R	Bristol VRT/SL3/6LXB	Eastern Coach Works	H43/31F	1977	Ex United Counties, 1986	
5016	OCY916R	Bristol VRT/SL3/501	Eastern Coach Works	H43/31F	1977	Ex South Wales, 1987	
5017	IAZ3977	Bristol VRT/SL3/501	Eastern Coach Works	H43/31F	1977	Ex South Wales, 1987	
5018	OVV852R	Bristol VRT/SL3/501(6LXB)	Eastern Coach Works	H43/31F	1976	Ex United Counties, 1986	
5019	OVV853R	Bristol VRT/SL3/501(6LXB)	Eastern Coach Works	H43/31F	1976	Ex United Counties, 1986	
5020	OVV855R	Bristol VRT/SL3/501(6LXB)	Eastern Coach Works	H43/31F	1976	Ex United Counties, 1986	
5021	WBD877S	Bristol VRT/SL3/6LXB	Eastern Coach Works	H43/31F	1977	Ex United Counties, 1986	
5022	YVV893S	Bristol VRT/SL3/6LXB	Eastern Coach Works	H43/31F	1978	Ex United Counties, 1986	
5023	YVV894S	Bristol VRT/SL3/6LXB	Eastern Coach Works	H43/31F	1978	Ex United Counties, 1986	
5024	YVV895S	Bristol VRT/SL3/6LXB	Eastern Coach Works	H43/31F	1978	Ex United Counties, 1986	

5025-5030

				Bristol VRT/SL3/6LXB	Eastern Coach Works	H43/31F	1978-80 Ex United Counties, 1986

5025	CBD897T	**5027w**	CBD900T	**5028**	ONH928V	**5029**	ONH929V	**5030**	CBD904T
5026	CBD899T								

5032	SNV932W	Bristol VRT/SL3/6LXB	Eastern Coach Works	H43/31F	1980	Ex United Counties, 1986	
5033	SNV933W	Bristol VRT/SL3/6LXB	Eastern Coach Works	H43/31F	1980	Ex United Counties, 1986	
5034	SNV934W	Bristol VRT/SL3/6LXB	Eastern Coach Works	H43/31F	1980	Ex United Counties, 1986	
5035	ONH925V	Bristol VRT/SL3/6LXB	Eastern Coach Works	H43/31F	1980	Ex United Counties, 1986	
5036	UDM448V	Bristol VRT/SL3/6LXB	Eastern Coach Works	H43/31F	1980	Ex Crosville Cymru, 1995	
5037	JPE237V	Leyland Atlantean AN68B/1R	Roe	H43/30F	1980	Ex London Country NW, 1990	
5038	SNV938W	Bristol VRT/SL3/6LXB	Eastern Coach Works	H43/31F	1980	Ex United Counties, 1986	

5039-5043

				Leyland Atlantean AN68B/1R	Roe	H43/30F	1980	Ex London Country NW, 1990

5039	JPE233V	**5040**	JPE236V	**5041**	KPJ241W	**5042**	KPJ242W	**5043**	KPJ243W

5044	TRN470V	Leyland Atlantean AN68A/1R	Eastern Coach Works	H45/31F	1979	Ex Ribble, 1994	
5045	TRN477V	Leyland Atlantean AN68A/1R	Eastern Coach Works	H45/31F	1980	Ex Ribble, 1994	

Route 747 links up most of the main airports which serve London. The Shires involvement includes 4035, H199AOD, a Volvo B10M with Plaxton Expressliner body, which here pulls into Hemel Hempstead bus station en route from Luton to Gatwick via Heathrow. As the index mark suggests, its origins lie down in the West Country. *Phillip Stephenson*

5046-5052

		Bristol VRT/SL3/6LXB		Eastern Coach Works		H43/31F*	1981	Ex United Counties, 1986
								*5048 is H40/31F

5046	URP946W	5048w	VVV955W	5050	VVV960W	5051	VVV951W	5052	VVV957W
5047	URP947W	5049	VVV956W						

5053-5060

		Leyland Olympian ONLXB/1R		Eastern Coach Works		H45/32F	1981-82	Ex United Counties, 1986

5053	ARP613X	5055	ARP615X	5057	ARP617X	5059	ARP619X	5060	ARP620X
5054	ARP614X	5056	ARP616X	5058	ARP618X				

5061	MUH287X	Leyland Olympian ONLXB/1R	Eastern Coach Works	H45/32F	1982	Ex Rhondda, 1994
5062	ARP612X	Leyland Olympian ONLXB/1R	Eastern Coach Works	H45/32F	1981	Ex United Counties, 1986
5063	MUH290X	Leyland Olympian ONLXB/1R	Eastern Coach Works	H45/32F	1982	Ex Rhondda, 1995
5064	MUH284X	Leyland Olympian ONLXB/1R	Eastern Coach Works	H45/32F	1982	Ex Rhondda, 1994
5065	BPF135Y	Leyland Olympian ONTL11/1R	Roe	H43/29F	1983	Ex Sovereign, 1990
5066	BPF136Y	Leyland Olympian ONTL11/1R	Roe	H43/29F	1983	Ex Sovereign, 1990
5067	IAZ2314	Leyland Olympian ONLXB/1R	Eastern Coach Works	H45/32F	1982	Ex Rhondda, 1995
5068	A141DPE	Leyland Olympian ONTL11/1R	Roe	H43/29F	1983	Ex Sovereign, 1990
5069	A149FPG	Leyland Olympian ONTL11/1R	Roe	H43/29F	1984	Ex London Country NW, 1990
5070	A143DPE	Leyland Olympian ONTL11/1R	Roe	H43/29F	1983	Ex Sovereign, 1990

5071-5075

		Leyland Olympian ONTL11/1R		Roe		H43/29F	1984	Ex London Country NW, 1990

5071	A151FPG	5072	A152FPG	5073	A153FPG	5074	A154FPG	5075	A155FPG

5076	B262LPH	Leyland Olympian ONTL11/1R	Eastern Coach Works	H43/29F	1985	Ex Sovereign, 1990
5077	B273LPH	Leyland Olympian ONTL11/1R	Eastern Coach Works	H43/29F	1985	Ex London Country NW, 1990
5078	A698EAU	Leyland Olympian ONTL11/1R	Northern Counties	H47/33D	1984	Ex Buffalo, Flitwick, 1995
5079	A699EAU	Leyland Olympian ONTL11/1R	Northern Counties	H47/33D	1984	Ex Buffalo, Flitwick, 1995
5080	B270LPH	Leyland Olympian ONTL11/1R	Eastern Coach Works	H43/29F	1985	Ex London Country NW, 1990
5081	B271LPH	Leyland Olympian ONTL11/1R	Eastern Coach Works	H43/29F	1985	Ex London Country NW, 1990
5082	B272LPH	Leyland Olympian ONTL11/1R	Eastern Coach Works	H43/29F	1985	Ex London Country NW, 1990

5083-5094

Leyland Olympian ONCL10/1RZ Alexander RL   H47/32F*   1988   *5086/91 are DPH47/29F

5083	F633LMJ	5086	F636LMJ	5089	F639LMJ	5091	F641LMJ	5093	F643LMJ
5084	F634LMJ	5087	F637LMJ	5090	F640LMJ	5092	F642LMJ	5094	F644LMJ
5085	F635LMJ	5088	F638LMJ

5095-5107

Leyland Olympian ON2R50C13Z4 Alexander RL   H47/32F*   1989-90 *5104 is DPH47/29F
5099-5103 are H47/34F

5095	G645UPP	5098	G648UPP	5101	G651UPP	5104	G654UPP	5106	G656UPP
5096	G646UPP	5099	G649UPP	5102	G652UPP	5105	G655UPP	5107	G657UPP
5097	G647UPP	5100	G650UPP	5103	G653UPP

5108	F506OYW	Leyland Olympian ONTL11/1RH Northern Counties	H47/30F	1988	Ex Yellow Bus, Stoke Mandeville, 1995
5109	G129YEV	Leyland Olympian ONCL10/2RZ Northern Counties	H49/34F	1989	Ex London Country NW, 1990
5110	G130YEV	Leyland Olympian ONCL10/2RZ Northern Counties	H49/34F	1989	Ex London Country NW, 1990

5111-5125

Leyland Olympian ONCL10/1RZ Leyland   H47/31F   1989-90 Ex London Country NW, 1990

5111	G281UMJ	5114	G284UMJ	5117	G287UMJ	5120	G290UMJ	5123	G293UMJ
5112	G282UMJ	5115	G285UMJ	5118	G288UMJ	5121	G291UMJ	5124	G294UMJ
5113	G283UMJ	5116	G286UMJ	5119	G289UMJ	5122	G292UMJ	5125	G295UMJ

5126	H196GRO	Leyland Olympian ON2R50C13Z4 Leyland	H47/29F	1991	
5127	H197GRO	Leyland Olympian ON2R50C13Z4 Leyland	H47/29F	1991	
5128	H198GRO	Leyland Olympian ON2R50C13Z4 Leyland	H47/29F	1991	
5129	H199GRO	Leyland Olympian ON2R50C13Z4 Leyland	H47/29F	1991	
5130	F747XCS	Leyland Olympian ONCL10/1RZ Alexander RL	H47/32F	1989	Ex A1 Service (McMenemy), 1995
5131	H201GRO	Leyland Olympian ON2R50C13Z4 Leyland	H47/29F	1991	
5132	H202GRO	Leyland Olympian ON2R50C13Z4 Leyland	H47/29F	1991	
5133	H203GRO	Leyland Olympian ON2R50C13Z4 Leyland	H47/29F	1991	
5134	G131YWC	Leyland Olympian ONCL10/2RZ Northern Counties	H49/33F	1989	Ex Ensign, Purfleet, 1991
5135	G132YWC	Leyland Olympian ONCL10/2RZ Northern Counties	H49/33F	1989	Ex London Country NW, 1990

In 1996 a batch of ten Volvo Olympian double-deckers were introduced into the fleet. Bearing Northern Counties Palatine 77-seater bodies, the vehicles were allocated to the Luton depot for dedicated services along the Luton to Dunstable corridor. Illustrating the batch is 5145, N45JPP.
Phillip Stephenson

5136-5145 Volvo Olympian YN2RV18Z4 Northern Counties Palatine H47/30F 1996

| 5136 | N36JPP | 5138 | N38JPP | 5140 | N46JPP | 5142 | N42JPP | 5144 | N35JPP |
| 5137 | N37JPP | 5139 | N39JPP | 5141 | N41JPP | 5143 | N43JPP | 5145 | N45JPP |

| 5866 | FKM866V | Bristol VRT/SL3/6LXB | Eastern Coach Works | H43/31F | 1979 | Ex Maidstone & District, 1997 |
| 5874 | FKM874V | Bristol VRT/SL3/6LXB | Eastern Coach Works | H43/31F | 1979 | Ex Maidstone & District, 1997 |

Heritage fleet:-

| 1178 | FEV178 | Leyland Titan TD5 | Eastern Coach Works (1949) | L28/27R | 1937 | Ex preservation, 1987 |

Ancilliary fleet:

1005	F273CEY	Iveco Daily 49.10	Robin Hood City Nippy	B21F	1988	Ex Crosville Cymru, 1994
1006	F689RKX	Iveco Daily 49.10	Carlyle Dailybus 2	B25F	1988	Ex Crosville Cymru, 1994
1007	F266CEY	Iveco Daily 49.10	Robin Hood City Nippy	B21F	1988	Ex Crosville Cymru, 1994
1008	F696GMA	Iveco Daily 49.10	Robin Hood City Nippy	B21F	1988	Ex Crosville Cymru, 1994
1201t	YMB938T	Bedford YLQ	Plaxton Supreme IV	C49F	1979	Ex ADS, Wem, 1993
1203t	RDS83W	Volvo B58-56	Duple Dominant	B53F	1980	Ex Buffalo, Flitwick, 1990
1204t	RDS84W	Volvo B58-56	Duple Dominant	B53F	1980	Ex Buffalo, Flitwick, 1990
1205t	NJF204W	Bedford YMQ	Plaxton Supreme IV	C45F	1980	Ex Lee & District, 1990
1206t	FJR776L	Bedford YRT	Plaxton Elite III	C53F	1972	Ex Rodham, Washington, 1994
1207	K657KNL	Iveco Daily 49.10	Carlyle Dailybus 2	B23F	1989	Ex OK, Bishop Auckland, 1996
2163t	D208SKD	Mercedes-Benz L608D	Reeve Burgess	B20F	1986	Ex London & Country (GWS), 1997
2164t	D210SKD	Mercedes-Benz L608D	Reeve Burgess	B20F	1986	Ex London & Country (GWS), 1997
3087t	G97VMM	Leyland Swift LBM6T/2RS	Wadham Stringer Vanguard II	B39F	1989	Ex London Country NW, 1990

There are 15 Volvo Olympians with Plaxton Palatine bodywork on order.

Previous Registrations:

ADZ4731	KNP3X
B118KPF	B118KPF, KBC193
BAZ6869	JTU577T
BTX152T	AYR329T, NIW4810
CAZ6852	HMA561T
DIL7916	D121EFH
FIL4919	D614FSL, D448FSP
GHB574V	EYH802V, NIW2309
GIL6253	D209LWX
GIL6949	D210LWX
H231KBH	CMN414C
HIL2358	AEG121Y
HIL7467	FUA387Y, 3408WY, NRV859Y
HIL7594	E662UNE
HIL7595	E663UNE
HIL7597	E660UNE
HIL8438	C212EKJ
HIL8439	C214EKJ
IAZ2314	MUH288X
IAZ3457	BVV548T
IAZ3977	RTH917S
IAZ4037	VRP532S
IIL4821	XPD299N
IIL4822	LPB180P
IIL4823	GMB659T
IIL4824	HNB20N
J65UNA	J59MHF, J6SLT
J964NLL	J413UUK
L500BUS	M289CUR
LAZ5765	D650CVN
LAZ5785	C203PCD
LAZ5929	C203EKJ
LAZ5962	C211EKJ
LAZ5964	D652CVN
LAZ6771	C207EKJ
LIL2288	B259AMG
MBZ6454	B572AVW, URY598
MBZ6455	E295VOM, 7178KP
MIL2350	G171BLH
NIB8459	E637NEL
RJI6861	HMA569T
RJI6862	MCA677T
SIB4846	E321OMG
SIB7480	E325OMG
SIB7481	E326OMG
SIB8529	E324OMG
SLU261	WET880, D969MDB
TIB4873	MCA671T
TIB4886	HPF322N
TIB5906	C264SPC
TIB7835	JTU594T
WIB1113	B504CGP
WIB1114	E428YDM
WIB1115	FKK615Y
WIB1118	YPD145Y
YIB2396	C510LGH
YIB2397	D296RKW

Allocations & Liveries:-

Livery : Blue and yellow; green, white and yellow (✈Green Line and Jetlink) silver, red and blue † (Lucketts) and white ♥ (Checker).

Aylesbury (Smeaton Close, Brunel Park) - Aylesbury & The Vale

Outstation - Leighton Buzzard

Mercedes-Benz	2054	2068	2069	2073	2083	2089	2095	2101
	2105	2106	2107	2113	2116	2117	2118	2145
National	3017	3018	3026					
Greenway	3044	3045	3047	3048				
Lynx	3065	3066	3067					
Scania	3163	3164	3165	3166				
Bristol VR	5000	5035	5038	5051	5866	5874		
Olympian	5053	5054	5055	5056	5057	5058	5059	5060
	5061	5062	5063	5064	5078	5079	5083	5085
	5088	5097	5099	5100	5101	5102	5103	5104

Dunstable (Tavistock Street) - Luton & Dunstable

Mercedes-Benz	2037	2038	2039	2040	2043	2048	2061	2062
	2064	2065	2067	2121	2122	2124	2126	
National	3035	3036	3037	3040				
Volvo B6	3130	3131						
Scania	3167	3169	3170					
Bristol VR	5018	5019	5020	5052				
Olympian	5087	5105	5106	5107				

Hemel Hempstead (Whiteleaf Road) - Gade Valley

Mercedes-Benz	2086	2087	2088	2127	2132	2181	2182	2183
	2184							
MetroRider	2002	2005	2006	2007	2009	2015	2016	
	2018	2021	2022	2023	2024	2102=		
Tiger	4001 ✈	4002 ✈	4003 ✈	4005 ✈	4017 ✈	4018 ✈	4019 ✈	4020 ✈
	4025 ✈	4026 ✈						
Volvo	4034 ✈	4035 ✈						
Dart	3090	3095	3097	3140	3141	3142	3150	3171
	3172	3173	3174	3175	3176	3177	3178	
Scania	3151	3152	3153	3154	3155	3156	3157	3158
	3159	3160	3161	3162				
Olympian	5084	5086	5092					

High Wycombe (Lincoln Road, Cressex Industrial Estate) - Chiltern Rover

Outstation - Old Amersham

Mercedes-Benz	2138	2139	2140	2141	2142	2143	
National	3010	3015	3027				
Greenway	3046	3050	3053	3055	3056	3057	
Volvo B6	3110	3115	3116	3126	3127	3138	3139
Tiger	4010 ✈	4012 ✈	4013 ✈	4023 ✈			
Atlantean	5037	5039	5040	5041	5042	5043	5045
Olympian	5066	5076	5108	5109	5110	5134	5135

Hitchin (Fishponds Road) - Hitchin & District

Mercedes-Benz	2055	2056	2057	2059	2063	2071	2080	2108
	2109	2111	2112	2146	2147	2148	2149	2150
	2151	2152	2153	2154	2155	2156	2157	2160
	2161	2162						
Iveco	2041	2045	2049	2051	2052	2053		
National	3031	3033	3051					
Greenway	3049	3054						
Volvo B6	3107	3109	3120	3128	3129			
Volvo B10	3089							
Lynx	3063							

Luton (Castle Street) - Luton & Dunstable - Challenger

Mercedes-Benz	2050	2058	2066	2072	2074	2075	2076	2077
	2078	2079	2081	2082	2120	2123	2125	2158
	2159	2801	2802	2803	2804	2805	2806	2807
	2808	2809	2810	2811	2812			
Iveco	2084	2085	2090	2091	2092	2093	2094	2096
	2097	2098	2099	2100				
Tiger	4016 ✈	4021 ✈	4022 ✈	4031 ✈	4032 ✈	4033 ✈		
Volvo Coach	4014 ✈	4015 ✈	4024 ✈	4027 ✈	4029 ✈			
National	3039	3041	3042	3043				
Volvo B10M	3059	3060	3077	3078	3079	3080	3081	
Volvo B6	3117	3118	3119	3121	3122	3123	3124	3125
	3132	3133	3134	3135	3136	3137		
Lynx	3068	3069						
Scania	3143	3144	3145	3146	3147	3148	3149	3168
	3192	3193	3194	3195				
Bristol VR	5011	5013	5015	5021	5022	5023	5024	5025
	5026	5028	5029	5030	5032	5033	5034	5036
	5046	5047	5049	5050				
Olympian	5089	5090	5091	5093	5094	5095	5096	5098
	5136	5137	5138	5139	5140	5141	5142	5143
	5144	5145						
Heritage	1178							

Stevenage (Norton Green Road) - The Stevenage Line

Volvo B6	3105	3106	3108	3111	3112	3113	3114	
Lynx	3061	3062	3064	3070	3071	3072	3073	3074
	3075	3076						
Scania	3196	3197	3198	3199	3201	3202		

Watford (Tolpits Lane) - Lucketts of Watford

Mercedes-Benz	2012					
MetroRider	2104†					
Iveco	4036					
Dart	3096	3098	3101†	3102†	3103†	3104†
Bedford	4004†	4011†				
Javelin	4028†					
Tiger	4006	4008				

Watford (St Albans Road, Garston) - Network Watford - Elstree & Borehamwood - Checker Travel

Mercedes-Benz	2060	2070	2100	2114	2115	2128	2129	2130
	2131	2134	2135	2136	2137	2144	2165	2166
	2171	2172	2173	2174	2175	2176	2177	2178
	2179	2180						
Iveco	2031							
Transit	2167	2168	2169	2170				
MetroRider	2003	2020	2025	2027	2028	2033	2103	
Dart	3091	3092	3093	3094	3099	3100	3179	3180
	3181	3182	3183	3184	3185	3186	3187	3188
	3189	3190						
National	3011	3014	3052					
Volvo B10M	3058♥	4009	4038♥	4039♥	4040♥			
Tiger	4007✈	4042♥	4043♥	4046✈				
Javelin	4037†							
DAF	4044♥							
Bristol VR	5014	5016	5017					
Olympian	5065	5067	5068	5069	5070	5071	5072	5073
	5074	5075	5077	5080	5081	5082	5111	5112
	5113	5114	5115	5116	5117	5118	5119	5120
	5121	5122	5123	5124	5125	5126	5127	5128
	5129	5130	5132	5133				

SOUTH LONDON

South London Transport Ltd; Croydon Bus Garage, Brighton Road,
South Croydon, CR2 6EL

DIB1	J929CYL	DAF SB220LC550	Ikarus Citi Bus	B48F	1992	Ex County, 1997
DIB2	J930CYL	DAF SB220LC550	Ikarus Citi Bus	B48F	1992	Ex Grey Green, 1997
DIB3	J931CYL	DAF SB220LC550	Ikarus Citi Bus	B48F	1992	Ex Grey Green, 1997
DIB4	J413NCP	DAF SB220LC550	Ikarus Citi Bus	B48F	1992	Ex The Birmingham Coach Company, 1997
DIB5	J414NCP	DAF SB220LC550	Ikarus Citi Bus	B48F	1992	Ex The Birmingham Coach Company, 1997

DR20-31

Dennis Dart 8.5SDL3003 — Plaxton Pointer — B28F — 1991 — Ex London Buses, 1995

20	H120THE	23	H123THE	26	H126THE	28	H128THE	30	H130THE
21	H621TKU	24	H124THE	27	H127THE	29	H129THE	31	H131THE
22	H122THE	25	H125THE						

DRL38-48

Dennis Dart 9SDL3016 — Plaxton Pointer — B34F — 1992 — Ex London Buses, 1995
47/8 ex County, 1997

38	K5380RH	40	K5400RH	42	K5420RH	44	K5440RH	48	K5480RH
39	K5390RH	41	K5410RH	43	K5430RH	47	K5470RH		

DRL147-158

Dennis Dart 9SDL3024 — Plaxton Pointer — B34F — 1993 — Ex London Buses, 1995

147	L147WAG	150	L150WAG	153	L153WAG	155	L155WAG	157	L157WAG
148	L148WAG	151	L151WAG	154	L154WAG	156	L156WAG	158	L158WAG
149	L149WAG	152	L152WAG						

DRL210	N710GUM	Dennis Dart 9SDL3053	Plaxton Pointer	B34F	1995
DRL211	N711GUM	Dennis Dart 9SDL3053	Plaxton Pointer	B34F	1995
DRL212	N712GUM	Dennis Dart 9SDL3053	Plaxton Pointer	B34F	1995

DRL213-218

Dennis Dart — Plaxton Pointer — B34F — 1996

213	P913PWW	215	P915PWW	216	P916PWW	217	P917PWW	218	P918PWW
214	P914PWW								

DT65-70

Dennis Dart 8.5SDL3003 — Carlyle Dartline — B28F — 1990 — Ex London Buses, 1995

65	H465UGO	67	H467UGO	68	H468UGO	69	H469UGO	70	H470UGO
66	H466UGO								

DT132	H132MOB	Dennis Dart 8.5SDL3003	Carlyle Dartine	B28F	1991	Ex Metroline, 1997
DT143	H143MOB	Dennis Dart 8.5SDL3003	Carlyle Dartine	B28F	1991	Ex Metroline, 1997
L1	A101SYE	Leyland Olympian ONTL11/1R	Eastern Coach Works	H47/28D	1984	
L2	A102SYE	Leyland Olympian ONLXB/1R	Eastern Coach Works	H47/28D	1984	
L3	A103SYE	Leyland Olympian ONLXB/1R	Eastern Coach Works	H47/28D	1984	

L4-20

Leyland Olympian ONLXB/1RH — Eastern Coach Works — H42/26D — 1986

4	C804BYY	6	C806BYY	13	VLT13	16	WLT916	20	C820BYY
5	C805BYY	8	WLT807	14	C814BYY	17	C817BYY		

L31-113

Leyland Olympian ONLXB/1RH — Eastern Coach Works — H42/26D — 1986

21	C21CHM	32	C32CHM	41	C41CHM	52	C52CHM	66	C66CHM
22	C22CHM	33	C33CHM	45	C45CHM	56	C56CHM	78	C78CHM
24	C24CHM	35	C35CHM	46	C46CHM	58	C58CHM	79	C79CHM
25	C25CHM	36	C36CHM	47	VLT47	59	C59CHM	99	C99CHM
26	C26CHM	37	C37CHM	49	C49CHM	63	C63CHM	102	C102CHM
27	VLT27	38	C38CHM	50	C50CHM	65	C65CHM	113	C113CHM
31	C31CHM								

Among the latest delivery of single-deck buses to South London comprise a batch of Dennis Darts with Plaxton Pointer bodywork. Seen on service 412 is DRL211, N711GUM, seen at East Croydon station. *Richard Godfrey*

London Buses commissioned design consultants Ogle to provide an improved interior layout for pay-as-you-board double-decks. many of the suggestions were incorporated into the large order for 260 Leyland Olympians. The features included split-entrance steps, high visibility handrails and straight forward-ascending staircases. In this view of L6, C803BYY at Waterloo, the enlarged panel encasing the staircase can be seen, in addition to the low-profile tyres fitted to these buses. *Richard Godfrey*

L135-259

| | | | | | | | | Leyland Olympian ONLXB/1RH | Eastern Coach Works | H42/26D | 1986-87 166-71 are DPH42/26D |

135	D135FYM	166	D166FYM	190	319CLT	214	D214FYM	237	D237FYM
139	D139FYM	167	D167FYM	191	D191FYM	215	815DYE	238	D238FYM
140	D140FYM	168	D168FYM	192	D192FYM	216	D216FYM	239	D239FYM
143	D143FYM	169	D169FYM	193	D193FYM	217	217CLT	240	D240FYM
146	D146FYM	170	7CLT	194	D194FYM	218	D218FYM	241	D241FYM
147	D147FYM	171	D171FYM	195	D195FYM	219	519CLT	242	D242FYM
148	D148FYM	172	WLT372	196	D196FYM	220	D220FYM	243	D243FYM
149	D149FYM	173	VLT173	197	D197FYM	221	D221FYM	244	VLT244
150	D150FYM	174	D174FYM	198	D198FYM	222	D222FYM	245	D245FYM
151	WLT751	175	D175FYM	199	D199FYM	223	D223FYM	246	D246FYM
152	D152FYM	176	D176FYM	200	D200FYM	224	D224FYM	247	D247FYM
153	D153FYM	177	D177FYM	201	D201FYM	225	D225FYM	248	D248FYM
154	WLT554	178	D178FYM	202	D202FYM	226	D226FYM	249	D249FYM
155	D155FYM	179	D179FYM	203	D203FYM	227	D227FYM	250	D250FYM
156	656DYE	180	480CLT	204	D204FYM	228	D228FYM	251	D251FYM
157	D157FYM	181	D181FYM	205	D205FYM	229	D229FYM	252	D252FYM
158	D158FYM	182	D182FYM	206	D206FYM	230	D230FYM	253	D253FYM
159	D159FYM	183	D183FYM	207	D207FYM	231	D231FYM	254	D254FYM
160	D160FYM	184	D184FYM	208	D208FYM	232	D232FYM	255	D255FYM
161	D161FYM	185	D185FYM	209	D209FYM	233	D233FYM	256	D256FYM
162	D162FYM	186	D186FYM	210	D210FYM	234	D234FYM	257	D257FYM
163	D163FYM	187	D187FYM	211	D211FYM	235	D235FYM	258	D258FYM
164	D164FYM	188	D188FYM	212	D212FYM	236	D236FYM	259	D259FYM
165	D165FYM	189	D189FYM	213	D213FYM				

LDR22-39

Dennis Dart SLF   Plaxton Pointer 2   B40F   1996

22	P822RWU	26	P826RWU	30	P830RWU	34	P834RWU	37	P837RWU
23	P823RWU	27	P827RWU	31	P831RWU	35	P835RWU	38	P838RWU
24	P824RWU	28	P828RWU	32	P832RWU	36	P836RWU	39	P839RWU
25	P825RWU	29	P829RWU	33	P833RWU				

M7-74

MCW Metrobus DR101/8*   MCW   H43/28D   1978-79 *66/9 are DR101/1
64/74 ex Leaside, 1997

7	WYW 7T	38	WYW38T	49	WYW49T	64	WYW64T	69	WYW69T
10	WYW10T	40	WYW40T	63	WYW63T	66	WYW66T	74	WYW74T

M129-314

MCW Metrobus DR101/9*   MCW   H43/28D   1979-80 *208-314 are DR101/2

129	BYX129V	208	BYX208V	233	BYX233V	277	BYX277V	296	BYX296V
168	BYX168V	210	BYX210V	240	BYX240V	280	BYX280V	298	BYX298V
173	BYX173V	225	BYX225V	248	BYX248V	283	BYX283V	299	BYX299V
182	BYX182V	230	BYX230V	251	BYX251V	290	BYX290V	314	BYX314V
200	BYX200V	232	BYX232V	263	BYX263V				

M346-601

MCW Metrobus DR101/12*   MCW   H43/28D   1980-81 *511-601 are DR101/14

346	GYE346W	399	GYE399W	464	GYE464W	515	GYE515W	534	GYE534W
365	GYE365W	400	GYE400W	474	GYE474W	517	GYE517W	541	GYE541W
372	GYE372W	402	GYE402W	492	GYE492W	518	GYE518W	552	GYE552W
378	GYE378W	410	GYE410W	496	GYE496W	519	GYE519W	555	GYE555W
384	GYE384W	417	GYE417W	500	GYE500W	520	GYE520W	568	GYE568W
388	GYE388W	439	GYE439W	503	GYE503W	521	GYE521W	577	GYE577W
395	GYE395W	454	GYE454W	507	GYE507W	522	GYE522W	580	GYE580W
396	GYE396W	456	GYE456W	508	GYE508W	525	GYE525W	584	GYE584W
398	398CLT	458	GYE458W	511	GYE511W	528	GYE528W	601	GYE601W

M629-805

MCW Metrobus DR101/14   MCW   H43/28D   1981-82

629	KYO629X	654	KYV654X	682	KYV682X	724	KYV724X	803	KYV803X
633	KYV633X	671	KYV671X	691	KYV691X	741	KYV741X	805	KYV805X
634	KYV634X	680	KYV680X	722	KYV722X	799	KYV799X		

Opposite:- **Leaside was acquired in 1994 and was renamed Cowie Leaside. Later in 1995 the previously troubled South London company was purchased becoming Cowie South London. These two acquisitions made Cowie the largest single operator in the London Buses area when taken with the existing Grey Green business. Two double-deck buses from the now South London fleet are L167, D167FYM , a Leyland Olympian, and M1354, C354BUV, a MCW Metrobus.**
Derek Akrigg/Gerald Mead

For a while, the Routemasters which operated route 159 carried a dedicated red and cream livery, though these buses have now recieved standard red with yellow band as shown by RM385, WLT385 seen in Park Lane. *Colin Lloyd*

M809-954

MCW Metrobus DR101/16   MCW   H43/28D   1983

809	OJD809Y	850	OJD850Y	865	OJD865Y	895	A895SUL	948	A948SUL
825	OJD825Y	858	OJD858Y	869	OJD869Y	927	A927SUL	954	WTL954
827	OJD827Y	863	OJD863Y	894	A894SUL	930	A930SUL		

M959	A959SYF	MCW Metrobus DR101/17	MCW	H43/24D	1984	
M973	A973SYF	MCW Metrobus DR101/17	MCW	H43/24D	1984	
M984	A984SYF	MCW Metrobus DR101/17	MCW	H43/24D	1984	
M998	A998SYF	MCW Metrobus DR101/17	MCW	H43/24D	1984	Ex Leaside, 1997
M1036	A736THV	MCW Metrobus DR101/17	MCW	DPH43/24F	1984	
M1062	B62WUL	MCW Metrobus DR101/17	MCW	H43/28D	1984	

M1084-1105

MCW Metrobus DR134/1   MCW   H43/28D   1984

1084	B84WUL	1089	B89WUL	1094	B94WUL	1098	B98WUL	1102	B102WUL
1085	B85WUL	1090	B90WUL	1095	B95WUL	1099	B99WUL	1103	B103WUL
1086	B86WUL	1091	B91WUL	1096	B96WUL	1100	B100WUL	1104	B104WUL
1087	B87WUL	1092	B92WUL	1097	B97WUL	1101	B101WUL	1105	B105WUL
1088	B88WUL	1093	B93WUL						

M1116	B116WUL	MCW Metrobus DR101/17	MCW	H43/28D	1984	
M1354	C354BUV	MCW Metrobus DR101/17	MCW	H43/28D	1985	
M1359	C359BUV	MCW Metrobus DR101/17	MCW	DPH43/28D	1985	
M1407	C407BUV	MCW Metrobus DR101/17	MCW	H43/28D	1985	
M1441	A441UUV	MCW Metrobus DR102/45	MCW	H43/24F	1984	
M1442	A442UUV	MCW Metrobus DR132/5	MCW	H43/24F	1984	
MR93	E873NJD	MCW MetroRider MF150/96	MCW	B25F	1988	

MRL107-129

MCW MetroRider MF158/16   MCW   B28F   1988   Ex London Buses, 1995

107	F107YVP	123	F123YVP	124	F124YVP	127	F127YVP	129	F129YVP
122	F122YVP								

South London have around seventy-seven of the longer 9.14-metre Routemaster including two of the original WLT batch. South London operate this type of bus on service 137, and RML892, WLT892, was seen at Clapham Common during the 1997 summer. *Gerald Mead*

MRL133	F133YVP	MCW MetroRider MF158/17	MCW			DP28F	1988	Ex London Buses, 1995		

RM6-719

AEC Routemaster R2RH(Iveco) Park Royal H36/28R 1959-61 Ex London Buses, 1995/97

6	VLT6	348	WLT348	432	SVS617	531	WLT531	676	WLT676
25	VLT25	385	WLT385	467	XVS997	664	WLT664	719	WLT719
275	VLT275								

RM970-2217

AEC Routemaster R2RH(Iveco) Park Royal H36/28R 1961-65 Ex London Buses, 1995

970	WLT970	1324	324CLT	1593	593CLT	1811	EGF220B	1978	ALD978B
997	WLT997	1361	VYJ808	1734	734DYE	1822	822DYE	2179	CUL179C
1003	3CLT	1398	KGJ118A	1801	801DYE	1872	ALD872B	2217	CUL217C
1124	VYJ806								

RML892	WLT892	AEC Routemaster R2RH/1(Iveco) Park Royal	H40/32R	1961	Ex London Buses, 1995
RML895	WLT895	AEC Routemaster R2RH/1(Iveco) Park Royal	H40/32R	1961	Ex London Buses, 1995

RM2264-2759

AEC Routemaster R2RH/1(Iveco) Park Royal H40/32R 1965-68

2264	CUV264C	2366	CUL366C	2521	JJD521D	2608	NML608E	2726	SMK726F
2307	CUV307C	2375	JJD375D	2545	JJD545D	2636	NML636E	2730	SMK730F
2324	CUV324C	2407	JJD407D	2549	JJD549D	2653	NML653E	2741	SMK741F
2333	CUV333C	2477	JJD477D	2572	JJD572D	2692	SMK692F	2753	SMK753F
2351	CUV351C	2491	JJD491D	2573	JJD573D	2718	SMK718F	2759	SMK759F

RML2266-2715

AEC Routemaster R2RH/1(Iveco) Park Royal H42/30R 1965-67 On extended loan from London Buses

2266	CUV266C	2383	JJD383D	2512	JJD512D	2533	JJD533D	2586	JJD586D
2301	CUV301C	2387	JJD387D	2514	JJD514D	2536	JJD536D	2591	JJD591D
2343	CUV343C	2410	JJD410D	2523	JJD523D	2548	JJD548D	2619	NML619E
2347	CUV347C	2452	JJD452D	2524	JJD524D	2574	JJD574D	2715	SMK715F
2382	JJD382D	2505	JJD505D	2531	JJD531D	2577	JJD577D		

Pictured in London's Pall Mall, Routemaster RML895 is one of the first delivery to the longer RML type. Currently with South London it is allocated to Brixton. The last refurbishment of the type saw the introduction of Iveco engines for these stalwarts of the London scene.
Tony Wilson

VE648-661   Volvo Citybus B10M-50   East Lancashire   H45/31D   1990   Ex Londonlinks, 1997

648	H648GPF	651	H651GPF	654	H654GPF	657	H657GPF	660	H660GPF
649	H649GPF	652	H652GPF	655	H655GPF	658	H658GPF	661	H661GPF
650	H650GPF	653	H653GPF	656	H656GPF	659	H659GPF		

VE662-684   Volvo Citybus B10M-50   East Lancashire   H45/31D   1990-91 Ex Londonlinks, 1997

662	H662GPF	668	H668GPF	673	H673GPF	677	H677GPF	681	H681GPF
663	H663GPF	669	H669GPF	674	H674GPF	678	H678GPF	682	H682GPF
664	H664GPF	670	H670GPF	675	H675GPF	679	H679GPF	683	H683GPF
665	H665GPF	671	H671GPF	676	H676GPF	680	H680GPF	684	H684GPF
667	H667GPF	672	H672GPF							

Previous Registrations:

7CLT	D170FYM	815DYE	D215FYM	VYJ806	124CLT
217CLT	D217FYM	EGF220B	811DYE	VYJ808	361CLT
319CLT	D190FYM	KGJ118A	398CLT	WLT372	D172FYM
324CLT	324CLT, VYJ807	SVS617	WLT432	WLT554	D154FYM
330CLT	C30CHM	VLT13	C813BYY	WLT751	D151FYM
398CLT	GYE398W	VLT27	C27CHM	WLT807	C808BYY
480CLT	D180FYM	VLT47	C47CHM	WLT916	C816BYY
519CLT	D219FYM	VLT173	D173FYM	WLT954	A954SUL
656DYE	D156FYM	VLT244	D244FYM	XVS851	WLT467

Allocations and liveries:-

Livery: Red and yellow

Brixton (Streatham Hill)

Dart	LDR22	LDR23	LDR24	LDR25	LDR26	LDR27	LDR28	LDR29
	LDR30	LDR31	LDR32	LDR33	LDR34	LDR35	LDR36	LDR37
	LDR38	LDR39						
Metrobus	M173t	M200	M230	M298	M365	M372	M396	M398
	M399	M400	M458	M492	M511	M517	M580	M584
	M634	M724	M741	M803	M805	M825	M827	M850
	M1062							
Routemaster	RM6	RM25	RM275	RM348	RM385	RM432	RM467	RM531
	RM664	RM676	RM719	RM970	RM997	RM1003	RM1124	RM1324
	RM1361	RM1398	RM1593	RM1734	RM1801	RM1811	RM1822	RM1872
	RM1978	RM2179	RM2217					
	RML892	RML895	RML2264	RML2307	RML2324	RML2333	RML2351	RML2366
	RML2375	RML2407	RML2477	RML2491	RML2521	RML2545	RML2549	RML2573
	RML2608	RML2636	RML2653	RML2692	RML2718	RML2726	RML2730	RML2741
	RML2753	RML2759						

Croydon (Brighton Road, South Croydon)

DAF	DIB1	DIB2	DIB3	DIB4	DIB5			
Dart	DRL39	DRL40	DRL41	DRL42	DRL43	DRL44	DRL47	DRL48
	DRL210	DRL211	DRL212	DRL213	DRL214	DRL215		
Olympian	L1	L2	L3	L17	L26	L99	L140	L210
	L213	L228	L241	L248	L253			
Metrobus	M7t	M10t	M38t	M40t	M49t	M60t	M63	M64
	M65t	M66	M69	M74	M129	M132	M149t	M168
	M182	M208	M210	M225	M232	M233	M240	M248
	M251	M263	M277	M280	M283	M290	M296	M299
	M314	M346	M378	M384	M388	M395	M402	M410
	M417	M439	M454	M456	M464	M474	M496	M500
	M503	M507	M515	M518	M519	M520	M521	M522
	M525	M528	M534	M541	M552	M555	M568	M577
	M601	M629	M633	M654	M671	M680	M682	M691
	M722	M799	M809	M858	M863	M865	M869	M894
	M895	M927	M930	M948	M954	M959	M973	M984
	M998	M1084	M1085	M1086	M1087	M1088	M1089	
	M1090	M1091	M1092	M1093	M1094	M1095	M1096	M1097
	M1098	M1099	M1100	M1101	M1102	M1103	M1104	M1105
	M1116	M1354	M1359	M1407	M1441	M1442		

Norwood (Knights Hill, West Norwood)

MetroRider	MR93							
Dart	DRL38	DRL147	DRL148	DRL149	DRL150	DRL151	DRL152	DRL153
	DRL154	DRL155	DRL156	DRL157	DRL158			
Olympian	L4	L6	L8	L13	L14	L16	L25	L31
	L32	L33	L36	L37	L38	L45	L46	L50
	L52	L59	L65	L102	L113	L146	L148	L155
	L156	L157	L160	L162	L163	L165	L166	L167
	L168	L169	L170	L171	L172	L174	L176	L177
	L180	L181	L185	L187	L189	L190	L191	L192
	L196	L197	L198	L199	L203	L207	L208	L211
	L214	L215	L216	L217	L218	L223	L224	L231
	L234	L237	L240	L242	L246	L250	L251	L252
	L256	L257	L258					
Citybus	VE648	VE649	VE650	VE651	VE652	VE653	VE654	VE655
	VE656	VE657	VE658	VE659	VE660	VE661	VE662	VE663
	VE664	VE665	VE667	VE668	VE669	VE670	VE671	VE672
	VE673	VE674	VE675	VE676	VE677	VE678	VE679	VE680
	VE681	VE682	VE683	VE684				

London Buses operated 263 Leyland Olympians and these carries the last Eastern Coachworks bodies. After privatisation, South London gained 161 of this batch including the trio of evaluation units. L172, WLT372, is one of many which now carry marks from other vehicles, notable Routemasters. These are retained by the company as cherished marks. *Ralph Stevens*

Thornton Heath (London Road)

MetroRider	MR107	MR122	MR123	MR124	MR127	MR129	MR133
Dart	DR20	DR21	DR22	DR23	DR24	DR25	DR26	DR27
	DR28	DR29	DR30	DR31	DRL216	DRL217	DRL218	DT65
	DT66	DT67	DT68	DT69	DT70	DT132	DT143
Olympian	L5	L20	L21	L22	L24	L27	L35	L41
	L47	L49	L56	L58	L63	L66	L78	L79
	L135	L139	L143	L147	L149	L150	L151	L152
	L153	L154	L158	L159	L161	L164	L173	L175
	L179	L182	L183	L184	L186	L188	L193	L194
	L195	L200	L201	L202	L204	L205	L206	L209
	L212	L219	L220	L221	L222	L225	L226	L227
	L229	L230	L232	L233	L235	L236	L238	L239
	L243	L244	L245	L247	L249	L254	L255	L259

Battersea (Hester Road)

Routemaster	RML2266	RML2301	RML2343	RML2347	RML2382	RML2383	RML2387	RML2410
	RML2452	RML2505	RML2512	RML2514	RML2523	RML2524	RML2531	RML2533
	RML2536	RML2548	RML2574	RML2577	RML2586	RML2591	RML2619	RML2715

SOUTHEND TRANSPORT

Southend Transport Ltd, 87 London Road, Southend-on-Sea, Essex, SS1 1PP

LSL001	M761JPA	Dennis Lance SLF 11SDA3201	Wright Endeavour	B39F	1995	
LSL002	M762JPA	Dennis Lance SLF 11SDA3201	Wright Endeavour	B39F	1995	
LSL003	M763JPA	Dennis Lance SLF 11SDA3201	Wright Endeavour	B39F	1995	
LSL004	M764JPA	Dennis Lance SLF 11SDA3201	Wright Endeavour	B39F	1995	
12	BVP812V	Leyland National 2 NL116L11/1R		B49F	1980	Ex Colchester, 1997
25	EON825V	Leyland National 2 NL116L11/1R		B49F	1980	Ex Colchester, 1997

DSL056-57

	Dennis Dart SLF	Plaxton Pointer	B39F	1997

056	P256FPK	**059**	P259FPK	**062**	P262FPK	**064**	P264FPK	**066**	P266FPK
057	P257FPK	**060**	P260FPK	**063**	P263FPK	**065**	P265FPK	**067**	P267FPK
058	P258FPK	**061**	P261FPK						

AN110	MPJ210L	Leyland Atlantean PDR1A/1	MCW	043/29D	1972	Ex Leaside, 1997
212	JTD392P	Daimler Fleetline CRL6-33	Northern Counties	H49/31D	1975	
216w	JTD396P	Daimler Fleetline CRL6-33	Northern Counties	H49/31D	1976	

221-242

	Leyland Fleetline FE33ALR	Northern Counties	H49/31D	1979-81 *233/5/7/8/42 are H49/33F

221	XTE221V	**226**	XTE226V	**231**	MRJ231W	**235**	MRJ235W	**239**	MRJ239W
222	XTE222V	**227**	XTE227V	**232**	MRJ232W	**236**	MRJ236W	**240**	MRJ240W
223	XTE223V	**228**	XTE228V	**233**	MRJ233W	**237**	MRJ237W	**241**	MRJ241W
224	XTE224V	**229**	XTE229V	**234**	MRJ234W	**238**	MRJ238W	**242**	MRJ242W
225	XTE225V	**230**	XTE230V						

250	Q475MEV	Daimler Fleetline CRL6-33	Northern Counties(1984)	H49/31D	1972	
251	Q476MEV	Daimler Fleetline CRL6-33	Northern Counties(1984)	H49/31D	1972	
252	Q552MEV	Daimler Fleetline CRL6-33	Northern Counties(1985)	H49/31D	1972	
253	Q553MEV	Daimler Fleetline CRL6-33	Northern Counties(1985)	H49/31D	1972	
254	Q554MEV	Daimler Fleetline CRL6-33	Northern Counties(1984)	H49/31D	1972	
256	A110FDL	Leyland Olympian ONLXB/1R	Eastern Coach Works	DPH41/23F	1984	Ex Southern Vectis, 1991
257	B185BLG	Leyland Olympian ONLXB/1R	Eastern Coach Works	H45/32F	1984	Ex Crosville Cymru, 1991
258	B189BLG	Leyland Olympian ONLXB/1R	Eastern Coach Works	H45/32F	1984	Ex Crosville Cymru, 1991
259	B183BLG	Leyland Olympian ONLXB/1R	Eastern Coach Works	H45/32F	1984	Ex Crosville Cymru, 1990
260	B184BLG	Leyland Olympian ONLXB/1R	Eastern Coach Works	H45/32F	1984	Ex Crosville Cymru, 1990
262	H262GEV	Leyland Olympian ON2R50G13Z4	Leyland	H47/31F	1990	
263	H263GEV	Leyland Olympian ON2R50G13Z4	Leyland	H47/31F	1990	
264	H264GEV	Leyland Olympian ON2R50G13Z4	Leyland	DPH43/29F	1990	
265	H265GEV	Leyland Olympian ON2R50G13Z4	Leyland	DPH43/29F	1990	

N706TPK carries the blue white and red Southend Transport livery. It is a Volvo Olympian which carries a Northern Counties body and on this vehicle is a low-height version of the Palatine type.
Malc McDonald

To find the names Green Line, its livery and Southend Transport together on one vehicle might appear unusual to the traditionalist, but the Green Line name is owned by British Bus and it has developed marketing of semi-express and commuter services between the Essex town and the City of London. *Above,* Southend 557, B83SWX, a Leyland Tiger pauses in Southend bus station before departure for London on route X1 while *opposite, bottom* is 549, A249SVW, a Duple Caribbean-bodied Leyland Tiger also seen on this service. *Phillip Stephenson/Richard Godfrey*

281	MUH281X	Leyland Olympian ONLXB/1R	Eastern Coach Works	H45/32F	1982	Ex Rhondda, 1992
282	MUH285X	Leyland Olympian ONLXB/1R	Eastern Coach Works	H45/32F	1982	Ex Rhondda, 1992
283	MUH283X	Leyland Olympian ONLXB/1R	Eastern Coach Works	H45/32F	1982	Ex Rhondda, 1992
284	MUH286X	Leyland Olympian ONLXB/1R	Eastern Coach Works	H45/32F	1982	Ex Rhondda, 1992
305	DGR477S	Bristol VRT/SL3/6LXB	Eastern Coach Works	H43/31F	1979	Ex West Riding, 1992
307	WTU473W	Bristol VRT/SL3/6LXB	Eastern Coach Works	H43/31F	1980	Ex Rhondda, 1992
351	YBF686S	Bristol VRT/SL3/501	Eastern Coach Works	H43/31F	1978	Ex PMT, 1992
MM478	P478DPE	Mercedes-Benz 711D	Plaxton Beaver 2	B27F	1997	
MM481	P481DPE	Mercedes-Benz 711D	Plaxton Beaver 2	B27F	1997	
MM482	P482DPE	Mercedes-Benz 711D	Plaxton Beaver 2	B27F	1997	
546	A246SVW	Leyland Tiger TRCTL11/3RP	Duple Caribbean	C57F	1984	
547	A247SVW	Leyland Tiger TRCTL11/3RP	Duple Caribbean	C57F	1984	
548	A248SVW	Leyland Tiger TRCTL11/3RP	Duple Caribbean	C57F	1984	
549	A249SVW	Leyland Tiger TRCTL11/3RP	Duple Caribbean	C57F	1984	
551	B100XTW	Leyland Tiger TRCTL11/3RP	Duple Caribbean	C57F	1984	
553	A141EPA	Leyland Tiger TRCTL11/2R	Plaxton Paramount 3200 E	C51F	1984	Ex London & Country, 1990
557	B83SWX	Leyland Tiger TRCTL11/3RH	Plaxton Paramount 3200 IIE	C57F	1985	Ex Yorkshire Voyager, 1990
558	B84SWX	Leyland Tiger TRCTL11/3RH	Plaxton Paramount 3200 IIE	C57F	1985	Ex Yorkshire Voyager, 1990
559	B85SWX	Leyland Tiger TRCTL11/3RH	Plaxton Paramount 3200 IIE	C53F	1985	Ex Yorkshire Voyager, 1991
563	A124EPA	Leyland Tiger TRCTL11/2R	Plaxton Paramount 3200 E	C51F	1984	Ex Kentish Bus, 1990

Opposite, top:- **The 1997 intake of new buses for Southend comprised a batch of Dennis Dart SLFs with Plaxton Pointer bodywork. Seen in the town is DSL58, P258FPK.** *Richard Godfrey*

Southend had found itself fighting a bus war with Thamesway, the Badgerline subsidiary and weakened by this extended competition found itself offered for sale by its owners. **After acquisition the operation was put under common management and the supervision of London and Country, a programme of rationalisation put both back onto a firm footing, though down sized. Both the type of vehicle now entering service, the registration and fleet number all lean towards that company's over-all operation. LSL003, M763JPA, a Wright bodied Dennis Lance, rests briefly in Southend bus station.** *Phillip Stephenson*

565	H845AHS	Volvo B10M-60		Plaxton Paramount 3500 III	C53F	1991	Ex Express Travel, 1995
566	H566MPD	Volvo B10M-60		Plaxton Paramount 3500 III	C53F	1991	Ex Express Travel, 1995
567	H567MPD	Volvo B10M-60		Plaxton Paramount 3500 III	C53F	1991	Ex Express Travel, 1995
568	H372PHK	Volvo B10M-60		Plaxton Paramount 3500 III	C53F	1991	Ex Express Travel, 1995
569	F425UVW	Volvo B10M-60		Plaxton Paramount 3200 III	C53F	1989	Ex Express Travel, 1995
570	F467UVW	Volvo B10M-60		Plaxton Paramount 3200 III	C53F	1989	Ex Express Travel, 1995
571	F523UVW	Volvo B10M-60		Plaxton Paramount 3200 III	C53F	1989	Ex Express Travel, 1995
572	F572UPB	Volvo B10M-60		Plaxton Paramount 3200 III	C53F	1989	Ex Express Travel, 1995

LR705-709

			Volvo Olympian YN2RV18Z4		Northern Counties Palatine II	H47/32F*	1996	*708/9 are DPH43/30F

705	N705TPK	**706**	N706TPK	**707**	N707TPK	**708**	N708TPK	**709**	N709TPK

745	PJI3745	Leyland National 10351A/1R (DAF)		B41F	1978	Ex Blackpool, 1991

902-909

		Leyland Olympian ONLXB/1RZ	Alexander RL	H47/32F	1988	Ex London & Country (GWS), 1996

902	F572SMG	**904**	F574SMG	**905**	F575SMG	**906**	F576SMG	**909**	F579SMG
903	F573SMG							

RMC1453	453CLT	AEC Routemaster R2RH	Park Royal	H32/25R	1962	Ex Leaside, 1997

Previous Registrations:

A110FDL	A701DDL, WDL748	H567MPD	H842AHS, NXI9001
F425UVW	F449PSL, NXI9004	PJI3745	GGE170T
F467UVW	F450PSL, NXI9005	Q475MEV	GHJ377L
F523UVW	F451PSL, NXI9006	Q476MEV	GHJ374L
F572UPB	F452PSL, NXI9007	Q552MEV	GHJ379L
H372PHK	H844AHS, NXI9003	Q553MEV	GHJ375L
H566MPD	H843AHS, NXI9002	Q554MEV	GHJ376L

With the ever increasing use of re-registrations from Northern Ireland DVLAs it is becoming more and more difficult to identify with ease the origins of vehicles. Even the effervescent Leyland National origins, while getting on a bit, are sometimes lost in the midst of these registrations. Now with Southend Transport 745, PJI3745 which was new to Greater Glasgow PTE though was last operated by Blackpool, pulls into the towns bus station. *Phillip Stephenson*

Allocations and liveries

Livery: Blue, white and red (buses); two-tone green white and yellow (Green Line)

Southend (London Road)

Mercedes-Benz	MM478	MM481	MM482					
Tiger	546	547	548	549	551	553	557	558
	559	563						
Volvo B10M	565	566	567	568	569	570	571	572
National	716	717	745					
Lance	LSL001	LSL002	LSL003	LSL004				
Dart	DSL37	DSL56	DSL57	DSL58	DSL59	DSL60	DSL61	DSL62
	DSL63	DSL64	DSL65	DSL66	DSL67			
Fleetline	208	211	212	216	221	222	223	224
	225	226	227	228	229	230	231	232
	233	234	235	236	237	238	239	240
	241	242	250	251	252	253	254	
Atlantean	110							
Bristol VR	305	307	351					
Olympian	256	257	258	259	260	262	263	264
	265	281	282	283	284	LR705	LR706	LR707
	LR708	LR709	902	903	904	905	906	909

UNITED / EDEN / TEES / TMS

Tees & District Transport Company Ltd,
Teesside Motor Services Ltd, Eden Bus Services Ltd
United Automobile Services Ltd, United House, Morton Road, Darlington,
DL1 4PT

202-238

| | | Leyland Olympian ONLXB/1R | Eastern Coach Works | H45/32F* | 1982-84 202-4/10 ex West Riding, 1993 |
| | | | | | *233/4 are DPH42/28F; 206/14 are H44/32F |

202	XWY477X	208	SPY208X	216	WDC216Y	226	AEF226Y	235	A235GHN
203	XWY478X	209	SPY209X	217	WDC217Y	227	AEF227Y	236	A236GHN
204	XWY479X	210	CWR505Y	218	WDC218Y	228	AEF228Y	237	A237GHN
206	SPY206X	214	WDC214Y	223	AEF223Y	233	A233GHN	238	A238GHN
207	SPY207X	215	WDC215Y	225	AEF225Y	234	A234GHN		

243	A563KWY	Leyland Olympian ONLXB/1R	Eastern Coach Works	DPH42/28F	1983	Ex West Riding, 1994
245	B45NDX	Leyland Olympian ONLXB/1RV	East Lancashire	H40/33F	1985	Ex Stevensons, 1993
251	B251NVN	Leyland Olympian ONLXB/1R	Eastern Coach Works	H45/32F	1985	
252	B252PHN	Leyland Olympian ONLXB/1R	Eastern Coach Works	H45/32F	1985	
253	B253PHN	Leyland Olympian ONLXB/1R	Eastern Coach Works	H45/32F	1985	
255	B255RAJ	Leyland Olympian ONLXB/1R	Eastern Coach Works	H45/32F	1985	
258	B598SWX	Leyland Olympian ONLXB/1R	Eastern Coach Works	DPH40/31F	1984	Ex West Riding, 1994
263	E963PME	Leyland Olympian ONLXB/1R	Optare	H47/29F	1988	Ex London Cityrama, 1992
265	C265XEF	Leyland Olympian ONLXB/1R	Eastern Coach Works	DPH42/30F	1986	
266	C266XEF	Leyland Olympian ONLXB/1R	Eastern Coach Works	DPH42/30F	1986	
267	C267XEF	Leyland Olympian ONLXB/1R	Eastern Coach Works	DPH42/30F	1986	
268	C268XEF	Leyland Olympian ONLXB/1R	Eastern Coach Works	DPH42/30F	1986	

271-275

| | | Leyland Olympian ON2R50C13Z4 | Alexander RH | H45/29F | 1993 |

271	L271FVN	272	L272FVN	273	L273FVN	274	L274FVN	275	L275FVN

Opposite:- **In 1990 United was split into two parts, the Durham and North Yorkshire section continuing to trade as United, the section in Cleveland trading as Tees and District. At this time the associated businesses of Trimdon Motor Services and Teeside Motor Services were acquired, with the Trimdon business being absorbed into United and the Teeside business continuing. Here are shown two of the liveries that resulted. The United livery, as illustrated by East Lancashire-bodied Olympian 245, B45NDX, which came from Stevensons, while in Tees' yellow and red livery is Optare Prisma-bodied Mercedes-Benz O405 3002, M302SAJ.**
Richard Godfrey/Tony Wilson

Durham is the location of this view of United 263, E963PME. This Leyland Olympian was previously in the London Cityrama fleet. It carries an Optare body which was built in the Roe/Eastern Coachworks style.
Malc McDonald

Trimdon Motor Services were acquired by United in 1990. As a result most of the Trimdon vehicles entered the fleet and a number remain in service. Number 1233, C76UHN now carries United fleetnames and is a Leyland Tiger which has 55 seats in its Duple Dominant bus body. *Malc McDonald*

276	G21HHG			Leyland Olympian ONCL10/1RZ	Leyland		H47/31F	1989	Ex Atlas Bus, 1994	

277-285

				Leyland Olympian ONCL10/1R	Northern Counties		H43/32F	1989	Ex Atlas Bus, 1994	
277	G754UYT	279	G756UYT	281	G758UYT	283	G760UYT	285	G762UYT	
278	G755UYT	280	G757UYT	282	G759UYT	284	G761UYT			

286-295

				Leyland Olympian ONLXB/1R	Roe		H47/29F	1982-83	Ex Metrobus, Orpington, 1997	
286	UWW13X	288	CUB60Y	290	CUB63Y	292	CUB66Y	294	CUB69Y	
287	UWW14X	289	CUB61Y	291	CUB64Y	293	CUB68Y	295	CUB71Y	

756-824

				Bristol VRT/SL3/6LXB	Eastern Coach Works		H43/31F*	1978-81	*804 is H42/31F; 814 is DPH41/29F	
756	DUP756S	804	XPT804V	812w	APT812W	822	MEF822W	824	MEF824W	
786	SGR786V	808	APT808W	814	APT814W	823	MEF823W			
801w	XPT801V									

831	RAU811R	Bristol VRT/SL3/501(Gardner)	Eastern Coach Works	H43/31F	1977	Ex Trent, 1992
832	URB822S	Bristol VRT/SL3/501(Gardner)	Eastern Coach Works	H43/31F	1977	Ex Trent, 1992
841w	UNW930R	Bristol VRT/SL3/6LXB	Eastern Coach Works	H43/31F	1977	Ex West Riding, 1990
864	CWU326T	Bristol VRT/SL3/6LXB	Eastern Coach Works	H43/31F	1978	Ex West Riding, 1991
879	JYG429V	Bristol VRT/SL3/6LXB	Eastern Coach Works	H43/31F	1980	Ex West Riding, 1991
892	PWR442W	Bristol VRT/SL3/6LXB	Eastern Coach Works	H43/31F	1981	Ex West Riding, 1992

1227w	TDC857X	Leyland Tiger TRCTL11/2R	Duple Dominant	B55F	1982	Ex Trimdon, 1990
1228w	B957LHN	Leyland Tiger TRBTL11/2RH	Duple Dominant	B55F	1984	Ex Trimdon, 1990
1229w	B958LHN	Leyland Tiger TRBTL11/2RH	Duple Dominant	B55F	1984	Ex Trimdon, 1990
1230w	B959LHN	Leyland Tiger TRBTL11/2RP	Duple Dominant	B55F	1984	Ex Trimdon, 1990
1231	C74UHN	Leyland Tiger TRCTL11/2RP	Duple Dominant	B55F	1985	Ex Trimdon, 1990
1232	C75UHN	Leyland Tiger TRCTL11/2RP	Duple Dominant	B55F	1985	Ex Trimdon, 1990
1233w	C76UHN	Leyland Tiger TRCTL11/2RP	Duple Dominant	B55F	1985	Ex Trimdon, 1990
1234	H278LEF	Leyland Tiger TRCL10/3ARZA	Alexander Q	B55F	1990	
1235	H279LEF	Leyland Tiger TRCL10/3ARZA	Alexander Q	B55F	1990	

B113GRR was once operated by the Trent Tigers coach unit for which the registration plate was appropriate. It is now used on Expressway services by Tees. This Plaxton Paramount-bodied Leyland Tiger is number 1405 in the Tees fleet. *Keith Lee*

1301	A516EVN	Leyland Tiger TRCTL11/2R	Plaxton Paramount 3200 E	C47F	1983
1302	A517EVN	Leyland Tiger TRCTL11/2R	Plaxton Paramount 3200 E	C47F	1983
1303	A518EVN	Leyland Tiger TRCTL11/2R	Plaxton Paramount 3200 E	DP55F	1983
1305	B266KPF	Leyland Tiger TRCTL11/2R	Plaxton Paramount 3200 IIE	C53F	1985	Ex Green, Kirkintilloch, 1990

1306-1315

		Leyland Tiger TRCTL11/2RP	Plaxton Paramount 3200 III	C53F*	1987	*1309/12 are C47F

1306	E266KEF	1308	E268KEF	1310	E270KEF	1312	E272KEF	1314	E274KEF
1307	E267KEF	1309	E269KEF	1311	E271KEF	1313	E273KEF	1315	E275KEF

1319	A105EPA	Leyland Tiger TRCTL11/2R	Plaxton Paramount 3200 E	C53F	1983	Ex Regal, Kirkintilloch, 1992
1322w	A31LWX	Leyland Tiger TRCTL11/2R	Alexander TE	DP55F	1983	Ex West Riding, 1990
1324	C39CWT	Leyland Tiger TRCTL11/2RH	Plaxton Paramount 3200 IIE	C53F	1986	Ex West Riding, 1991
1325	C40CWT	Leyland Tiger TRCTL11/2RH	Plaxton Paramount 3200 IIE	C53F	1986	Ex West Riding, 1991
1327	NLG35Y	Leyland Tiger TRCTL11/2R	Plaxton Paramount 3200 E	C51F	1983	Ex Careline, Coventry, 1992
1328	LHO992Y	Leyland Tiger TRCTL11/2R	Plaxton Paramount 3200 E	C53F	1983	Ex Tillingbourne, 1992
1329	C36CWT	Leyland Tiger TRCTL11/2RH	Plaxton Paramount 3200 IIE	C53F	1986	Ex West Riding, 1992
1330	C37CWT	Leyland Tiger TRCTL11/2RH	Plaxton Paramount 3200 IIE	C53F	1986	Ex West Riding, 1992
1331	C38CWT	Leyland Tiger TRCTL11/2RH	Plaxton Paramount 3200 IIE	C53F	1986	Ex West Riding, 1992
1332	A116EPA	Leyland Tiger TRCTL11/2R	Plaxton Paramount 3200 E	C53F	1983	Ex London & Country, 1992
1333	A117EPA	Leyland Tiger TRCTL11/2R	Plaxton Paramount 3200 E	C53F	1983	Ex London & Country, 1992
1334	A119EPA	Leyland Tiger TRCTL11/2R	Plaxton Paramount 3200 E	C53F	1983	Ex London & Country, 1992
1335	A120EPA	Leyland Tiger TRCTL11/2R	Plaxton Paramount 3200 E	C53F	1983	Ex London & Country, 1992
1336	A122EPA	Leyland Tiger TRCTL11/2R	Plaxton Paramount 3200 E	C53F	1983	Ex London & Country, 1992
1337	A132EPA	Leyland Tiger TRCTL11/2R	Plaxton Paramount 3200 E	C49F	1984	Ex London & Country, 1992
1338	REP328Y	Leyland Tiger TRCTL11/2R	Plaxton Paramount 3200 E	C53F	1983	Ex Chisholm, Ramsgate, 1993
1339	RMO202Y	Leyland Tiger TRCTL11/2R	Plaxton Paramount 3200 E	C53F	1983	Ex Pulham, Bourton, 1993
1340	RMO204Y	Leyland Tiger TRCTL11/2R	Plaxton Paramount 3200 E	C53F	1983	Ex Pulham, Bourton, 1993
1341	RMO201Y	Leyland Tiger TRCTL11/2R	Plaxton Paramount 3200 E	C53F	1983	Ex Pulham, Bourton, 1993

Photographed while turning on Rippon bus station, Optare MetroRider 2632, P632FHN is seen with route-branding for the North Yorkshire Roadranger service between the town and Darlington.
Tony Wilson

1342-1346		Leyland Tiger TRCTL11/2RH	Plaxton Paramount 3200 IIE	C53F*	1986	Ex West Riding, 1993
						*1344/6 are C49F

1342	C42CWT	**1343**	C43CWT	**1344**	C34CWT	**1345**	C35CWT	**1346**	C41CWT

1401	C131HJN	Leyland Tiger TRCTL11/3RH	Plaxton Paramount 3200 IIE	C53F	1986	Ex Eastern National, 1989
1402	C132HJN	Leyland Tiger TRCTL11/3RH	Plaxton Paramount 3200 IIE	C53F	1986	Ex Eastern National, 1989
1403	C133HJN	Leyland Tiger TRCTL11/3RH	Plaxton Paramount 3200 IIE	C53F	1986	Ex Eastern National, 1989
1404	B112GRR	Leyland Tiger TRCTL11/3RH	Plaxton Paramount 3200 II	C51F	1985	Ex Trent, 1991
1405	B113GRR	Leyland Tiger TRCTL11/3RH	Plaxton Paramount 3200 II	C51F	1985	Ex Trent, 1991
1406	A949KAJ	Leyland Tiger TRCTL11/3R	Plaxton Paramount 3200 E	C57F	1983	Ex Vanguard, Bedworth, 1991
1410	B110GRR	Leyland Tiger TRCTL11/3R	Plaxton Paramount 3200 II	C51F	1985	Ex Trent, 1991
1411	B906RVF	Leyland Tiger TRCTL11/3RH	Plaxton Paramount 3200 IIE	C53F	1985	Ex Ambassador Travel, 1991
1412	B907RVF	Leyland Tiger TRCTL11/3RH	Plaxton Paramount 3200 IIE	C53F	1985	Ex Ambassador Travel, 1991
1413w	ERF23Y	Leyland Tiger TRCTL11/3R	Plaxton Paramount 3200 E	C51F	1983	Ex Bell, Sunderland, 1991
1414	EAH887Y	Leyland Tiger TRCTL11/3R	Plaxton Paramount 3200 E	DP57F	1983	Ex Ambassador Travel, 1991
1415	B111GRR	Leyland Tiger TRCTL11/3RH	Plaxton Paramount 3200 II	C51F	1985	Ex Trent, 1991
1416	B114GRR	Leyland Tiger TRCTL11/3RH	Plaxton Paramount 3200 II	C51F	1985	Ex Trent, 1991
1417	B115GRR	Leyland Tiger TRCTL11/3RH	Plaxton Paramount 3200 II	C51F	1985	Ex Trent, 1991
1418	B908RVF	Leyland Tiger TRCTL11/3RH	Plaxton Paramount 3200 IIE	C53F	1985	Ex Ambassador Travel, 1991
1419	A146EPA	Leyland Tiger TRCTL11/3R	Plaxton Paramount 3200 E	DP57F	1984	Ex Luton & District, 1992
1420	B283KPF	Leyland Tiger TRCTL11/3RH	Plaxton Paramount 3200 IIE	C53F	1985	Ex Luton & District, 1992
1422	CVN174Y	Leyland Tiger TRCTL11/3R	Plaxton Paramount 3200	C53F	1983	Ex Vanguard, Bedworth, 1992
1423	B281KPF	Leyland Tiger TRCTL11/3RH	Plaxton Paramount 3200 IIE	C53F	1985	Ex Luton & District, 1992
1425	B280KPF	Leyland Tiger TRCTL11/3RH	Plaxton Paramount 3200 IIE	C53F	1985	Ex Luton & District, 1992
1426	A909LWU	Leyland Tiger TRCTL11/3R	Plaxton Paramount 3200 E	DP57F	1983	Ex Scutt, Owston Ferry, 1993
1431	YLX281	Leyland Tiger TRCTL11/3R	Duple Laser	C50F	1983	Ex Maidstone & District, 1997
1432	445YMU	Leyland Tiger TRCTL11/3R	Duple Laser	C50F	1983	Ex Maidstone & District, 1997
1433	681CXM	Leyland Tiger TRCTL11/3R	Duple Laser	C50F	1983	Ex Maidstone & District, 1997
1434	648WHK	Leyland Tiger TRCTL11/3R	Duple Laser	C53F	1983	Ex Maidstone & District, 1997

| 1501 | J661UHN | MAN 11.190 HOCLR | Optare Vecta | B42F | 1991 |
| 1502 | J620UHN | MAN 11.190 HOCLR | Optare Vecta | B42F | 1991 |

1503-1543

MAN 11.190 HOCLR — Optare Vecta — B42F — 1993 — *1509-13 are DP42F

1503	K503BHN	1512	K512BHN	1520	L520FHN	1528	L528FHN	1536	L536FHN
1504	K504BHN	1513	K513BHN	1521	L521FHN	1529	L529FHN	1537	L537FHN
1505	K505BHN	1514	K514BHN	1522	L522FHN	1530	L530FHN	1538	L538FHN
1506	K506BHN	1515	K515BHN	1523	L523FHN	1531	L531FHN	1539	L539FHN
1507	K507BHN	1516	K516BHN	1524	L524FHN	1532	L532FHN	1540	L540FHN
1508	K508BHN	1517	K517BHN	1525	L525FHN	1533	L533FHN	1541	L541FHN
1509	K509BHN	1518	K518BHN	1526	L526FHN	1534	L534FHN	1542	L542FHN
1510	K510BHN	1519	L519FHN	1527	L527FHN	1535	L535FHN	1543	L543FHN
1511	K511BHN								

1544-1551

MAN 11.190 HOCLR — Optare Vecta — B42F — 1993-94

1544	L544GHN	1546	L546GHN	1548	L548GHN	1550	L550GHN	1551	L551GHN
1545	L545GHN	1547	L547GHN	1549	L549GHN				

1601-1609

Dennis Dart SLF — Plaxton Pointer 2 — B39F — On order

1601	R601MHN	1603	R603MHN	1605	R685MHN	1607	R607MHN	1609	R609MHN
1602	R602MHN	1604	R604MHN	1606	R606MHN	1608	R608MHN		

2443-2460

Mercedes-Benz L608D — Reeve Burgess — B20F — 1986

2443	D643CVN	2447	D647CVN	2451	D651CVN	2456	D656CVN	2459	D659CVN
2446	D646CVN	2448	D648CVN	2453	D653CVN	2458	D658CVN	2460	D660CVN

2464-2480

Mercedes-Benz L608D — Reeve Burgess — B20F — 1987

2464	D464EAJ	2469	D469EAJ	2473	D473EAJ	2477	D477EAJ	2479	D479EAJ
2465	D465EAJ	2471	D471EAJ	2474	D474EAJ	2478	D478EAJ	2480	D480EAJ
2466w	D466EAJ	2472	D472EAJ	2475	D475EAJ				

2601-2605

Optare MetroRider MR33 — Optare — B25F — 1994

2601	L601FHN	2602	L602FHN	2603	L603FHN	2604	L604FHN	2605	L605FHN

2606-2645

Optare MetroRider MR35 — Optare — B25F — 1996-97

2606	P606FHN	2614	P614FHN	2622	P622FHN	2630	P630FHN	2638	P638FHN
2607	P607FHN	2615	P615FHN	2623	P623FHN	2631	P631FHN	2639	P639FHN
2608	P608FHN	2616	P616FHN	2624	P624FHN	2632	P632FHN	2640	P640FHN
2609	P609FHN	2617	P617FHN	2625	P625FHN	2633	P633FHN	2641	P641FHN
2610	P610FHN	2618	P618FHN	2626	P626FHN	2634	P634FHN	2642	P642FHN
2611	P611FHN	2619	P619FHN	2627	P627FHN	2635	P635FHN	2643	P643FHN
2612	P612FHN	2620	P620FHN	2628	P628FHN	2636	P636FHN	2644	P644FHN
2613	P613FHN	2621	P621FHN	2629	P629FHN	2637	P637FHN	2645	P645FHN

2701-2725

Optare MetroRider MR15 — Optare — B31F — On order

2701	R701MHN	2706	R706MHN	2711	R711MHN	2716	R716MHN	2721	R721MHN
2702	R702MHN	2707	R707MHN	2712	R712MHN	2717	R717MHN	2722	R722MHN
2703	R703MHN	2708	R708MHN	2713	R713MHN	2718	R718MHN	2723	R723MHN
2704	R704MHN	2709	R709MHN	2714	R714MHN	2719	R719MHN	2724	R724MHN
2705	R705MHN	2710	R710MHN	2715	R715MHN	2720	R720MHN	2725	R725MHN

3001-3025

Mercedes-Benz 0405 — Optare Prisma — B49F — 1995

3001	M301SAJ	3006	N806XHN	3011	N511XVN	3016	N516XVN	3021	N521XVN
3002	M302SAJ	3007	N807XHN	3012	N512XVN	3017	N517XVN	3022	N522XVN
3003	M303SAJ	3008	N808XHN	3013	N513XVN	3018	N518XVN	3023	N523XVN
3004	M304SAJ	3009	N809XHN	3014	N514XVN	3019	N519XVN	3024	N524XVN
3005	M305SAJ	3010	N810XHN	3015	N515XVN	3020	N520XVN	3025	N525XVN

ARN895Y has been in the Ribble, Cumberland and Shearings fleets. This Leyland National 2 joined the United fleet as number 3147 in 1991. It is fitted with a Gardner 6HLX engine rather than the more usual Leyland TL11 unit. *Keith Lee*

3100-3109

Leyland National 11351A/1R (DAF)   B49F*   1979   *3109 is DP49F

3100	LUP900T	3104	LUP904T	3106	PUP506T	3107	RUP307V	3109	RUP309V

3111-3126

Leyland National 2 NL116L11/1R   B49F   1980

3111	UBR111V	3116	APT116W	3118	APT118W	3121	APT121W	3123	APT123W
3112	UBR112V	3117	APT117W	3119	APT119W	3122	APT122W	3126	APT126W
3114	UBR114V								

3130-3142

Leyland National 2 NL116HLXCT/1R   B49F   1983-84

3130	A130FDC	3134	A134FDC	3136	A136FDC	3138	A138FDC	3142	A142FDC
3131	A131FDC	3135	A135FDC	3137	A137FDC	3140	A140FDC		

3143	RHG882X	Leyland National 2 NL116AL11/1R (6HLXCT)	B52F	1982	Ex Shearings, 1991
3145	RHG885X	Leyland National 2 NL116AL11/1R	B52F	1982	Ex Shearings, 1991
3146	RHG887X	Leyland National 2 NL116AL11/1R	B52F	1982	Ex Shearings, 1991
3147	ARN895Y	Leyland National 2 NL116AHLXB/1R	B52F	1983	Ex Shearings, 1991
3148	ARN896Y	Leyland National 2 NL116AHLXB/1R	B52F	1983	Ex Shearings, 1991
3149	ARN897Y	Leyland National 2 NL116AHLXB/1R	B52F	1983	Ex Shearings, 1991
3150	ARN898Y	Leyland National 2 NL116AHLXB/1R	B52F	1983	Ex Shearings, 1991
3152	A542PCW	Leyland National 2 NL116AHLXCT/1R	B49F	1984	Ex Blackpool, 1991
3153	A543PCW	Leyland National 2 NL116AHLXCT/1R	B49F	1984	Ex Blackpool, 1991
3502w	RJI5344	Leyland National 10351A/2R(Volvo)	DP42F	1976	Ex The Eden, 1995
3503w	RJI5755	Leyland National 10351A/2R(Volvo)	DP42F	1979	Ex The Eden, 1995
3601	HHA122L	Leyland National 1151/2R/0501(Volvo)	B51F	1973	Ex West Midlands Travel, 1995
3602	NTC627M	Leyland National 1151/1R/0402(Volvo)	B49F	1974	Ex West Midlands Travel, 1995
3603	NTC640M	Leyland National 1151/1R/0402(Volvo)	B49F	1974	Ex West Midlands Travel, 1995

Opposite:- **Two products from the Optare vehicle range are illustrated here. The upper picture shows Optare MetroRider 2624 with Darlington Roadranger markings and route-branding for service 23, while the lower picture shows the blue TMS colours though here specifically lettered for the Stockton Thornaby Connection. This Optare Delta is based on the DAF SB220 chassis, and the series will continue with the arrival of the new DAF low floor chassis early in 1998.** *Terry Wightman*

3604w	JTH757P	Leyland National 11351A/1R(Volvo)	B52F	1975	Ex West Midlands Travel, 1995
3605	XOV748T	Leyland National 11351A/1R(Volvo)	B49F	1979	Ex West Midlands Travel, 1995
3606	OOX826R	Leyland National 11351A/1R(Volvo)	B49F	1977	Ex West Midlands Travel, 1995
3607	TVP863S	Leyland National 11351A/1R(Volvo)	B49F	1978	Ex West Midlands Travel, 1995
3608w	YXI3751	Leyland National 11351A/1R(Volvo)	B49F	1977	Ex The Eden, 1995
3652	TOE482N	Leyland National 11351/1R(DAF)	B50F	1974	Ex West Midlands Travel, 1995
3653w	TOE525N	Leyland National 11351/1R(DAF)	B50F	1974	Ex West Midlands Travel, 1995
3654	JOX500P	Leyland National 11351/1R(DAF)	B49F	1976	Ex West Midlands Travel, 1995
3655	PUK636R	Leyland National 11351A/1R(DAF)	B49F	1977	Ex West Midlands Travel, 1995
3657	VOD601S	Leyland National 11351A/1R(DAF)	B52F	1978	Ex West Midlands Travel, 1995
3658	TOF714S	Leyland National 11351A/1R(DAF)	B49F	1978	Ex West Midlands Travel, 1995
3659	EGB79T	Leyland National 11351A/1R(DAF)	B52F	1978	Ex West Midlands Travel, 1995
3660w	GSX865T	Leyland National 11351A/1R(DAF)	B52F	1978	Ex West Midlands Travel, 1995
3661	TOE521N	Leyland National 11351/1R(DAF)	B50F	1974	Ex West Midlands Travel, 1995
3662	ROK467M	Leyland National 11351/1R(DAF)	B50F	1974	Ex West Midlands Travel, 1995
3664	TOE480N	Leyland National 11351/1R(DAF)	B50F	1974	Ex West Midlands Travel, 1995
3665	TVP836S	Leyland National 11351A/1R(DAF)	B50F	1978	Ex West Midlands Travel, 1995
3666	XOV759T	Leyland National 11351A/1R(DAF)	B49F	1979	Ex West Midlands Travel, 1995
3667	KHT118P	Leyland National 11351/1R(DAF)	B52F	1976	Ex West Midlands Travel, 1996
3668	PUK630R	Leyland National 11351A/1R(DAF)	B49F	1977	Ex West Midlands Travel, 1996
3718w	WPT718R	Leyland National 11351A/1R(DAF)	B49F	1977	
3720	WPT720R	Leyland National 11351A/1R(DAF)	B49F	1977	
3723	WPT723R	Leyland National 11351A/1R(DAF)	B49F	1977	
3724	WPT724R	Leyland National 11351A/1R(DAF)	B49F	1977	

3730-3739

		Leyland National 2 NL116L11/1R			B49F	1981		
3730	MHN128W	**3732**	MHN130W	**3734**	RDC734X	**3737**	RDC737X	**3739** RDC739X
3731	MHN129W							

3740	NAT198V	Leyland National 2 NL116L11/1R	B52F	1980	Ex East Yorkshire, 1990
3741	NAT199V	Leyland National 2 NL116L11/1R	B52F	1980	Ex East Yorkshire, 1990
3743	MNW131V	Leyland National 2 NL116L11/1R	B52F	1980	Ex Harrogate & District, 1990
3744	WAO399Y	Leyland National 2 NL116HLXB/1R	B52F	1983	Ex Shearings, 1991
3745	WAO395Y	Leyland National 2 NL116HLXB/1R	B52F	1983	Ex Shearings, 1991
3747	WRA224Y	Leyland National 2 NL116AHLXB/1R	B52F	1983	Ex Trent, 1991
3748	WRA225Y	Leyland National 2 NL116AHLXB/1R	B52F	1983	Ex Trent, 1991
3749	RRA219X	Leyland National 2 NL116AHLXB/1R	B52F	1981	Ex Trent, 1991
3750	DOC40V	Leyland National 2 NL116L11/1R	B50F	1980	Ex West Midlands Travel, 1995
3751	DOC31V	Leyland National 2 NL116L11/1R	B50F	1980	Ex West Midlands Travel, 1995
3752	DOC24V	Leyland National 2 NL116L11/1R	B50F	1980	Ex West Midlands Travel, 1995
3753	DOC33V	Leyland National 2 NL116L11/1R(DAF)	B49F	1980	Ex West Midlands Travel, 1995
3754	DOC19V	Leyland National 2 NL116L11/1R	B50F	1980	Ex West Midlands Travel, 1995
3758	CCY819V	Leyland National 2 NL116L11/1R(6HLXB)	DP49F	1980	Ex Yorkshire Bus (WR), 1997
3759	HED204V	Leyland National 2 NL116AL11/1R(6HLXB)	B49F	1980	Ex Yorkshire Bus (WR), 1997
3760	HED205V	Leyland National 2 NL116AL11/1R(6HLXB)	B49F	1980	Ex Yorkshire Bus (WR), 1997
3761	VBG93V	Leyland National 2 NL116AL11/1R(6HLXB)	B49F	1980	Ex Yorkshire Bus (WR), 1997
3762	XWA72X	Leyland National 2 NL116L11/1R(6HLXB)	B49F	1982	Ex Yorkshire Bus (WR), 1997
3763	XWA73X	Leyland National 2 NL116L11/1R(6HLXB)	B49F	1982	Ex Yorkshire Bus (WR), 1997
3764	XWA74X	Leyland National 2 NL116L11/1R(6HLXB)	B49F	1982	Ex Yorkshire Bus (WR), 1997
3765	XWA75X	Leyland National 2 NL116L11/1R(6HLXB)	B49F	1982	Ex Yorkshire Bus (WR), 1997
3766	EWT206Y	Leyland National 2 NL116HLXB/1R	B49F	1982	Ex Yorkshire Bus (WR), 1997
3767	EWT208Y	Leyland National 2 NL116HLXB/1R	B49F	1983	Ex Yorkshire Bus (WR), 1997
3768	EWT210Y	Leyland National 2 NL116HLXB/1R	B49F	1983	Ex Yorkshire Bus (WR), 1997
3769	BPR48Y	Leyland National 2 NL116HLXB/1R	B49F	1983	Ex Yorkshire Bus (WR), 1997
3770	BPR49Y	Leyland National 2 NL116HLXB/1R	B49F	1983	Ex Yorkshire Bus (WR), 1997

4001-4005

		DAF SB220LC550	Optare Delta		B51F	1990		
4001	G209HCP	**4002**	G210HCP	**4003**	G211HCP	**4004**	G212HCP	**4005** G214HCP

4006	J866UPY	DAF SB220LC550	Optare Delta	B49F	1992
4007	J867UPY	DAF SB200LC550	Optare Delta	B49F	1992

4008-4022

		DAF SB220LC550	Optare Delta		B49F	1993		
4008	K408BHN	**4011**	K411BHN	**4014**	K414BHN	**4017**	K417BHN	**4020** L420FHN
4009	K409BHN	**4012**	K412BHN	**4015**	K415BHN	**4018**	L418FHN	**4021** L421FHN
4010	K410BHN	**4013**	K413BHN	**4016**	K416BHN	**4019**	L419FHN	**4022** L422FHN

The Leyland Lynx 2 can be distinguished from the earlier model of this type by the protruding front dash panel. This feature can be seen on United 5001, G508EAJ which as part of a batch of five were purchased to compare with the DAF chassis. The vehicle carries the red and cream livery of its owner and, like all the Lynx, is based at Bishops Auckland. *Terry Wightman*

4023-4058

DAF DE02   Plaxton Prestige   B46F   On order

4023	4031	4038	4045	4052
4024	4032	4039	4046	4053
4025	4033	4040	4047	4054
4026	4034	4041	4048	4055
4027	4035	4042	4049	4056
4028	4036	4043	4050	4057
4029	4037	4044	4051	4058
4030				

5001-5005

Leyland Lynx LX2R11C15Z4S   Leyland Lynx   B49F   1990

5001	G508EAJ	5002	G509EAJ	5003	G510EAJ	5004	G511EAJ	5005	G512EAJ

5006-5018

Leyland Lynx LX2R11C15Z4S   Leyland Lynx 2   B49F   1991

5006	H31PAJ	5009	H253PAJ	5012	J652UHN	5015	J655UHN	5017	J657UHN
5007	H32PAJ	5010	H254PAJ	5013	J653UHN	5016	J656UHN	5018	J658UHN
5008	H34PAJ	5011	J651UHN	5014	J654UHN				

Ancilliary Vehicles:-

LH92	WAE192T	Bristol LH6L	Eastern Coach Works	B43F	1979	Ex Provincial, 1994
LH93	LPT703T	Bristol LH6L	Eastern Coach Works	B43F	1983	
VRT95	UGR698R	Bristol VRT/SL3/6LXB	Eastern Coach Works	H43/31F	1976	
1743	AFB589V	Bristol LH6L	Eastern Coach Works	B43F	1980	Ex Provincial, 1994

Previous Registrations:

445YMU	A177MKE	CVN174Y	CDG214Y, 7694VC
648WHK	A185MKE	LHO992Y	AEF992Y, TBC658
681CXM	A178MKE	YLX281	A170MKE
A949KAJ	A672OKX, 7694VC		

Allocations and liveries

Livery: Red and cream (United and The Eden); red and yellow (Tees); blue and cream (TMS); blue and yellow ♣(Expressway).

Bishop Auckland (Morland Street) - United - The Eden ♦

Outstations - Crook and Fishburn

Bristol VR	786	808	814	824	831	832	892	
Tiger	1324	1325	1329	1330	1331	1342	1343	1344
	1345	1346	1404♣	1410	1415♣			
Vecta	1514♦	1515	1526	1527	1528	1529	1539	1546
	1547	1548	1549					
Lynx	5001♦	5002♦	5003	5004	5005	5006	5007	5008
	5009	5010	5011	5012	5013	5014	5015	5016
	5017	5018						
Mercedes-Benz	2446	2458	2464	2465♦	2469	2471♦	2472♦	
MetroRider	2643	2644	2645					

Darlington (Feethams) - United

Outstation - Barnard Castle

Bristol VR	822	823					
Olympian	214	215	216	266	271	272	
Tiger	1234	1235	1303				
Vecta	1516	1517	1518	1550	1551		
National	3111	3112	3114	3116	3117	3118	3119	3121
	3122	3123	3145	3146			
MetroRider	2606	2607	2608	2611	2612	2613	2614	2615
	2616	2617	2618	2619	2620	2621	2622	2623
	2624	2625	2626	2627	2628	2629	2630	2631
	2640	2641	2642				

Durham (Waddington Steet) - United

Mercedes-Benz	2443	2451	2456	2473	2474	2477	2478	2479
	2480							
National	3130	3131	3134	3135	3136	3137	3138	3140
	3142	3143	3147	3148	3149	3150	3152	3153
Delta	4016	4017	4018	4019	4020	4021	4022	
Olympian	207	208	209	217	218	227	228	245
	251	252	253	255	263	265	273	274
	275							

Loftus (Whitby Road) - Tees & District

Outstation at Whitby

MetroRider	2635	2636	2637	2638	2639		
National	3744	3745	3747	3748	3749	3758	3759	3760
Tiger	1231	1232	1311	1312	1313	1314	1315	1319
	1332	1335	1336	1338	1339	1340	1341	1414
	1422	1431♣	1432♣	1433♣	1434♣			
Vecta	1509	1510	1511	1512	1513	1534	1535	

Middlesbrough (Union Street) - Tees & District

National	3126	3730	3731	3732	3734	3737	3739	3740
	3741	3743	3750	3751	3752	3754		
Tiger	1327	1414	1418	1420	1422	1423	1425	
Vecta	1503	1504	1505	1506	1507	1508	1519	1520
	1521	1522	1523	1524	1525			
Bristol VR	756	804	864	879				
Olympian	202	203	204	206	210	233	234	235
	236	237	238	243	258			

B45NDX has lead a chequered life. It was new to Ipswich in 1985 but was by 1989 to be found in the Stevensons fleet. This East Lancashire-bodied Leyland Olympian moved to the North East in 1993 when it joined the United fleet as number 245. This Durham based vehicle is seen on service 43 to Esh Winning. *Derek Akrigg*

Peterlee (Davey Drive) - United

Mercerdes-Benz	2447	2448						
National	3720	3761	3763	3764	3765	3766	3767	3768
	3769							
Tiger	1301	1302	1328	1333	1334 .	1337	1401	1402
	1403	1411	1412					
Bristol VR	756							
Olympian	286	287	288	289	290	291	292	293
	294	295						

Redcar (Railway Terrace) - Tees & District

Tiger	1405♣	1416♣	1417♣					
Prisma	3002	3003	3004	3005	3006	3007	3008	3009
	3010	3011	3012	3013	3014	3015	3016	3017
	3018	3019	3020	3021	3022	3023	3024	3025
Olympian	279	280	281	282	283	284	285	

Richmond (Station Yard) - United

Outstation - Hawes

MetroRider	2601	2602	2603	2604	2605	2609	2610	2632
	2633	2634						
Tiger	1305	1306	1307	1308	1309	1310	1406	
Vecta	1530	1531	1532	1533				
Olympian	267	268						

Mercedes-Benz have been keen to enter the British bus market for some time, providing chassis for British bodybuilders to complete rather than import the complete integral unit frequently seen in central Europe. While 1998 may well see large numbers of O405 completed units being imported. An earlier version bodied by Optare is Tees 3010, N810XHN, pictured as the vehicle was leaving Darlington for its home base of Redcar. *Richard Godfrey*

Stockton (Boathouse Lane) - TMS

National	3100	3104	3106	3107	3109	3601	3602	3603
	3605	3606	3607	3652	3654	3655	3657	3658
	3659	3661	3662	3664	3665	3666	3667	3668
	3723	3724	3753					
Vecta	1501	1502	1540	1541	1542	1543	1544	1545
Delta	4001	4002	4003	4004	4005	4006	4007	4008
	4009	4010	4011	4012	4013	4014	4015	

Stokesley (North Road) - Tees & District

Mercedes-Benz	2453	2459	2460	2475
Tiger	1419	1426		
Vecta	1536	1537	1538	
Prisma	3001			
Olympian	223	226	276	277	278

Withdrawn & unallocated:-

Mercedes-Benz	2403	2466						
Tiger	1227	1228	1229	1230	1233	1322	1413	
National	3502	3503	3604	3608	3651	3653	3660	3718
Bristol VR	801	812	841					

YORKSHIRE BUS

West Riding Automobile Co Ltd; South Yorkshire Road Transport Ltd;
Selby & District Bus Co Ltd,
24 Barnsley Road, Wakefield, West Yorkshire, WF1 5JX
Yorkshire Woollen District Transport Co Ltd, Mill Street East, Dewsbury,
West Yorkshire, WF12 9AG

31	P31XUG	DAF DE33WSSB3000	Van Hool Alizée		C FT	1997		

51-56   Scania K113CRB   Van Hool Alizée   C44FT   1995

51	M51AWW	53	M53AWW	54	M54AWW	55	M55AWW	56	M56AWW
52	M52AWW							

170-199   Dennis Dart SLF   Alexander ALX200   B40F   1997

170	P170VUA	176	P176VUA	182	P182VUA	188	P188VUA	194	P194VUA
171	P171VUA	177	P177VUA	183	P183VUA	189	P189VUA	195	P195VUA
172	P172VUA	178	P178VUA	184	P184VUA	190	P190VUA	196	P196VUA
173	P173VUA	179	P179VUA	185	P185VUA	191	P191VUA	197	P197VUA
174	P174VUA	180	P180VUA	186	P186VUA	192	P192VUA	198	P198VUA
175	P175VUA	181	P181VUA	187	P187VUA	193	P193VUA	199	P199VUA

252	C920FMP	Leyland Lynx LX1126LXCTFR1	Leyland Lynx	B51F	1986	Ex Leyland Bus, 1987	
253	D204FBK	Leyland Lynx LX112TL11ZR1	Leyland Lynx	B51F	1986	Ex Solent Blue Line, 1987	
254	E254TUB	Leyland Lynx LX1126LXCTFR2	Leyland Lynx	B50F	1987		

255-264   Leyland Lynx LX1126LXCTFR1S Leyland Lynx   B49F   1987-88

255	E255TUB	257	E257TUB	259	E259TUB	261	E261TUB	263	E263TUB
256	E256TUB	258	E258TUB	260	E260TUB	262	E262TUB	264	E264TUB

Thirty low floor single deck buses entered the Yorkshire Woollen fleet in 1997. All carry the new Alexander ALX200 body on Dennis Dart SLF chassis. 186, P186VUA is one of the batch which operate a number of routes including 281 to Fieldhead.
Phillip Stephenson

With the disposal of the last Leyland National 2 vehicles, the oldest single deck buses in the Yorkshire Bus Group fleets are Leyland Lynxes. 277, F277AWW is one of the substantial batch of this type purchased when the company was part of the Caldaire group. It carries the latest version of the Yorkshire Woollen red and cream livery. *Richard Godfrey*

265-314

Leyland Lynx LX112L10ZR1S   Leyland Lynx   B49F   1988-89

265	E265WUB	275	F275AWW	285	F285AWW	295	F295AWW	305	F305AWW
266	E266WUB	276	F276AWW	286	F286AWW	296	F296AWW	306	F306AWW
267	E267WUB	277	F277AWW	287	F287AWW	297	F297AWW	307	F307AWW
268	E268WUB	278	F278AWW	288	F288AWW	298	F298AWW	308	F308AWW
269	E269WUB	279	F279AWW	289	F289AWW	299	F299AWW	309	F309AWW
270	E270WUB	280	F280AWW	290	F290AWW	300	F300AWW	310	F310AWW
271	E271WUB	281	F281AWW	291	F291AWW	301	F301AWW	311	F311AWW
272	F272AWW	282	F282AWW	292	F292AWW	302	F302AWW	312	F312AWW
273	F273AWW	283	F283AWW	293	F293AWW	303	F303AWW	313	F313AWW
274	F274AWW	284	F284AWW	294	F294AWW	304	F304AWW	314	F314AWW

315	E116UTX	Leyland Lynx LX112L10ZR1R	Leyland Lynx	B51F	1988	Ex Merthyr Tydfil, 1989
316	F117XTX	Leyland Lynx LX112L10ZR1R	Leyland Lynx	B51F	1988	Ex Merthyr Tydfil, 1989
317	F118XTX	Leyland Lynx LX112L10ZR1R	Leyland Lynx	B51F	1988	Ex Merthyr Tydfil, 1989

318-332

Leyland Lynx LX2R11C15Z4S   Leyland Lynx   B49F   1990

318	G317NNW	321	G321NNW	324	G324NUM	327	G327NUM	330	G330NUM
319	G319NNW	322	G322NNW	325	G110OUG	328	G109OUG	331	G331NUM
320	G324NNW	323	G108OUG	326	G326NUM	329	G329NUM	332	G332NUM

333-337

Leyland Lynx LX2R11C15Z4S   Leyland Lynx 2   B49F   1990

333	H338TYG	334	H334TYG	335	H335TYG	336	H336TYG	337	H337TYG

338-347

Leyland Lynx LX2R11C15Z4S   Leyland Lynx 2   B49F   1990-91

338	H338UWT	340	H343UWT	342	H342UWT	344	H344UWX	346	H346UWX
339	H339UWT	341	H341UWT	343	H343UWX	345	H345UWX	347	H347UWX

Service 402 runs from Leeds to York via Selby providing passengers with cross Selby journeys which before de-regulation involved a change of bus. Depicted on this service is 405, K405HWX a Volvo B10B which carries an Alexander Strider body. This view shows the previous Selby and District livery with the upsweep of green towards the front of the vehicle.

348	G542GAC	Leyland Lynx LX2R11C15Z4R	Leyland Lynx	B49F	1990	Ex Volvo Bus, Warwick, 1991
349	G148CHP	Leyland Lynx LX2R11C15Z4R	Leyland Lynx	B49F	1990	Ex Volvo Bus, Warwick, 1991
350	G149CHP	Leyland Lynx LX2R11C15Z4R	Leyland Lynx	B51F	1990	Ex Volvo Bus, Warwick, 1991
351	G49CVC	Leyland Lynx LX112L10ZR1R	Leyland Lynx	B51F	1990	Ex Volvo Bus, Warwick, 1991

352-382

| | Leyland Lynx LX2R11C15Z4S* | Leyland Lynx 2 | B49F | 1991 | *378 is LX2R11V18Z4S |

352	H755WWW	359	H359WWY	365	J365YWX	371	J371YWX	377	J377AWT
353	H756WWW	360	H460WWY	366	J366YWX	372	J372AWT	378	J371AWT
354	H757WWW	361	H393WWY	367	J367YWX	373	J373AWT	379	J379BWU
355	H355WWX	362	J362YWX	368	J368YWX	374	J374AWT	380	J380BWU
356	H356WWX	363	J363YWX	369	J369YWX	375	J375AWT	381	J381BWU
357	H357WWX	364	J364YWX	370	J370YWX	376	J376AWT	382	J382BWU
358	H358WWY								

401-405

| | Volvo B10B-58 | Alexander Strider | B51F | 1993 |

401	K401HWW	402	K402HWW	403	K403HWW	404	K404HWW	405	K405HWX

406	L406NUA	Volvo B10B-58	Wright Endeavour	DP49F	1993
407	L407NUA	Volvo B10B-58	Wright Endeavour	DP49F	1993
408	L408NUA	Volvo B10B-58	Wright Endeavour	DP49F	1993
409	L409NUA	Volvo B10B-58	Wright Endeavour	DP49F	1993

410-433

| | Volvo B10B-58 | Alexander Strider | B51F | 1994 |

410	M410UNW	415	M415UNW	420	M420UNW	425	M425UNW	430	M430UNW
411	M411UNW	416	M416UNW	421	M421UNW	426	M426UNW	431	M431UNW
412	M412UNW	417	M417UNW	422	M422UNW	427	M427UNW	432	M432UNW
413	M413UNW	418	M418UNW	423	M423UNW	428	M428UNW	433	M433UNW
414	M414UNW	419	M419UNW	424	M424UNW	429	M429UNW		

There has recently been an exchange of work between operators on the White Rose Express network. As a result all journeys on service X33 between Sheffield and Bradford are now in the hands of Yorkshire Woollen. Seen on this route is 409, L409NUA one of four Wright Endeavour, Volvo B10B buses fitted with high backed seating especially purchased for White Rose services. When photographed, the vehicle carried West Riding fleetnames. It has recently been transferred to Yorkshire Woollen but still carries the green and cream West Riding livery. *Richard Godfrey*

508-552   Leyland Olympian ONLXB/1R   Eastern Coach Works   H45/33F   1982-83

508	CWR508Y	518	CWR518Y	531	EWX531Y	538	EWX538Y	545	EWW545Y
510	CWR510Y	519	CWR519Y	532	EWX532Y	539	EWW539Y	546	EWW546Y
511	CWR511Y	520	CWR520Y	533	EWX533Y	540	EWW540Y	547	EWW547Y
512	CWR512Y	521	CWR521Y	534	EWX534Y	541	EWW541Y	548	EWW548Y
514	CWR514Y	524	CWR524Y	535	EWX535Y	542	EWW542Y	550	EWW550Y
515	CWR515Y	528	CWR528Y	536	EWX536Y	543	EWW543Y	551	EWW551Y
516	CWR516Y	529	CWR529Y	537	EWX537Y	544	544WRA	552	EWW552Y
517	CWR517Y	530	CWR530Y						

560-612   Leyland Olympian ONLXB/1R   Eastern Coach Works   H45/32F*   1983-85 *seating varies

560	A560KWY	572	A572NWX	582	A582NWX	592	B592SWX	603	B603UUM
562	A562KWY	573	A573NWX	583	A583NWX	593	B593SWX	604	B604UUM
564	A564KWY	574	A574NWX	584	A584NWX	594	B594SWX	605	B605UUM
565	A565NWX	575	A575NWX	585	A585NWX	595	B595SWX	606	B606UUM
566	A566NWX	576	A576NWX	586	A586NWX	596	B596SWX	607	B607UUM
567	A567NWX	577	A577NWX	587	A587NWX	597	B597SWX	608	B608UUM
568	A568NWX	578	A578NWX	588	A588NWX	599	B599SWX	609	B609UUM
569	A569NWX	579	A579NWX	589	A589NWX	600	B601UUM	610	C610ANW
570	A570NWX	580	A580NWX	590	A590NWX	601	B602UUM	611	C611ANW
571	A571NWX	581	A581NWX	591	B591SWX	602	B603UUM	612	C612ANW

Opposite, top: - The oldest of the double-deck buses remaining with West Yorkshire are the Eastern Coach Works-bodied Leyland Olympians, and these are now starting their migration to other fleets within the group. Pictured earlier in 1997, 509 is one of those to have left. It is seen here in South Yorkshire's blue livery before being moved to Crosville Cymru. *Tony Wilson*
Opposite, bottom: - One of the 1992 delivery of Optare MetroRiders is 722, J722CUM which is seen here in West Riding livery. This locally-built product is expected to be one of the first new buses to be delivered in the new Arriva livery, being part of the current Northumbria batch, with deliveries for several other group members to take place in 1998. *Tony Wilson*

Having operated Sherpa and Dodge minibuses, the Yorkshire Bus Group has until recently standardised on Optare and Mercedes-Benz for its small buses. The 1991 batch of Optare MetroRider 23 seaters have now been transferred to Clydeside. A 31 seat example is 748, M748WWR seen leaving Wakefield bus station on local service 102 to Portobello. *Richard Godfrey*

613	E205TUB	Leyland Olympian ONTL11/1RH	Northern Counties	H43/28F	1988	Ex South Yorkshire, Pontefract, 1995
614	TWY7	Leyland Olympian ONCL10/1RZ	Northern Counties	H43/28F	1988	Ex South Yorkshire, Pontefract, 1995
615	H106RWT	Leyland Olympian ON2R50C13Z4	Northern Counties	H43/28F	1990	Ex South Yorkshire, Pontefract, 1995
616	H108RWT	Leyland Olympian ON2R50C13Z4	Northern Counties	H43/28F	1990	Ex South Yorkshire, Pontefract, 1995
621	N621KUA	Volvo Olympian YN2RV18Z4	Northern Counties Palatine II	H43/30F	1996	
622	N622KUA	Volvo Olympian YN2RV18Z4	Northern Counties Palatine II	H43/30F	1996	
623	N623KUA	Volvo Olympian YN2RV18Z4	Northern Counties Palatine II	H43/30F	1996	

701-711   Optare MetroRider MR09   Optare   B23F   1991

705w	H705UNW	707w	H707UNW	708w	H708UNW	709w	H709UNW	711w	H711UNW

714-729   Optare MetroRider MR05   Optare   B31F   1992-93

714	J714CUM	718	J718CUM	721	J721CUM	724	K724HUG	727	K727HUG
715	J715CUM	719	J719CUM	722	J722CUM	725	K725HUG	728	K728HUG
716	J716CUM	720	J720CUM	723	K723HUG	726	K726HUG	729	K729HUG
717	J717CUM								

730-745   Optare MetroRider MR15   Optare   B31F   1993-94

730	L730MWW	734	L734MWW	737	L737PUA	740	L740PUA	743	M743UUA
731	L731MWW	735	L735PUA	738	L738PUA	741	L741PUA	744	M744UUA
732	L732MWW	736	L736PUA	739	L739PUA	742	M742UUA	745	M745UUA
733	L733MWW								

746-750   Optare MetroRider MR15   Optare   B31F   1995

746	M746WWX	747	M247WWX	748	M748WWX	749	M749WWR	750	M750WWR

Opposite:- The Yorkshire Buses livery is seen on two of the 'standard' models in the fleet. The Leyland Lynx, 351, G49CVC was one of four that joined the fleet after spending some time with the compay on loan while other members of the type returned to Lillyhall for attention. The lower picture, 562, A562KWY, was pictured in Eastgate, Leeds, when operating the 201 Huddersfield service. *Les Peters/Tony Wilson*

751	M751WWR	Optare MetroRider MR31	Optare	B25F	1995			
752	M752WWR	Optare MetroRider MR31	Optare	B25F	1995			
753	M753WWR	Optare MetroRider MR31	Optare	B25F	1995			
754	N754LWW	Optare MetroRider MR15	Optare	B31F	1996			
755	N755LWW	Optare MetroRider MR15	Optare	B31F	1996			
756	N756LWW	Optare MetroRider MR15	Optare	B31F	1996			
757	N757LWW	Optare MetroRider MR15	Optare	B31F	1996			

758-770
Mercedes-Benz Vario O810   Plaxton Beaver 2   B27F   1997

758	R758DUB	761	R761DUB	764	R764DUB	767	R767DUB	769	R769DUB
759	R758DUB	762	R762DUB	765	R765DUB	768	R768DUB	770	R770DUB
760	R760DUB	763	R763DUB	766	R766DUB				

771-778
Mercedes-Benz 811D   Plaxton Beaver   B31F   1994

771	L771RWW	773	L773RWW	775	L775RWW	777	L779RWW	778	L778RWW
772	L772RWW	774	L774RWW	776	L776RWW				

779-784
Mercedes-Benz 811D   Plaxton Beaver   B31F*   1995   *779 is B27F

779	N779EUA	781	N781EUA	782	N782EUA	783	N783EUA	784	N784EUA
780	N780EUA							

785-799
Mercedes-Benz Vario O810   Plaxton Beaver 2   B27F   1997

785	R785DUB	789	R789DUB	792	R792DUB	795	R795DUB	798	R798DUB
787	R787DUB	790	R790DUB	793	R793DUB	796	R796DUB	799	R799DUB
788	R788DUB	791	R791DUB	794	R794DUB	797	R797DUB		

801-830
Dennis Lance 11SDA3107   Alexander Strider   B47F   1993

801	K801HWW	807	L807NNW	813	L813NNW	819	L819NWY	825	L825NWY
802	K802HWW	808	L808NNW	814	L814NNW	820	L820NWY	826	L826NYG
803	K803HWW	809	L809NNW	815	L815NNW	821	L821NWY	827	L827NYG
804	K804HWW	810	L810NNW	816	L816NWY	822	L822NWY	828	L828NYG
805	K805HWX	811	L811NNW	817	L817NWY	823	L823NWY	829	L829NYG
806	L806NNW	812	L812NNW	818	L818NWY	824	L824NWY	830	L830NYG

Previous Registrations:

544WRA	EWX544Y		
		TWY7	From new

Allocations and liveries:-

Livery: Cream and green (West Riding); cream and red (Yorkshire); cream and green (Selby & District); cream and blue (South Yorkshire); cream and red ✈ (Flightlink).

Castleford (Wheldon Road) - West Riding

MetroRider	720	721	722	723	724	725	726	727
	728	729	743	744	745	753		
Lynx	267	269	276	289	290	293	294	299
	301	329	330	331	332	333	334	335
	336	337	338	339	340	341	342	343
	344	345	346	347	352	353	354	355
	356	357	360	366	367	368	369	370
	371							
Olympian	515	528	529	537	538	539	541	595
	596	597	598	599				

Yorkshire Buses' 829, L829NYG is a Dennis Lance which carries a stylish Alexander Strider body. It is seen leaving Huddersfield bus station bound for Leeds. There is an extensive network of services between these two points with buses operated jointly by Yorkshire Woollen and Yorkshire Traction. *Phillip Stephenson*

Dewsbury (Mill Street East) - Yorkshire

Coach	31🠖	51🠖	52🠖	53🠖	54🠖	56🠖		
Mercedes-Benz	771	772	773	774	775	776	777	778
	779	780	781	782	783	784		
Dart	170	171	172	173	174	175	176	177
	178	179	180	181	182	183	184	185
	186	187	188	189	190	191	192	193
	194	195	196	197	198	199		
Lynx	275	277	279	280	281	284	285	287
	288	291	295	296	303	304	328	350
	351							

Heckmondwike (Beck Lane) - Yorkshire

Volvo B10B	405	406	407	408	409	410	411	412
	413	414	415	416	417	418		
Lance	801	802	803	804	805	806	807	808
	809	810	811	812	813	814	815	816
	817	818	819	820	821	822	823	824
	825	826	827	828	829	830		
Olympian	521	524	527	540	547	548	562	564
	565	568	569	570	571	585	586	587
	588	589	600	601	602			

Pontefract (Northgate) - South Yorkshire

MetroRider	749	750	754	755	756	757		
Lynx	315	316	317	318	319	320	321	322
	323	324	325	326	327			
Olympian	508	510	518	519	613	614	615	616

Selby (Cowie Drive, Ousegate) - Selby & District

Mercedes-Benz	758	759	760	761	762			
Volvo B10B	401	402	403	404	421	422		
Olympian	512	520	534	535	542	591	592	593
	594	603	621	622	623			

Wakefield (Belle Isle, Barnsley Road) - West Riding

Coach	55✈							
MetroRider	714	715	716	717	718	719	730	731
	732	733	734	735	736	737	738	739
	740	741	742	746	747	748	751	752
Mercedes-Benz	763	764	765	766	767	768	769	770
Lynx	252	253	254	255	256	257	258	259
	260	261	262	263	264	265	266	268
	270	271	272	273	274	278	282	283
	286	292	297	298	300	302	305	306
	307	308	309	310	311	312	312	313
	314	348	349	358	359	361	362	363
	364	365	372	373	374	375	376	377
	378	379	380	381	382			
Volvo B10B	419	420	423	424	425	426	427	428
	429	430	431	432	433			
Olympian	511	513	514	515	516	517	530	531
	532	533	536	543	544	545	546	550
	551	552	560	566	567	572	573	574
	575	576	577	578	579	580	581	582
	583	584	590	604	605	606	607	
	608	609	610	611	612			

Withdrawn and unallocated

Mercedes-Benz	785	786	787					
	788	789	790	791	792	793	794	795
	796	797	798	799				
MetroRider	701	705	707	708	709	710	711	

UNIBUS

Unibus, København.

151	ME94.576	DAB-Silkeborg 11-0860S	DAB	B..D	1990	Ex Hovedstadsområdets Trafikselskab,
155	MY91.485	DAB-Silkeborg 11-0860S	DAB	B..D	1992	Ex Hovedstadsområdets Trafikselskab,
156	MY91.576	DAB-Silkeborg 11-0860S	DAB	B..D	1992	Ex Hovedstadsområdets Trafikselskab,
165	MN92.651	DAB-Silkeborg 11-0860S	DAB	B..D	1991	Ex Hovedstadsområdets Trafikselskab,
166	MJ89.343	DAB-Silkeborg 11-0860S	DAB	B..D	1993	Ex Linjebuss
170	MY91.536	DAB-Silkeborg 11-0860S	DAB	B..D	1992	Ex Linjebuss
171	MY91.537	DAB-Silkeborg 11-0860S	DAB	B..D	1992	Ex Linjebuss
175	NJ97.918	DAB-Silkeborg 11-0860S	DAB	B..D	1993	Ex Hovedstadsområdets Trafikselskab,
701	OX94.934	MAN SD200	Waggon Union	O53/35F	1980	Ex BVG, Berlin, 1996
702	OV97.450	MAN SD200	Waggon Union	O53/35F	1980	Ex BVG, Berlin, 1996
7016	MB92.556	Leyland-DAB 7-2	DAB	B..D	1983	Ex Søndergaard, Fjerritslev, 1993
7017	MB92.557	Leyland-DAB 7-1200L	DAB	B..D	1985	Ex Kirsten Jensen, Hallund, 1993
7024	MB88.889	Leyland-DAB LS575-690	DAB	B..D	1980	Ex Therkildsens, Rutter, 1993
7026	MV95.774	Scania N113CLB	WIIMA K202L	B..D	1992	
7027	MV95.777	Scania N113CRB	WIIMA K202L	B..D	1992	
7028	MV95.782	Scania N113CRB	WIIMA K202L	B..D	1992	
7029	MV95.794	Scania N113CRB	WIIMA K202L	B..D	1992	
7030	MV95.793	Scania N113CRB	WIIMA K202L	B..D	1992	
7040	MV91.327	Leyland-DAB 7-1200B	DAB	B..D	1993	
7045	NC97.438	DAB-Silkeborg 7-1200B	DAB RS2001	B41T	1993	
7046	NC97.439	DAB-Silkeborg 7-1200B	DAB RS2001	B41T	1993	
7047	NC97.440	DAB-Silkeborg 7-1200B	DAB RS2001	B41T	1993	
7048	NC97.441	DAB-Silkeborg 7-1200B	DAB RS2001	B41T	1993	
7051	NJ89.354	DAB-Silkeborg 7-1200B	DAB RS2001	B41T	1993	
7052	NJ89.355	DAB-Silkeborg 7-1200B	DAB RS2001	B41T	1993	
7053	NJ89.356	DAB-Silkeborg 7-1200B	DAB RS2001	B41T	1993	
7054	NJ97.966	DAB-Silkeborg 7-1200B	DAB RS2001	B41T	1993	
7055	NJ97.967	DAB-Silkeborg 7-1200B	DAB RS2001	B41T	1993	
7056	NJ97.968	DAB-Silkeborg 7-1200B	DAB RS2001	B41T	1993	
7059	NR96.580	Leyland-DAB 7-1200B	DAB 1200L	B35T	1986	
7060	NR96.578	Leyland-DAB 7-1200B	DAB 1200L	B35T	1986	Ex .. 1994
7061	NN97.769	Leyland-DAB 7-1200B	DAB 1200L	B35T	1986	
7062	NR96.577	Leyland-DAB 7-1200B	DAB 1200L	B35T	1987	
7064	NR96.581	DAB-Silkeborg 7-1200B	DAB	B41T	1989	

The lowest numberin the Unibus fleet belongs to DAB minibus 151, ME94.576 which is seen here at the depot. The rear-view illustrates the unusual arrangement of the access doors and engine.
Unibus,

7072	NR96.555	DAB-Silkeborg 12-1200B	DAB	B41T	1989	Ex City Trafik, 1993
7073	NR96.556	Scania DAB	Silkeborg		1994	Ex ??, 1997
7074	NR96.557	Scania DAB	Silkeborg		1994	Ex ??, 1997
7075	NR96.558	Scania DAB	Silkeborg		1994	Ex ??, 1997
7076	NR96.559	Scania DAB	Silkeborg		1994	Ex ??, 1997
7077	NR96.601	Leyland-DAB 7-1200B	DAB 1200L	B35T	1985	
7078	NN97.602	Leyland-DAB 7-1200B	DAB 1200L	B35T	1985	
7079	NR96.603	Leyland-DAB 7-1200B	DAB 1200L	B35T	1986	
7080	NR96.622	Leyland-DAB 7-1200B	DAB 1200L	B35T	1986	
7081	NR96.641	Leyland-DAB 7-1200B	DAB 1200L	B35T	1986	
7083	NN97.642	Leyland-DAB 7-1200B	DAB 1200L	B35T	1987	
7084	NR96.604	Leyland-DAB 7-1200B	DAB 1200L	B35T	1987	
7084	NR96.627	Leyland-DAB 7-1200B	DAB 1200L	B35T	1988	
7087	NR96.625	Scania N112CL	Aabenraa	B42T	1987	Ex Therkildsens Ruter, 1994
7088	NR96.589	DAB-Silkeborg 15-1200C	DAB Citybus 2	B41T	1994	
7089	NR96.590	DAB-Silkeborg 15-1200C	DAB Citybus 2	B41T	1994	
7090	NR96.591	DAB-Silkeborg 15-1200C	DAB Citybus 2	B41T	1994	
7091	NR96.592	DAB-Silkeborg 15-1200C	DAB Citybus 2	B41T	1994	
7092	NR96.593	DAB-Silkeborg 15-1200C	DAB Citybus 2	B41T	1994	
7093	NR96.594	DAB-Silkeborg 15-1200C	DAB Citybus 2	B41T	1994	
7094	NR96.595	DAB-Silkeborg 15-1200C	DAB Citybus 2	B41T	1994	
7095	NR96.618	DAB-Silkeborg 15-1200C	DAB Citybus 2	B41T	1994	
7096	NR96.619	DAB-Silkeborg 15-1200C	DAB Citybus 2	B41T	1994	
7097	NR96.620	DAB-Silkeborg 15-1200C	DAB Citybus 2	B41T	1994	
7098	NR96.643	DAB-Silkeborg 15-1200C	DAB Citybus 2	B41T	1994	
7099	NR96.621	DAB-Silkeborg 15-1200C	DAB Citybus 2	B41T	1994	
7100	NR96.674	DAB-Silkeborg 15-1200C	DAB Citybus 2	B41T	1994	
7101	NS95.940	DAB-Silkeborg 15-1200C	DAB Citybus 2	B41T	1994	
7102	NS95.941	DAB-Silkeborg 15-1200C	DAB Citybus 2	B41T	1994	
7103	NS95.942	DAB-Silkeborg 15-1200C	DAB Citybus 2	B41T	1994	
7104	NS95.943	DAB-Silkeborg 15-1200C	DAB Citybus 2	B41T	1994	
7105	NS95.944	DAB-Silkeborg 15-1200C	DAB Citybus 2	B41T	1994	
7106	NS95.973	DAB-Silkeborg 15-1200C	DAB Citybus 2	B41T	1994	
7107	NS95.974	DAB-Silkeborg 15-1200C	DAB Citybus 2	B41T	1994	
7108	NS96.987	DAB-Silkeborg 15-1200C	DAB Citybus 2	B41T	1994	
7109	NS95.988	DAB-Silkeborg 15-1200C	DAB Citybus 2	B41T	1994	
7110	NS95.989	DAB-Silkeborg 15-1200C	DAB Citybus 2	B41T	1994	
7111	NS95.990	DAB-Silkeborg 15-1200C	DAB Citybus 2	B41T	1994	
7112	NS96.012	DAB-Silkeborg 15-1200C	DAB Citybus 2	B41T	1994	
7113	NS96.013	DAB-Silkeborg 15-1200C	DAB Citybus 2	B41T	1994	
7114	NS96.034	DAB-Silkeborg 15-1200C	DAB Citybus 2	B41T	1994	
7115	NS96.035	DAB-Silkeborg 15-1200C	DAB Citybus 2	B41T	1994	
7116	NS96.052	DAB-Silkeborg 15-1200C	DAB Citybus 2	B41T	1994	
7117	NS96.053	DAB-Silkeborg 15-1200C	DAB Citybus 2	B41T	1994	
7118	NS96.073	DAB-Silkeborg 15-1200C	DAB Citybus 2	B41T	1994	
7119	NS96.074	DAB-Silkeborg 15-1200C	DAB Citybus 2	B41T	1994	
7122	NV93.256	DAB RS200L(DAF)	DAB Citybus	B40T	1994	
7127	NY90.312	Mercedes-Benz 602	Mercedes-Benz	B00C	1995	
7128	NY90.313	Mercedes-Benz 602	Mercedes-Benz	B00C	1995	
7129	NY90.314	Mercedes-Benz 602	Mercedes-Benz	B00C	1995	
7130	NY90.315	Mercedes-Benz 602	Mercedes-Benz	B00C	1995	
7131	NY90.316	Mercedes-Benz 602	Mercedes-Benz	B00C	1995	
7132	NY90.317	Mercedes-Benz 602	Mercedes-Benz	B00C	1995	
7133	NY90.318	Mercedes-Benz 602	Mercedes-Benz	B00C	1995	
7136	NZ95.428	Mercedes-Benz 602	Mercedes-Benz	B00C	1995	
7137	NZ95.429	Mercedes-Benz 602	Mercedes-Benz	B00C	1995	
7138	NU91.449	Mercedes-Benz 602	Mercedes-Benz	B00C	1995	
7139	LT97.100(?)	Mercedes-Benz 602	Mercedes-Benz	B00C	1995	
7140	OC91.462	Mercedes-Benz 602	Mercedes-Benz	B00C	1995	
7143	OL88.190	Volvo B10L-60	Säffle-Aabenraa	B41T	1996	
7144	OL88.191	Volvo B10L-60	Säffle-Aabenraa	B41T	1996	
7145	OL88.192	Volvo B10L-60	Säffle-Aabenraa	B41T	1996	
7146	OL88.193	Volvo B10L-60	Säffle-Aabenraa	B41T	1996	
7147	OL88.194	Volvo B10L-60	Säffle-Aabenraa	B41T	1996	
7148	OL88.238	Volvo B10L-60	Säffle-Aabenraa	B41T	1996	

Opposite, top:- **Copenhagen serviced are placed by tender, with vehicles painted in standard yellow livery. Here are seen two of the vehicle currently service with Unibus. The upper picture shows 7030, MV95.793, shortly after delivery and before the last renumbering. This is a Scania N113CRB which has a Wiima K202L body which was seen in the spring of 1994.** *Bill Potter*
Opposite, bottom:- **The majority of the buses in the fleet are Volvo B10Ls with Säffle-designed bodywork which was assembled by Aabenraa. Representing these buses is 7151, OL88242.** *Unibus*

7149	OL88.239	Volvo B10L-60	Säffle	B41T	1996	
7150	OL88.240	Volvo B10L-60	Säffle	B41T	1996	
7151	OL88.241	Volvo B10L-60	Säffle	B41T	1996	
7152	OL88.242	Volvo B10L-60	Säffle	B41T	1996	
7153	OL88.243	Volvo B10L-60	Säffle	B41T	1996	
7154	OL88.250	Volvo B10L-60	Säffle	B41T	1996	
7155	OL88.260	Volvo B10L-60	Säffle	B41T	1996	
7156	OL88.261	Volvo B10L-60	Säffle	B41T	1996	
7157	OL88.262	Volvo B10L-60	Säffle	B41T	1996	
7158	OL88.279	Volvo B10L-60	Säffle	B41T	1996	
7159	OL88.280	Volvo B10L-60	Säffle	B41T	1996	
7160	NY90.163	Mercedes-Benz 602	Mercedes-Benz	B00C	1995	
7161	HV89.713	Volvo B10M-70	Säffle		1996	Ex Vejle, 1996
7162	HV89.714	Volvo B10M-70	Säffle		1996	Ex Vejle, 1996
7163	JC94.330	Leyland-DAB 7-2	DAB		1983	Ex Vejle, 1996
7165	JK93.651	Leyland-DAB 7-1200B	DAB		1983	Ex Vejle, 1996
7166	OM94.884	Mercedes-Benz 309D	Mercedes-Benz	M..	1982	
7167	JR89.516	Volvo B10M-70	Säffle		1996	Ex Vejle, 1996
7168	HP91.335	Leyland-DAB LS575-690	DAB		1983	Ex Vejle, 1996
7169	OU96.504	Mercedes-Benz Sprinter 300	Mercedes-Benz	B00C	1997	
7170	OU96.508	Mercedes-Benz Sprinter 300	Mercedes-Benz	B00C	1997	
7171	OU96.503	Mercedes-Benz Sprinter 300	Mercedes-Benz	B00C	1997	
7172	OU96.506	Mercedes-Benz Sprinter 300	Mercedes-Benz	B00C	1997	
7173	OU96.490	Mercedes-Benz Sprinter 300	Mercedes-Benz	B00C	1997	
7174	OU96.501	Mercedes-Benz Sprinter 300	Mercedes-Benz	B00C	1997	
7175	OU96.489	Mercedes-Benz Sprinter 300	Mercedes-Benz	B00C	1997	
7176	OU96.509	Mercedes-Benz Sprinter 300	Mercedes-Benz	B00C	1997	
7177	OU96.505	Mercedes-Benz Sprinter 300	Mercedes-Benz	B00C	1997	
7178	OU96.502	Mercedes-Benz Sprinter 300	Mercedes-Benz	B00C	1997	
7179	OU96.510	Mercedes-Benz Sprinter 300	Mercedes-Benz	B00C	1997	
7180	OU96.512	Mercedes-Benz Sprinter 300	Mercedes-Benz	B00C	1997	
7181	OU96.511	Mercedes-Benz Sprinter 300	Mercedes-Benz	B00C	1997	
7182	OU96.507	Mercedes-Benz Sprinter 300	Mercedes-Benz	B00C	1997	
7183	OU96.578	Mercedes-Benz Sprinter 300	Mercedes-Benz	B00C	1997	
7184	OU96.571	Mercedes-Benz Sprinter 300	Mercedes-Benz	B00C	1997	
7185	OU96.	Mercedes-Benz Sprinter 300	Mercedes-Benz	B00C	1997	
7186	OU96.647	Mercedes-Benz Sprinter 300	Mercedes-Benz	B00C	1997	
7187	OU96.	Mercedes-Benz Sprinter 300	Mercedes-Benz	B00C	1997	
7188	OU96.	Mercedes-Benz Sprinter 300	Mercedes-Benz	B00C	1997	
7189	OU96.661	Mercedes-Benz Sprinter 300	Mercedes-Benz	B00C	1997	
7190	OU96.	Mercedes-Benz Sprinter 300	Mercedes-Benz	B00C	1997	
7191	OU96.660	Mercedes-Benz Sprinter 300	Mercedes-Benz	B00C	1997	
7192	OU96.662	Mercedes-Benz Sprinter 300	Mercedes-Benz	B00C	1997	
7193	OU96.648	Mercedes-Benz Sprinter 300	Mercedes-Benz	B00C	1997	

Livery: Operations within København carry Hovedstadsområdets Trafikselskab's yellow livery onto which Unibus have applied a blue and white striped banner to the roof-line. The open-top double-decks operate as '*Copenhagen Pride*' in a red and grey livery.

Operations:

Gilleleje Turistart AF 1994:-
7165   7167   7168

Unibus Handicapbefordring A/s

7127	7128	7129	7130	7131	7132	7133	7136	7137	7138
7139	7140	7160	7166	7169	7170	7171	7172	7173	7174
7175	7176	7177	7178	7179	7180	7181	7182	7183	7184
7186	7189	7191	7192	7193	+ 5 un-numbered and 2 undelivered				

Unibus Rutetrafik:- remainder

Vehicle Index

Reg	Operator	Reg	Operator	Reg	Operator	Reg	Operator
3CLT	South London	A103OUG	Crosville Cymru	A151FPG	The Shires	A543PCW	United
7CLT	South London	A103SYE	South London	A151UDM	North Western	A560KWY	Yorkshire Bus
70CLT	County	A104OUG	Crosville Cymru	A152EPA	The Shires	A562KWY	Yorkshire Bus
81SVO	Midland Fox	A105EPA	United	A152FPG	The Shires	A563KWY	United
82HBC	Midland Red	A108EPA	Midland Fox	A152UDM	Midland Red	A564KWY	Yorkshire Bus
109CRC	Midland Fox	A110FDL	Southend	A153EPA	The Shires	A565NWX	Yorkshire Bus
111XKT	Midland Fox	A113EPA	The Shires	A153FPG	The Shires	A566NWX	Yorkshire Bus
123TKM	Midland Red	A115EPA	Midland Red	A153UDM	North Western	A567NWX	Yorkshire Bus
124CLT	County	A116EPA	United	A154EPA	London & Country	A568NWX	Yorkshire Bus
124YTW	Midland Red	A117EPA	United	A154FPG	The Shires	A569NWX	Yorkshire Bus
185CLT	County	A118EPA	Midland Red	A154UDM	Midland Red	A570NWX	Yorkshire Bus
205CLT	County	A119EPA	United	A155EPA	The Shires	A571NWX	Yorkshire Bus
217CLT	South London	A120EPA	United	A155FPG	The Shires	A572NWX	Yorkshire Bus
319CLT	South London	A121EPA	Midland Red	A155UDM	Midland Red	A573NWX	Yorkshire Bus
324CLT	South London	A122EPA	United	A156EPA	London & Country	A574NWX	Yorkshire Bus
361CLT	County	A124EPA	Southend	A157EPA	The Shires	A575NWX	Yorkshire Bus
398CLT	South London	A125EPA	Midland Fox	A160EPA	Midland Red	A576NWX	Yorkshire Bus
407CLT	Clydeside	A129DTO	Midland Fox	A172VFM	Midland Red	A577NWX	Yorkshire Bus
422AKN	Midland Red	A130DTO	Midland Fox	A195KKF	Midland Red	A578NWX	Yorkshire Bus
429UFM	Midland Red	A130FDC	United	A201OKJ	Maidstone & Dist	A579NWX	Yorkshire Bus
430UFM	Midland Red	A131DTO	Midland Fox	A202OKJ	Maidstone & Dist	A580NWX	Yorkshire Bus
445YMU	United	A131FDC	United	A203OKJ	Maidstone & Dist	A581NWX	Yorkshire Bus
453CLT	Southend	A132DTO	Midland Fox	A204OKJ	Maidstone & Dist	A582NWX	Yorkshire Bus
464CLT	County	A132EPA	United	A205OKJ	Maidstone & Dist	A583NWX	Yorkshire Bus
468KPX	Midland Red	A132SMA	Midland Fox	A207OKJ	Maidstone & Dist	A584NWX	Yorkshire Bus
479BOC	Midland Red	A133DTO	Midland Fox	A208OKJ	Maidstone & Dist	A585NWX	Yorkshire Bus
480CLT	South London	A133SMA	Midland Fox	A209OKJ	Maidstone & Dist	A586NWX	Yorkshire Bus
488BDN	Midland Red	A134FDC	United	A210OKJ	Maidstone & Dist	A587NWX	Yorkshire Bus
494WYA	Maidstone & Dist	A134SMA	Midland Fox	A215PEV	Midland Red	A588NWX	Yorkshire Bus
519CLT	South London	A135FDC	United	A222DRM	Maidstone & Dist	A589NWX	Yorkshire Bus
530MUY	County	A135SMA	Midland Fox	A233GHN	United	A590NWX	Yorkshire Bus
544WRA	Yorkshire Bus	A136EPA	Midland Red	A234GHN	United	A698EAU	The Shires
544XVW	Maidstone & Dist	A136FDC	United	A235GHN	United	A699EAU	The Shires
558LKP	Maidstone & Dist	A137FDC	United	A236GHN	United	A700THV	Leaside
565LON	Midland Red	A138FDC	United	A237GHN	United	A701HVT	Midland Red
593CLT	South London	A139EPA	Midland Red	A238GHN	United	A702HVT	Midland Red
614WEH	Midland Red	A139MRN	North Western	A240GHN	Kentish Bus	A703HVT	Midland Red
648WHK	United	A139SMA	North Western	A241GHN	Kentish Bus	A704HVT	Midland Red
656DYE	South London	A140FDC	United	A242GHN	Kentish Bus	A705HVT	Midland Red
662NKR	Midland Fox	A140MRN	North Western	A243GHN	Kentish Bus	A706HVT	Midland Red
681CXM	United	A140SMA	North Western	A244GHN	Kentish Bus	A707HVT	Midland Red
725DYE	Leaside	A141DPE	The Shires	A246SVW	Southend	A708HVT	Midland Red
734DYE	South London	A141EPA	Southend	A247SVW	Southend	A709HVT	Midland Red
784RBF	Midland Red	A141MRN	North Western	A248SVW	Southend	A736THV	South London
796UHT	Midland Fox	A141SMA	North Western	A249SVW	Southend	A744THV	Leaside
801DYE	South London	A142FDC	United	A250SVW	Southend	A829JLT	Maidstone & Dist
803HOM	Midland Red	A142SMA	North Western	A278ROW	Midland Fox	A855UYM	Colchester
815DYE	South London	A143DPE	The Shires	A280ROW	Midland Fox	A856UYM	Colchester
822DYE	South London	A143EPA	The Shires	A441UUV	South London	A858YOX	Midland Red
838AFM	North Western	A144EPA	London & Country	A442UUV	South London	A859YOX	Midland Red
852YYC	Midland Fox	A144OFR	North Western	A501EJF	Midland Fox	A888PKR	Maidstone & Dist
869SVX	Northumbria	A146EPA	United	A502EJF	Midland Fox	A889PKR	Maidstone & Dist
904AXY	Midland Red	A146FPG	London & Country	A503EJF	Midland Fox	A890PKR	Maidstone & Dist
4225FM	Clydeside	A146OFR	North Western	A504EJF	Midland Fox	A894SUL	South London
A11GTA	Maidstone & Dist	A147FPG	Clydeside	A505EJF	Midland Fox	A895SUL	South London
A14GTA	Maidstone & Dist	A147OFR	North Western	A507EJF	Midland Fox	A898KAH	Midland Red
A31LWX	United	A147UDM	North Western	A508EJF	Midland Fox	A903SUL	Leaside
A37SMA	Midland Fox	A148FPG	London & Country	A509EJF	Midland Fox	A909LWU	United
A39SMA	Midland Red	A148UDM	North Western	A510EJF	Midland Fox	A919SUL	Leaside
A41SMA	Midland Red	A149FPG	The Shires	A511EJF	Midland Fox	A927SUL	South London
A42SMA	Midland Red	A149UDM	North Western	A512EJF	Midland Fox	A929SUL	Leaside
A50LHG	North Western	A150EPA	The Shires	A516EVN	United	A930SUL	South London
A101EPA	Midland Red	A150FPG	London & Country	A517EVN	United	A936SUL	Leaside
A101SYE	South London	A150UDM	Midland Red	A518EVN	United	A939SUL	Leaside
A102SYE	South London	A151EPA	The Shires	A542PCW	United	A948SUL	South London

A949KAJ	United	ARP620X	The Shires	B136WUL	Leaside	B228WUL	Leaside
A959SYF	South London	AVT345S	Midland Red	B137GAU	Midland Fox	B229WUL	Leaside
A973SYF	South London	AYR313T	London & Country	B137WUL	Leaside	B231WUL	Leaside
A984SYF	South London	B26ADW	North Western	B138GAU	Midland Fox	B233WUL	Leaside
A988SYF	Leaside	B27ADW	North Western	B138WUL	Leaside	B239WUL	Leaside
A996SYF	Leaside	B45NDX	United	B139GAU	Midland Fox	B245NVN	Kentish Bus
A998SYF	South London	B51XFV	North Western	B139WUL	Leaside	B246NVN	Kentish Bus
AAK112T	Clydeside	B62WUL	South London	B140GAU	Midland Fox	B247NVN	Kentish Bus
AAL303A	Midland Red	B70WUL	Leaside	B140WUL	Leaside	B248NVN	Kentish Bus
AAL404A	Midland Red	B74WUL	Leaside	B141GAU	Midland Fox	B248WUL	County
AAX590A	Midland Red	B75WUL	Leaside	B142GAU	Midland Fox	B249WUL	Leaside
ACM705X	Midland Fox	B83SWX	Southend	B143GAU	Midland Fox	B251NVN	United
ACM706X	Midland Fox	B84SWX	Southend	B145ALG	Midland Red	B252PHN	United
ACM707X	Midland Fox	B84WUL	South London	B146ALG	Midland Fox	B252WUL	Leaside
ACM710X	Midland Fox	B85SWX	Southend	B147ALG	Midland Red	B253PHN	United
ACM711X	Midland Fox	B85WUL	South London	B148ALG	Midland Red	B253WUL	Leaside
ACW764R	North Western	B86WUL	South London	B149ALG	Midland Red	B254WUL	Leaside
ADZ4731	The Shires	B87WUL	South London	B149TRN	North Western	B255RAJ	United
AEF221Y	Crosville Cymru	B88WUL	South London	B150ALG	Midland Red	B255WUL	Leaside
AEF222Y	Crosville Cymru	B89WUL	South London	B150TRN	North Western	B256RAJ	Kentish Bus
AEF223Y	United	B90WUL	South London	B151ALG	Midland Fox	B261KPF	County
AEF224Y	Crosville Cymru	B91WUL	South London	B151TRN	North Western	B262KPF	Northumbria
AEF225Y	United	B92WUL	South London	B152WUL	Leaside	B262LPH	The Shires
AEF226Y	United	B93WUL	South London	B153TRN	North Western	B263WUL	Leaside
AEF227Y	United	B94WUL	South London	B154TRN	North Western	B265KPF	Northumbria
AEF228Y	United	B95WUL	South London	B154WUL	Leaside	B265WUL	Leaside
AEF229Y	Crosville Cymru	B96WUL	South London	B155TRN	North Western	B266KPF	United
AEF990Y	London & Country	B97WUL	South London	B155WUL	Leaside	B270LPH	The Shires
AFB589V	United	B98WUL	South London	B162WUL	Leaside	B271LPH	The Shires
AFB593V	Northumbria	B99WUL	South London	B164WUL	Leaside	B272LPH	The Shires
AFB597V	North Western	B100WUL	South London	B165WUL	Leaside	B273KPF	Northumbria
AFM2W	North Western	B100XTW	Southend	B169WUL	Leaside	B273LPH	The Shires
AFM3W	North Western	B101WUL	South London	B170WUL	Leaside	B274KPF	London & Country
AFM4W	North Western	B102KPF	Midland Red	B173WUL	Leaside	B274LPH	London & Country
AHW206V	Midland Red	B102WUL	South London	B175WUL	Leaside	B275LPH	London & Country
AJA118	North Western	B103KPF	Midland Red	B176WUL	Leaside	B275WUL	Leaside
AJA142B	North Western	B103WUL	South London	B179WUL	Leaside	B276KPF	Northumbria
AKP430T	Maidstone & Dist	B104KPF	Midland Red	B182WUL	Leaside	B276WUL	Leaside
ALD872B	South London	B104WUL	South London	B183BLG	Southend	B277KPF	Northumbria
ALD978B	South London	B105KPF	Midland Red	B184BLG	Southend	B278WUL	Leaside
AOL11T	North Western	B105WUL	South London	B185BLG	Southend	B279KPF	Northumbria
APM113T	London & Country	B108KPF	Midland Red	B186BLG	Midland Fox	B279WUL	Leaside
APT116W	United	B109KPF	Midland Red	B187BLG	Midland Fox	B280KPF	United
APT117W	United	B109WUL	Leaside	B189BLG	Southend	B280WUL	Leaside
APT118W	United	B110GRR	United	B190BLG	Midland Fox	B281KPF	United
APT119W	United	B111GRR	United	B191BLG	Crosville Cymru	B281WUL	Leaside
APT120W	Northumbria	B112GRR	United	B192BLG	Crosville Cymru	B282WUL	Leaside
APT121W	United	B112WUL	Leaside	B193BLG	Crosville Cymru	B283KPF	United
APT122W	United	B113GRR	United	B194BLG	Crosville Cymru	B283WUL	Leaside
APT123W	United	B114GRR	United	B196BLG	Crosville Cymru	B284KPF	Northumbria
APT126W	United	B115GRR	United	B197DTU	Midland Red	B285KPF	London & Country
APT808W	United	B116WUL	South London	B198DTU	Midland Red	B285WUL	Leaside
APT810W	Northumbria	B118KPF	The Shires	B203DTU	Midland Red	B286WUL	Leaside
APT811W	Northumbria	B121WUL	Leaside	B204DTU	Midland Red	B288KPF	London & Country
APT812W	United	B122WUL	Leaside	B208GTU	Crosville Cymru	B288WUL	Leaside
APT814W	United	B123WUL	Leaside	B209GTU	Crosville Cymru	B289WUL	Leaside
APT816W	Northumbria	B124WUL	Leaside	B209WUL	Leaside	B290WUL	Leaside
APT817W	Northumbria	B126WUL	Leaside	B210GTU	Crosville Cymru	B291WUL	Leaside
ARN895Y	United	B127WUL	Leaside	B210WUL	Leaside	B292KPF	The Shires
ARN896Y	United	B128WUL	Leaside	B211GTU	Crosville Cymru	B293KPF	The Shires
ARN897Y	United	B129WUL	Leaside	B212GTU	Crosville Cymru	B293WUL	Leaside
ARN898Y	United	B130WUL	Leaside	B212JTY	North Western	B294WUL	Leaside
ARP612X	The Shires	B131WUL	Leaside	B213WUL	Leaside	B295WUL	Leaside
ARP613X	The Shires	B132WUL	Leaside	B214WUL	Leaside	B296WUL	Leaside
ARP614X	The Shires	B133WUL	Leaside	B216WUL	Leaside	B297WUL	Leaside
ARP615X	The Shires	B134GAU	Midland Fox	B217WUL	Leaside	B298WUL	Leaside
ARP616X	The Shires	B134WUL	Leaside	B219WUL	Leaside	B299WUL	Leaside
ARP617X	The Shires	B135GAU	Midland Fox	B221WUL	Leaside	B300WUL	Leaside
ARP618X	The Shires	B135WUL	Leaside	B227WUL	Leaside	B303WUL	Leaside
ARP619X	The Shires	B136GAU	Midland Fox	B227WUL	Leaside	B504PRF	Midland Red

Reg	Operator	Reg	Operator	Reg	Operator	Reg	Operator
B513LFP	Midland Fox	BKE833T	Maidstone & Dist	BYW413V	North Western	C63CHM	South London
B514LFP	Midland Fox	BKE837T	Maidstone & Dist	BYW430V	North Western	C63JTU	Crosville Cymru
B516OEH	Midland Red	BKE840T	Maidstone & Dist	BYW432V	North Western	C65CHM	South London
B591SWX	Yorkshire Bus	BKE842T	Maidstone & Dist	BYW437V	North Western	C66CHM	South London
B592SWX	Yorkshire Bus	BKE843T	Maidstone & Dist	BYX129V	South London	C74UHN	United
B593SWX	Yorkshire Bus	BKE845T	Maidstone & Dist	BYX168V	South London	C75UHN	United
B594SWX	Yorkshire Bus	BKE846T	Maidstone & Dist	BYX170V	County	C76UHN	United
B595SWX	Yorkshire Bus	BKE847T	The Shires	BYX173V	South London	C78CHM	South London
B596SWX	Yorkshire Bus	BKE848T	Maidstone & Dist	BYX175V	County	C78WRE	Midland Red
B597SWX	Yorkshire Bus	BKE852T	Maidstone & Dist	BYX182V	South London	C79CHM	South London
B598SWX	United	BKE853T	Maidstone & Dist	BYX200V	South London	C85AUB	Midland Red
B599SWX	Yorkshire Bus	BMA520W	Crosville Cymru	BYX205V	Leaside	C89NNV	London & Country
B601UUM	Yorkshire Bus	BMA521W	Crosville Cymru	BYX208V	South London	C99CHM	South London
B602UUM	Yorkshire Bus	BMA522W	Crosville Cymru	BYX210V	South London	C102CHM	South London
B603UUM	Yorkshire Bus	BMA523W	Midland Red	BYX220V	Leaside	C113CHM	South London
B603UUM	Yorkshire Bus	BMA524W	Crosville Cymru	BYX225V	South London	C131HJN	United
B604OEH	Midland Red	BOK364T	Midland Red	BYX230V	South London	C132HJN	United
B604UUM	Yorkshire Bus	BPF135Y	The Shires	BYX232V	South London	C133HJN	United
B605OEH	Midland Red	BPF136Y	The Shires	BYX233V	South London	C141SPB	Midland Red
B605UUM	Yorkshire Bus	BPL459T	London & Country	BYX240V	South London	C144NRR	Midland Fox
B606OEH	Midland Red	BPL475T	London & Country	BYX248V	South London	C144SPB	London & Country
B606UUM	Yorkshire Bus	BPL491T	London & Country	BYX251V	South London	C145NRR	Midland Red
B607OEH	Midland Red	BPL495T	North Western	BYX263V	South London	C146NRR	Midland Fox
B607UUM	Yorkshire Bus	BPR48Y	United	BYX266V	Leaside	C147NRR	Midland Fox
B608UUM	Yorkshire Bus	BPR49Y	United	BYX277V	South London	C147SPB	The Shires
B609UUM	Yorkshire Bus	BPR102Y	Midland Red	BYX280V	South London	C148NRR	Midland Fox
B724AGD	Clydeside	BPR103Y	Midland Fox	BYX282V	Leaside	C148SPB	The Shires
B725AGD	Clydeside	BPR106Y	Midland Red	BYX283V	South London	C149SPB	The Shires
B732YUD	Midland Red	BPR107Y	Midland Red	BYX290V	South London	C201EKJ	Midland Red
B733YUD	Midland Red	BPR108Y	Midland Fox	BYX296V	South London	C202EKJ	Midland Red
B734YUD	Midland Red	BPT917S	Northumbria	BYX298V	South London	C206EKJ	The Shires
B857XYR	Colchester	BPT919S	Northumbria	BYX299V	South London	C210EKJ	Midland Red
B858XRY	Colchester	BPT923S	Northumbria	BYX301V	Colchester	C214UPD	Clydeside
B859XYR	Colchester	BRC834T	Maidstone & Dist	BYX310V	Leaside	C218EKJ	Midland Red
B860XYR	Colchester	BRC835T	Maidstone & Dist	BYX314V	South London	C221EKJ	Crosville Cymru
B861XYR	Colchester	BRC837T	Maidstone & Dist	C21CHM	South London	C246SPC	London & Country
B863XYR	Grey-Green	BSJ891T	Clydeside	C22CHM	South London	C253SPC	County
B864XYR	Grey-Green	BSJ899T	Clydeside	C24CHM	South London	C254SPC	County
B865XYR	Grey-Green	BSJ902T	Clydeside	C25CHM	South London	C255SPC	County
B866XYR	Grey-Green	BSJ912T	Clydeside	C26CHM	South London	C257UAJ	Kentish Bus
B867XYR	Grey-Green	BSJ916T	Clydeside	C30EUH	Midland Fox	C258UAJ	Crosville Cymru
B868XYR	Grey-Green	BSJ921T	Clydeside	C31CHM	South London	C259UAJ	Northumbria
B870XYR	Grey-Green	BSJ922T	Clydeside	C32CHM	South London	C260SPC	County
B871XYR	Grey-Green	BSJ923T	Clydeside	C33CHM	South London	C260UAJ	Northumbria
B872XYR	Grey-Green	BSJ925T	Clydeside	C34CWT	United	C261UAJ	Northumbria
B875EOM	Midland Red	BSN878V	Midland Red	C35CHM	South London	C262SPC	Midland Red
B906RVF	United	BTU374S	North Western	C35CWT	United	C262UAJ	Northumbria
B907RVF	United	BTX152T	The Shires	C36CHM	South London	C263FGG	Clydeside
B908RVF	United	BVP763V	Midland Red	C36CWT	United	C263SPC	County
B911NBF	Midland Red	BVP764V	Midland Red	C37CHM	South London	C263XEF	Northumbria
B912NBF	Midland Red	BVP765V	Midland Red	C37CWT	United	C264FGG	Clydeside
B913NBF	Midland Red	BVP767V	Midland Red	C37WBF	Midland Red	C264XEF	Northumbria
B957LHN	United	BVP768V	Midland Red	C38CHM	South London	C265SPC	County
B958LHN	United	BVP784V	Midland Fox	C38CWT	United	C265XEF	United
B959LHN	United	BVP785V	Midland Fox	C39CWT	United	C266XEF	United
B960WRN	North Western	BVP809V	Colchester	C40CWT	United	C267XEF	United
B962WRN	North Western	BVP810V	Colchester	C41CHM	South London	C268XEF	United
B963WRN	North Western	BVP811V	North Western	C41CWT	United	C286BBP	Midland Fox
B964WRN	North Western	BVP812V	Southend	C41HHJ	Colchester	C307BUV	Leaside
B965WRN	North Western	BVP813V	Midland Fox	C42CWT	United	C308BUV	Leaside
B966WRN	North Western	BVP821V	Colchester	C42HHJ	Midland Fox	C309BUV	Leaside
B967WRN	North Western	BVV542T	The Shires	C43CWT	United	C310BUV	Leaside
B968WRN	North Western	BVV545T	The Shires	C45CHM	South London	C312BUV	Leaside
B969WRN	North Western	BVV547T	The Shires	C46CHM	South London	C313BUV	Leaside
BAZ6869	The Shires	BYW359V	North Western	C49CHM	South London	C314BUV	Leaside
BAZ7384	County	BYW367V	North Western	C50CHM	South London	C316BUV	Leaside
BHS206X	Clydeside	BYW379V	North Western	C52CHM	South London	C317BUV	Leaside
BHS207X	Clydeside	BYW402V	North Western	C56CHM	South London	C318BUV	Leaside
BKE831T	Maidstone & Dist	BYW406V	North Western	C58CHM	South London	C319BUV	Leaside
BKE832T	Maidstone & Dist	BYW412V	North Western	C59CHM	South London	C320BUV	Leaside

Reg	Operator	Reg	Operator	Reg	Operator	Reg	Operator
C321BUV	Leaside	CKE168Y	London & Country	CWR511Y	Yorkshire Bus	D139FYM	South London
C322BUV	Leaside	CKE169Y	London & Country	CWR512Y	Yorkshire Bus	D140FYM	South London
C323BUV	Leaside	CKS386X	Midland Fox	CWR513Y	Crosville Cymru	D143FYM	South London
C324BUV	Leaside	CKS390X	Midland Fox	CWR514Y	Yorkshire Bus	D146FYM	South London
C326BUV	Leaside	CPG160T	London & Country	CWR515Y	Yorkshire Bus	D147FYM	South London
C327BUV	Leaside	CPT734S	Northumbria	CWR516Y	Yorkshire Bus	D148FYM	South London
C332BUV	Leaside	CPT736S	Northumbria	CWR517Y	Yorkshire Bus	D149FYM	South London
C354BUV	South London	CPT738S	Northumbria	CWR518Y	Yorkshire Bus	D150FYM	South London
C359BUV	South London	CPT739S	Northumbria	CWR519Y	Yorkshire Bus	D152FYM	South London
C362BUV	Leaside	CTN637V	Maidstone & Dist	CWR520Y	Yorkshire Bus	D152RAK	Midland Fox
C367BUV	County	CUB60Y	United	CWR521Y	Yorkshire Bus	D153FYM	South London
C398BUV	County	CUB61Y	United	CWR522Y	Crosville Cymru	D154RAK	Midland Fox
C399BUV	Leaside	CUB63Y	United	CWR523Y	Crosville Cymru	D154THG	North Western
C401BUV	Leaside	CUB64Y	United	CWR524Y	Yorkshire Bus	D154VRP	Crosville Cymru
C402BUV	Leaside	CUB66Y	United	CWR527Y	Crosville Cymru	D155FYM	South London
C404BUV	Leaside	CUB68Y	United	CWR528Y	Yorkshire Bus	D155HML	Maidstone & Dist
C405BUV	Leaside	CUB69Y	United	CWR529Y	Yorkshire Bus	D156HML	London & Country
C406BUV	Leaside	CUB71Y	United	CWR530Y	Yorkshire Bus	D157FYM	South London
C407BUV	South London	CUL83V	County	CWU326T	United	D157HML	Maidstone & Dist
C413BUV	Leaside	CUL88V	Clydeside	D22KKP	Midland Red	D158FYM	South London
C417BUV	Leaside	CUL94V	Clydeside	D23KKP	Midland Red	D159FYM	South London
C424BUV	Leaside	CUL95V	Leaside	D23RPP	The Shires	D160FYM	South London
C449BKM	Clydeside	CUL100V	County	D24KKP	Midland Red	D161FYM	South London
C450BKM	Clydeside	CUL143V	Clydeside	D25KKP	Clydeside	D162FYM	South London
C451BKM	Clydeside	CUL152V	Clydeside	D27KKP	Midland Red	D162RAK	Midland Fox
C452GKE	Clydeside	CUL179C	South London	D28KKP	Crosville Cymru	D163FYM	South London
C453GKE	Clydeside	CUL217C	South London	D31RWC	Crosville Cymru	D164FYM	South London
C454GKE	Clydeside	CUL366C	South London	D32KKP	Midland Red	D165FYM	South London
C475TAY	Midland Fox	CUV185C	Leaside	D32RWC	Crosville Cymru	D166FYM	South London
C610ANW	Yorkshire Bus	CUV261C	Leaside	D36KKP	The Shires	D167FYM	South London
C611ANW	Yorkshire Bus	CUV264C	South London	D38KKP	Midland Red	D167VRP	Crosville Cymru
C612ANW	Yorkshire Bus	CUV266C	South London	D40MAG	County	D168FYM	South London
C613ANW	Northumbria	CUV267C	Leaside	D43RWC	Colchester	D168VRP	Clydeside
C614ANW	Northumbria	CUV277C	Leaside	D44RWC	Midland Fox	D169FYM	South London
C616ANW	Northumbria	CUV280C	Leaside	D45OKH	County	D170VRP	Crosville Cymru
C617ANW	Northumbria	CUV287C	Leaside	D59TLV	Midland Fox	D171FYM	South London
C632PAU	Midland Fox	CUV292C	Leaside	D79VCC	Crosville Cymru	D171VRP	Crosville Cymru
C707JMB	Clydeside	CUV294C	Leaside	D80UTF	Midland Fox	D172VRP	Crosville Cymru
C708JMB	Clydeside	CUV301C	South London	D80VCC	Crosville Cymru	D173VRP	Crosville Cymru
C726JJO	Midland Red	CUV304C	Leaside	D81UTF	Midland Fox	D174FYM	South London
C802SDY	Midland Red	CUV307C	South London	D82VCC	Crosville Cymru	D174VRP	Crosville Cymru
C804BYY	South London	CUV315C	Leaside	D85VCC	Crosville Cymru	D175FYM	South London
C805BYY	South London	CUV323C	Leaside	D86VCC	Crosville Cymru	D176FYM	South London
C806BYY	South London	CUV324C	South London	D88CFA	Midland Red	D176LNA	Midland Red
C814BYY	South London	CUV325C	Leaside	D88VCC	Crosville Cymru	D177FYM	South London
C817BYY	South London	CUV326C	Leaside	D89VCC	Crosville Cymru	D178FYM	South London
C820BYY	South London	CUV328C	Leaside	D91CFA	Midland Red	D179FYM	South London
C822SDY	Midland Red	CUV329C	Leaside	D91VCC	Crosville Cymru	D181FYM	South London
C823SDY	Midland Red	CUV330C	Leaside	D92CFA	Midland Red	D182FYM	South London
C874CYX	County	CUV333C	South London	D92VCC	Crosville Cymru	D183FYM	South London
C876CYX	County	CUV334C	Leaside	D94VCC	Crosville Cymru	D184FYM	South London
C920FMP	Yorkshire Bus	CUV340C	South London	D95CFA	Midland Red	D185FYM	South London
CAZ6852	The Shires	CUV343C	South London	D96CFA	Midland Red	D186FYM	South London
CBD779K	The Shires	CUV344C	Leaside	D98CFA	Midland Red	D187FYM	South London
CBD897T	The Shires	CUV346C	Leaside	D98VCC	Crosville Cymru	D188FYM	South London
CBD899T	The Shires	CUV347C	South London	D99VCC	Crosville Cymru	D188VRP	Crosville Cymru
CBD900T	The Shires	CUV350C	Leaside	D101NDW	London & Country	D189FYM	South London
CBD904T	The Shires	CUV351C	South London	D102CFA	Midland Red	D189VRP	Crosville Cymru
CBF21Y	Midland Fox	CUV354C	Leaside	D102NDW	London & Country	D191FYM	South London
CBV791S	North Western	CUV355C	Leaside	D104CFA	Midland Red	D192FYM	South London
CBV792S	North Western	CUV356C	Leaside	D107CFA	Midland Red	D193FYM	South London
CBV794S	North Western	CUV359C	Leaside	D108NDW	Maidstone & Dist	D194FYM	South London
CCY817V	North Western	CVA110V	Maidstone & Dist	D111OWG	Midland Fox	D195FYM	South London
CCY819V	United	CVN174Y	United	D118OWG	Midland Fox	D196FYM	South London
CCY820V	Crosville Cymru	CWR505Y	United	D124OWG	Midland Fox	D197FYM	South London
CEF230Y	Crosville Cymru	CWR506Y	Crosville Cymru	D130OWG	Midland Fox	D198FYM	South London
CEF231Y	Kentish Bus	CWR507Y	Crosville Cymru	D134OWG	Midland Fox	D199FYM	South London
CEF232Y	Crosville Cymru	CWR508Y	Yorkshire Bus	D135FYM	South London	D200FYM	South London
CFM350S	North Western	CWR509Y	Crosville Cymru	D135NUS	Midland Red	D201FYM	South London
CFM351S	North Western	CWR510Y	Yorkshire Bus	D138OWG	Midland Fox	D202FYM	South London

Reg	Operator	Reg	Operator	Reg	Operator	Reg	Operator
D202SKD	Clydeside	D387VKJ	Maidstone & Dist	DCA525X	Crosville Cymru	E51UKL	Crosville Cymru
D203FYM	South London	D401MHS	Midland Red	DCA527X	Crosville Cymru	E52UKL	Maidstone & Dist
D203RGH	The Shires	D406NNA	North Western	DCA528X	Crosville Cymru	E53UKL	Maidstone & Dist
D203SKD	The Shires	D413NNA	North Western	DCA529X	Crosville Cymru	E54UKL	Maidstone & Dist
D204FBK	Yorkshire Bus	D427NNA	North Western	DCA530X	Crosville Cymru	E55UKL	Maidstone & Dist
D204FYM	South London	D433UHC	Crosville Cymru	DCA532X	Crosville Cymru	E56UKL	Maidstone & Dist
D204SKD	Clydeside	D434UHC	Crosville Cymru	DCA533X	Crosville Cymru	E57UKL	Maidstone & Dist
D205FYM	South London	D435UHC	Crosville Cymru	DCA534X	Crosville Cymru	E58UKL	Maidstone & Dist
D205SKD	Clydeside	D436UHC	Crosville Cymru	DDX741T	County	E59UKL	Crosville Cymru
D206FYM	South London	D437UHC	Crosville Cymru	DGR477S	Southend	E60UKL	Crosville Cymru
D206SKD	The Shires	D438UHC	Crosville Cymru	DIL7916	The Shires	E61UKL	Midland Fox
D207FYM	South London	D439NNA	Clydeside	DJN25X	Midland Red	E62UKL	Midland Fox
D208FYM	South London	D439UHC	Crosville Cymru	DOC19V	United	E63UKL	Maidstone & Dist
D208SKD	The Shires	D440UHC	Crosville Cymru	DOC20V	North Western	E64UKL	Maidstone & Dist
D209FYM	South London	D441RKE	Crosville Cymru	DOC21V	North Western	E65KXE	Maidstone & Dist
D209SKD	Midland Fox	D441UHC	Crosville Cymru	DOC22V	North Western	E72KBF	Midland Red
D210FYM	South London	D442UHC	Crosville Cymru	DOC24V	United	E88OJT	London & Country
D210SKD	The Shires	D443UHC	Crosville Cymru	DOC26V	Midland Red	E89OJT	London & Country
D211FYM	South London	D444UHC	Crosville Cymru	DOC29V	Midland Red	E90OJT	London & Country
D212FYM	South London	D445UHC	Crosville Cymru	DOC30V	North Western	E90WCM	Midland Red
D213FYM	South London	D446UHC	Crosville Cymru	DOC31V	United	E91WCM	Midland Red
D214FYM	South London	D464EAJ	United	DOC32V	North Western	E93WCM	Midland Red
D216FYM	South London	D465EAJ	United	DOC33V	United	E94WCM	Midland Red
D218FYM	South London	D466EAJ	United	DOC36V	North Western	E95WCM	Midland Red
D220FYM	South London	D469EAJ	United	DOC37V	Midland Red	E96WCM	Midland Red
D221FYM	South London	D471EAJ	United	DOC38V	North Western	E99WCM	Midland Red
D222FYM	South London	D472EAJ	United	DOC40V	United	E104JYV	Grey-Green
D222SKD	Midland Fox	D473EAJ	United	DOC43V	North Western	E105JYV	Grey-Green
D223FYM	South London	D474EAJ	United	DOC45V	North Western	E107JYV	Grey-Green
D223SKD	Midland Fox	D475EAJ	United	DOC47V	North Western	E109JYV	Grey-Green
D224FYM	South London	D477EAJ	United	DPH502T	London & Country	E110JYV	Grey-Green
D224SKD	Midland Fox	D478EAJ	United	DTG366V	County	E111KYN	Grey-Green
D225FYM	South London	D479EAJ	United	DTG367V	County	E112KYN	Grey-Green
D226FYM	South London	D480EAJ	United	DTG372V	County	E113KYN	Grey-Green
D226SKD	Midland Fox	D534FAE	Midland Red	DUP745S	Northumbria	E114KYN	Grey-Green
D227FYM	South London	D538FAE	Midland Red	DUP747S	Northumbria	E116UTX	Yorkshire Bus
D228FYM	South London	D603ACW	The Shires	DUP753S	Northumbria	E136KYW	London & Country
D229FYM	South London	D643CVN	United	DUP756S	United	E141KYW	London & Country
D230FYM	South London	D646CVN	United	E21ECH	Midland Red	E145KYW	London & Country
D231FYM	South London	D647CVN	United	E23ECH	Midland Fox	E149BTO	Midland Fox
D232FYM	South London	D648CVN	United	E24ECH	Midland Fox	E150BTO	Midland Fox
D233FYM	South London	D651CVN	United	E25ECH	Midland Fox	E151BTO	Midland Fox
D234FYM	South London	D653CVN	United	E25UNE	Midland Red	E151OMD	Kentish Bus
D235FYM	South London	D656CVN	United	E26ECH	Midland Fox	E152BTO	Midland Fox
D236FYM	South London	D658CVN	United	E26UNE	Midland Red	E152OMD	Kentish Bus
D237FYM	South London	D659CVN	United	E27UNE	Midland Red	E153BTO	Midland Fox
D238FYM	South London	D660CVN	United	E28UNE	Midland Red	E153OMD	Kentish Bus
D239FYM	South London	D676MHS	Midland Red	E29UNE	Midland Red	E154OMD	Kentish Bus
D240FYM	South London	D678MHS	Midland Red	E30UNE	Midland Red	E155OMD	Kentish Bus
D241FYM	South London	D680MHS	Midland Red	E31NEF	North Western	E156OMD	Kentish Bus
D242FYM	South London	D682MHS	Midland Red	E31UNE	Midland Red	E157OMD	Kentish Bus
D243FYM	South London	D683MHS	Midland Red	E32NEF	North Western	E158OMD	Kentish Bus
D245FYM	South London	D906MVU	Midland Fox	E32UNE	Midland Red	E159OMD	Kentish Bus
D246FYM	South London	D916VCN	Northumbria	E33EVW	Crosville Cymru	E160OMD	Kentish Bus
D247FYM	South London	D954VCN	London & Country	E33NEF	North Western	E161OMD	Kentish Bus
D248FYM	South London	D959UDY	Crosville Cymru	E34EVW	Crosville Cymru	E164OMD	Kentish Bus
D249FYM	South London	D960EOW	Northumbria	E34NEF	Kentish Bus	E168OMD	London & Country
D249NCS	North Western	D960UDY	Crosville Cymru	E35EVW	Crosville Cymru	E181UWF	Midland Fox
D250FYM	South London	D963UDY	Crosville Cymru	E36EVW	Crosville Cymru	E188CNE	Midland Fox
D251FYM	South London	D964UDY	Crosville Cymru	E37EVW	Crosville Cymru	E188UWF	Midland Fox
D252FYM	South London	D965UDY	Crosville Cymru	E41UKL	Maidstone & Dist	E201HRY	Midland Fox
D253FYM	South London	D966UDY	Crosville Cymru	E42UKL	Maidstone & Dist	E202HRY	Midland Fox
D254FYM	South London	D967UDY	Crosville Cymru	E43UKL	Maidstone & Dist	E203HRY	Midland Fox
D255FYM	South London	D973VCN	Northumbria	E44UKL	Maidstone & Dist	E205TUB	Yorkshire Bus
D256FYM	South London	D975VCN	Northumbria	E45UKL	Maidstone & Dist	E206HRY	Midland Fox
D257FYM	South London	D989JYG	The Shires	E46UKL	Maidstone & Dist	E208HRY	Midland Fox
D257NCS	North Western	DBV133Y	North Western	E47UKL	Maidstone & Dist	E209HRY	Midland Fox
D258FYM	South London	DBV135Y	North Western	E48UKL	Crosville Cymru	E212HRY	Midland Fox
D259FYM	South London	DBV136Y	North Western	E49UKL	Crosville Cymru	E213HRY	Midland Fox
D319DEF	Midland Red	DBV845W	North Western	E50UKL	Crosville Cymru	E214HRY	Midland Fox

Reg	Operator	Reg	Operator	Reg	Operator	Reg	Operator
E254TUB	Yorkshire Bus	E420EBH	The Shires	E896KYW	Grey-Green	ERF23Y	United
E255TUB	Yorkshire Bus	E448TYG	County	E897KYW	Grey-Green	ESK987	London & Country
E256TUB	Yorkshire Bus	E478NSC	Midland Red	E898KYW	Grey-Green	ESK988	London & Country
E257TUB	Yorkshire Bus	E479CNM	The Shires	E933UBO	Midland Fox	EWF474V	Midland Fox
E258TUB	Yorkshire Bus	E486CNM	The Shires	E963PME	United	EWF484V	Midland Fox
E259TUB	Yorkshire Bus	E564BNK	County	E965PME	The Shires	EWF488V	Midland Fox
E260TUB	Yorkshire Bus	E564YBU	Midland Red	E966PME	The Shires	EWT206Y	United
E261TUB	Yorkshire Bus	E565BNK	County	E967PME	Crosville Cymru	EWT207Y	Crosville Cymru
E262TUB	Yorkshire Bus	E611LFV	Midland Red	E968PME	Crosville Cymru	EWT208Y	United
E263TUB	Yorkshire Bus	E661AWJ	The Shires	E969PME	The Shires	EWT209Y	Crosville Cymru
E264TUB	Yorkshire Bus	E662AWJ	The Shires	E970NMK	The Shires	EWT210Y	United
E265WUB	Yorkshire Bus	E663AWJ	The Shires	E970PME	The Shires	EWW539Y	Yorkshire Bus
E266KEF	United	E667YDT	County	E971DNK	The Shires	EWW540Y	Yorkshire Bus
E266WUB	Yorkshire Bus	E673DCU	North Western	E972DNK	The Shires	EWW541Y	Yorkshire Bus
E267KEF	United	E676DCU	Northumbria	E973DNK	The Shires	EWW542Y	Yorkshire Bus
E267WUB	Yorkshire Bus	E677DCU	Crosville Cymru	E975DNK	The Shires	EWW543Y	Yorkshire Bus
E268KEF	United	E678DCU	Crosville Cymru	E976DNK	The Shires	EWW545Y	Yorkshire Bus
E268WUB	Yorkshire Bus	E701XKR	Midland Fox	E977DNK	The Shires	EWW546Y	Yorkshire Bus
E269KEF	United	E702XKR	Midland Fox	E978DNK	The Shires	EWW547Y	Yorkshire Bus
E269WUB	Yorkshire Bus	E801BTN	Northumbria	E979DNK	The Shires	EWW548Y	Yorkshire Bus
E270KEF	United	E802BTN	Northumbria	E980NMK	Crosville Cymru	EWW550Y	Yorkshire Bus
E270WUB	Yorkshire Bus	E803BTN	Northumbria	E985DNK	The Shires	EWW551Y	Yorkshire Bus
E271KEF	United	E804BTN	Northumbria	E986DNK	The Shires	EWW552Y	Yorkshire Bus
E271WUB	Yorkshire Bus	E805BTN	Northumbria	E988DNK	The Shires	EWX211Y	Crosville Cymru
E272KEF	United	E806BTN	Northumbria	E990DNK	The Shires	EWX212Y	Crosville Cymru
E273KEF	United	E809BTN	Northumbria	E990NMK	Midland Red	EWX213Y	Crosville Cymru
E274KEF	United	E810BTN	Northumbria	E991DNK	The Shires	EWX214Y	Crosville Cymru
E275KEF	United	E812BTN	Northumbria	E992DNK	The Shires	EWX215Y	Crosville Cymru
E296VOM	County	E813BTN	Northumbria	E992NMK	Midland Red	EWX531Y	Yorkshire Bus
E299OMG	Crosville Cymru	E813JSX	Clydeside	E993DNK	The Shires	EWX532Y	Yorkshire Bus
E323OMG	The Shires	E814BTN	Northumbria	E993NMK	Midland Red	EWX533Y	Yorkshire Bus
E323WYS	Clydeside	E815BTN	Northumbria	E994DNK	The Shires	EWX534Y	Yorkshire Bus
E324WYS	Clydeside	E816BTN	Northumbria	E995DNK	The Shires	EWX535Y	Yorkshire Bus
E325WYS	Clydeside	E817BTN	Northumbria	E997DNK	The Shires	EWX536Y	Yorkshire Bus
E326LHN	Midland Fox	E818BTN	Northumbria	E999DNK	The Shires	EWX537Y	Yorkshire Bus
E327LHN	Midland Fox	E819BTN	Northumbria	EAH887Y	United	EWX538Y	Yorkshire Bus
E328LHN	Midland Fox	E820BTN	Northumbria	EDZ215	Northumbria	EYE317V	Leaside
E328OMG	Crosville Cymru	E821BTN	Northumbria	EEH901Y	Northumbria	EYE336V	Colchester
E329EJR	Northumbria	E822BTN	Northumbria	EEH902Y	Midland Red	F22XVP	Midland Fox
E330LHN	Midland Fox	E823BTN	Northumbria	EEH903Y	Midland Red	F23XVP	Midland Fox
E330WYS	Clydeside	E824BTN	Northumbria	EEH904Y	Midland Red	F24XVP	Midland Fox
E331LHN	Midland Fox	E825BTN	Northumbria	EEH905Y	Midland Red	F25XVP	Midland Fox
E331WYS	Clydeside	E826BTN	Northumbria	EEH906Y	Midland Red	F26XVP	Midland Fox
E332LHN	Midland Fox	E827BTN	Northumbria	EEH907Y	Midland Red	F27JRC	Midland Fox
E332WYS	Clydeside	E829AWA	Midland Red	EEH908Y	Northumbria	F27XVP	Midland Fox
E334LHN	Midland Fox	E829BTN	Northumbria	EEH909Y	Midland Red	F28JRC	Midland Fox
E334WYS	Clydeside	E830BTN	Northumbria	EEH910Y	Midland Red	F28XVP	Midland Fox
E335DRO	The Shires	E831BTN	Northumbria	EGB79T	United	F29XVP	Midland Fox
E335WYS	Clydeside	E832BTN	Northumbria	EGF220B	South London	F33ENF	Midland Red
E337WYS	Clydeside	E833BTN	Northumbria	EKL456K	Maidstone & Dist	F34ENF	Midland Red
E338WYS	Clydeside	E834BTN	Northumbria	EMB360S	North Western	F35ENF	Midland Red
E339WYS	Clydeside	E836BKL	Maidstone & Dist	EMB366S	North Western	F36ENF	Midland Red
E341DRO	The Shires	E836BTN	Northumbria	EMB367S	North Western	F39ENF	Midland Red
E342WYS	Clydeside	E840BTN	Northumbria	EON823V	North Western	F39HOD	Midland Red
E343WYS	Clydeside	E841BTN	Northumbria	EON825V	Southend	F40ENF	Midland Red
E344WYS	Clydeside	E842BTN	Northumbria	EON826V	Colchester	F44XVP	Midland Red
E345WYS	Clydeside	E844BTN	Northumbria	EON829V	Colchester	F45ENF	Maidstone & Dist
E348WYS	Clydeside	E845BTN	Northumbria	EON831V	Midland Fox	F46ENF	Maidstone & Dist
E349WYS	Clydeside	E873NJD	South London	EPD511V	London & Country	F47ENF	Maidstone & Dist
E350WYS	Clydeside	E881YKY	The Shires	EPD523V	The Shires	F48ENF	Maidstone & Dist
E351WYS	Clydeside	E882YKY	The Shires	EPD530V	London & Country	F51ENF	Midland Red
E352NEG	County	E885KYW	Maidstone & Dist	EPD538V	London & Country	F52ENF	Midland Red
E353NEG	County	E886KYW	Maidstone & Dist	EPD543V	London & Country	F61PRE	Midland Red
E353WYS	Clydeside	E887KYW	Maidstone & Dist	EPH210V	Kentish Bus	F61SMC	County
E354NEG	County	E888KYW	County	EPH220V	Kentish Bus	F62SMC	County
E354WYS	Clydeside	E889KYW	County	EPH221V	Kentish Bus	F63SMC	County
E355WYS	Clydeside	E890KYW	Maidstone & Dist	EPH223V	London & Country	F66BKK	Maidstone & Dist
E413EPE	Midland Fox	E891AKN	Maidstone & Dist	EPH228V	London & Country	F66FKW	Crosville Cymru
E415EPE	Midland Fox	E891KYW	County	EPH229V	London & Country	F67BKK	Maidstone & Dist
E417EPE	Midland Fox	E895KYW	Grey-Green	EPH232V	Kentish Bus	F67FKW	Crosville Cymru

Reg	Operator	Reg	Operator	Reg	Operator	Reg	Operator
F68BKK	Maidstone & Dist	F144PHM	Grey-Green	F291AWW	Yorkshire Bus	F576SMG	Southend
F68FKW	Crosville Cymru	F151KGS	The Shires	F292AWW	Yorkshire Bus	F577SMG	London & Country
F69FKW	Crosville Cymru	F152KGS	The Shires	F293AWW	Yorkshire Bus	F578SMG	London & Country
F70FKW	Crosville Cymru	F153DET	Midland Fox	F294AWW	Yorkshire Bus	F579SMG	Southend
F77ERJ	Midland Red	F153KGS	The Shires	F295AWW	Yorkshire Bus	F580SMG	London & Country
F96PRE	Midland Red	F154DET	Midland Fox	F296AWW	Yorkshire Bus	F598CET	The Shires
F97PRE	Midland Red	F154DKV	County	F297AWW	Yorkshire Bus	F601EHA	Midland Red
F101TML	Leaside	F154KGS	The Shires	F298AWW	Yorkshire Bus	F602EHA	Midland Red
F102TML	Kentish Bus	F155DET	Midland Fox	F299AWW	Yorkshire Bus	F602RPG	London & Country
F102YVP	Leaside	F155DKU	Midland Red	F300AWW	Yorkshire Bus	F603EHA	Midland Red
F103TML	Leaside	F155KGS	The Shires	F300MNK	The Shires	F603RPG	London & Country
F104TML	Leaside	F156DET	Midland Fox	F301AWW	Yorkshire Bus	F604EHA	Midland Red
F104YVP	Leaside	F157DET	Midland Fox	F301MNK	The Shires	F604RPG	London & Country
F105TML	Leaside	F158DET	Midland Fox	F301RUT	Midland Fox	F605EHA	Midland Red
F105YVP	Leaside	F170DET	Midland Fox	F302AWW	Yorkshire Bus	F605RPG	London & Country
F106TML	Leaside	F181YDA	Midland Red	F302MNK	The Shires	F606EHA	Midland Red
F107TML	Leaside	F185PRE	Midland Red	F302RUT	Midland Fox	F606RPG	London & Country
F107YVP	South London	F186PRE	Midland Red	F303AWW	Yorkshire Bus	F607EHA	Midland Red
F108TML	Leaside	F187REH	Midland Red	F303JTY	Northumbria	F607RPG	London & Country
F109TML	Leaside	F188HKK	Maidstone & Dist	F303MNK	The Shires	F608EHA	Midland Red
F110SRF	Midland Red	F188REH	Midland Red	F304AWW	Yorkshire Bus	F608RPG	London & Country
F110TML	Leaside	F189HKK	Maidstone & Dist	F304JTY	Northumbria	F609EHA	Midland Red
F111TML	Kentish Bus	F189RRF	Midland Red	F305AWW	Yorkshire Bus	F609RPG	London & Country
F112TML	Leaside	F190RRF	Midland Red	F305JTY	Northumbria	F610EHA	Midland Red
F113TML	Leaside	F191SRF	Midland Red	F306AWW	Yorkshire Bus	F611EHA	Midland Red
F114TML	Kentish Bus	F192VFA	Midland Red	F306JTY	Northumbria	F612EHA	Midland Red
F115JGS	County	F201OPD	London & Country	F307AWW	Yorkshire Bus	F613EHA	Midland Red
F115PHM	Grey-Green	F210DCC	Crosville Cymru	F307JTY	Northumbria	F614EHA	Midland Red
F116PHM	Grey-Green	F211DCC	Crosville Cymru	F308AWW	Yorkshire Bus	F615EHA	Midland Red
F117PHM	Grey-Green	F212DCC	Crosville Cymru	F308JTY	Northumbria	F616EHA	Midland Red
F117XTX	Yorkshire Bus	F213DCC	Crosville Cymru	F309AWW	Yorkshire Bus	F619EHA	Midland Red
F118PHM	Grey-Green	F214DCC	Crosville Cymru	F309JTY	Northumbria	F619HGO	London & Country
F118XTX	Yorkshire Bus	F215DCC	Crosville Cymru	F310AWW	Yorkshire Bus	F621HGO	Maidstone & Dist
F119PHM	Grey-Green	F216DCC	Crosville Cymru	F310JTY	Northumbria	F622EHA	Midland Red
F120PHM	Grey-Green	F217DCC	Crosville Cymru	F311AWW	Yorkshire Bus	F623EHA	Midland Red
F121PHM	Grey-Green	F218DCC	Crosville Cymru	F311JTY	Northumbria	F624EHA	Midland Red
F121TRU	The Shires	F219DCC	Crosville Cymru	F312AWW	Yorkshire Bus	F625EHA	Midland Red
F122PHM	Grey-Green	F220DCC	Crosville Cymru	F312JTY	Northumbria	F626EHA	Midland Red
F122TRU	The Shires	F221DCC	Crosville Cymru	F313AWW	Yorkshire Bus	F630BKD	North Western
F122YVP	South London	F222DCC	Crosville Cymru	F314AWW	Yorkshire Bus	F631BKD	London & Country
F123PHM	Grey-Green	F223DCC	Crosville Cymru	F314RMH	The Shires	F632BKD	North Western
F123TRU	The Shires	F245MTW	Colchester	F326PPO	Midland Red	F633BKD	North Western
F123YVP	South London	F246MTW	Colchester	F367CHE	County	F633LMJ	The Shires
F124PHM	Grey-Green	F258GWJ	Midland Red	F379UCP	Midland Fox	F634BKD	North Western
F124TRU	The Shires	F266CEY	The Shires	F393DOA	Maidstone & Dist	F634LMJ	The Shires
F124YVP	South London	F272AWW	Yorkshire Bus	F400PUR	The Shires	F635BKD	North Western
F125PHM	Grey-Green	F272OPX	Midland Fox	F401PUR	The Shires	F635LMJ	The Shires
F125TRU	The Shires	F273AWW	Yorkshire Bus	F402PUR	The Shires	F636BKD	North Western
F126PHM	Grey-Green	F273CEY	The Shires	F403PUR	The Shires	F636LMJ	The Shires
F127PHM	Grey-Green	F274AWW	Yorkshire Bus	F404PUR	The Shires	F637BKD	North Western
F127YVP	South London	F275AWW	Yorkshire Bus	F406DUG	Midland Fox	F637LMJ	The Shires
F128PHM	Grey-Green	F275CEY	Midland Red	F407DUG	Midland Fox	F638LMJ	The Shires
F128TRU	The Shires	F276AWW	Yorkshire Bus	F424EJC	Crosville Cymru	F639LMJ	The Shires
F129PHM	Grey-Green	F276CEY	Midland Red	F425EJC	Crosville Cymru	F640LMJ	The Shires
F129YVP	South London	F277AWW	Yorkshire Bus	F425UVW	Southend	F641LMJ	The Shires
F130PHM	Grey-Green	F278AWW	Yorkshire Bus	F426EJC	Crosville Cymru	F642LMJ	The Shires
F131PHM	Grey-Green	F278HOD	Midland Red	F427EJC	Crosville Cymru	F643LMJ	The Shires
F132PHM	Grey-Green	F279AWW	Yorkshire Bus	F428EJC	Crosville Cymru	F644LMJ	The Shires
F133PHM	Grey-Green	F280AWW	Yorkshire Bus	F467UVW	Southend	F660KNL	Midland Fox
F133YVP	South London	F281AWW	Yorkshire Bus	F484EJC	Midland Red	F689RKX	The Shires
F134PHM	Grey-Green	F282AWW	Yorkshire Bus	F485EJC	Midland Red	F696GMA	The Shires
F135PHM	Grey-Green	F283AWW	Yorkshire Bus	F486EJC	Midland Red	F700LCA	Midland Red
F136PHM	Grey-Green	F284AWW	Yorkshire Bus	F506OYW	The Shires	F701ECC	Northumbria
F137PHM	Grey-Green	F285AWW	Yorkshire Bus	F523UVW	Southend	F701KMA	Crosville Cymru
F138PHM	Grey-Green	F286AWW	Yorkshire Bus	F571SMG	London & Country	F702ECC	Northumbria
F139PHM	Grey-Green	F287AWW	Yorkshire Bus	F572SMG	Southend	F702KMA	Crosville Cymru
F140PHM	Grey-Green	F287FGL	The Shires	F572UPB	Southend	F703KFM	Midland Red
F141PHM	Grey-Green	F288AWW	Yorkshire Bus	F573SMG	Southend	F704KMA	Crosville Cymru
F142PHM	Grey-Green	F289AWW	Yorkshire Bus	F574SMG	Southend	F705KFM	Midland Red
F143PHM	Grey-Green	F290AWW	Yorkshire Bus	F575SMG	Southend	F711CWJ	County

F712CWJ	County	FTU382T	Midland Fox	G113TND	London & Country	G184DRF	Midland Red
F713CWJ	County	FYT335V	County	G114TND	Midland Red	G192NWY	Clydeside
F714CWJ	County	FYT336V	County	G115TND	Midland Red	G193NWY	Clydeside
F715CWJ	County	G21HHG	United	G116TND	North Western	G194NWY	Clydeside
F718CWJ	County	G32OHS	Clydeside	G117TND	Midland Red	G195NWY	Clydeside
F719CWJ	County	G34HKY	North Western	G118TND	North Western	G196NWY	Clydeside
F747XCS	The Shires	G34VME	London & Country	G119TND	North Western	G197NWY	Clydeside
F760VNH	Clydeside	G35HKY	North Western	G120TJA	London & Country	G199NWY	Clydeside
F792DWT	Midland Red	G35VME	London & Country	G121TJA	Midland Red	G201RKK	Maidstone & Dist
F795JKX	County	G36HKY	North Western	G122RGT	Maidstone & Dist	G202RKK	Maidstone & Dist
F796JKX	County	G36VME	Kentish Bus	G122TJA	Midland Red	G203RKK	Maidstone & Dist
F822GDT	Midland Red	G37HKY	North Western	G123RGT	Kentish Bus	G209HCP	United
F835BCW	Northumbria	G37VME	Kentish Bus	G123TJA	North Western	G210HCP	United
F836BCW	Northumbria	G38HKY	North Western	G124TJA	North Western	G211HCP	United
F847EKP	North Western	G38VME	Kentish Bus	G125RGT	Kentish Bus	G212HCP	United
F860LCU	London & Country	G38YHJ	Crosville Cymru	G125TJA	North Western	G214HCP	United
F861LCU	London & Country	G39VME	Kentish Bus	G126RGT	Kentish Bus	G217LGK	Kentish Bus
F862LCU	Kentish Bus	G39YHJ	Crosville Cymru	G126TJA	Midland Red	G218LGK	Maidstone & Dist
F863LCU	Kentish Bus	G40OHS	The Shires	G127RGT	Kentish Bus	G229FJC	Crosville Cymru
F864LCU	Kentish Bus	G40VME	Kentish Bus	G127TJA	Midland Red	G230EOA	Midland Fox
F865LCU	London & Country	G40YHJ	Crosville Cymru	G128RGT	Kentish Bus	G230FJC	Crosville Cymru
F892BKK	Maidstone & Dist	G41HKY	Midland Red	G128TJA	Midland Red	G231EOA	Midland Fox
F893BKK	Maidstone & Dist	G41VME	Kentish Bus	G129YEV	The Shires	G232EOA	Midland Fox
F894BKK	Maidstone & Dist	G42VME	Kentish Bus	G130YEV	The Shires	G232FJC	Crosville Cymru
F895BKK	Maidstone & Dist	G43VME	Kentish Bus	G131YWC	The Shires	G233FJC	Crosville Cymru
F896DKK	Maidstone & Dist	G44VME	Kentish Bus	G132YWC	The Shires	G234FJC	Crosville Cymru
F897DKK	Maidstone & Dist	G45VME	Kentish Bus	G141GOL	Midland Red	G235EOA	Midland Fox
F898DKK	Maidstone & Dist	G49CVC	Yorkshire Bus	G142GOL	Midland Fox	G235FJC	Crosville Cymru
F899DKK	Maidstone & Dist	G58BEL	The Shires	G143GOL	Midland Fox	G236EOA	Midland Fox
F899GUM	Maidstone & Dist	G58RGG	Clydeside	G145TYT	Grey-Green	G236FJC	Crosville Cymru
F900DKK	Maidstone & Dist	G64SNN	Midland Fox	G146TYT	Grey-Green	G237FJC	Crosville Cymru
F901GUM	Maidstone & Dist	G65SNN	Midland Fox	G147TYT	Grey-Green	G238FJC	Crosville Cymru
F907PFH	Midland Red	G69PKR	Maidstone & Dist	G148CHP	Yorkshire Bus	G239EOA	Midland Fox
F932LKE	Kentish Bus	G70PKR	Maidstone & Dist	G148TYT	Grey-Green	G239FJC	Crosville Cymru
F956XCK	Midland Red	G71PKR	Maidstone & Dist	G149CHP	Yorkshire Bus	G240EOA	Midland Fox
F969GKJ	The Shires	G72PKR	Maidstone & Dist	G149TYT	Grey-Green	G240FJC	Crosville Cymru
F985EDS	Midland Red	G73PKR	Maidstone & Dist	G150GOL	Midland Red	G241GCC	Crosville Cymru
F985GKJ	The Shires	G74PKR	Maidstone & Dist	G150TYT	Grey-Green	G242GCC	Crosville Cymru
F991UME	Kentish Bus	G75PKR	Maidstone & Dist	G151FJC	Crosville Cymru	G243GCC	Crosville Cymru
F997EKM	North Western	G76PKR	Maidstone & Dist	G151TYT	Grey-Green	G245GCC	Midland Fox
FAZ2784	Midland Fox	G77PKR	Maidstone & Dist	G152FJC	Crosville Cymru	G247GCC	Midland Fox
FAZ3194	Midland Red	G78SKR	Maidstone & Dist	G152TYT	Grey-Green	G249GCC	Midland Fox
FAZ3195	Midland Red	G79SKR	Maidstone & Dist	G153TYT	Grey-Green	G250GCC	Midland Fox
FAZ5181	Midland Red	G80SKR	Maidstone & Dist	G154TYT	Grey-Green	G251SRG	Northumbria
FAZ5279	Midland Red	G82SKR	Maidstone & Dist	G160YRE	Crosville Cymru	G252SRG	Northumbria
FBV506W	North Western	G84SKR	Maidstone & Dist	G161YRE	Crosville Cymru	G253SRG	Northumbria
FCA7X	North Western	G85SKR	Maidstone & Dist	G162YRE	Crosville Cymru	G254SRG	Northumbria
FCA10X	North Western	G86SKR	Maidstone & Dist	G163YRE	Crosville Cymru	G255UVK	Northumbria
FEV178	The Shires	G87OTU	Midland Fox	G164YRE	Midland Red	G256UVK	Northumbria
FIL3451	Midland Fox	G87SKR	Crosville Cymru	G165YRE	Midland Red	G257UVK	Northumbria
FIL3452	Midland Fox	G97VMM	The Shires	G166YRE	Midland Red	G258UVK	Northumbria
FIL4919	The Shires	G98VMM	Midland Red	G167YRE	Midland Red	G281UMJ	The Shires
FJR776L	The Shires	G100TND	North Western	G168YRE	Midland Red	G282UMJ	The Shires
FKM713L	Maidstone & Dist	G101TND	London & Country	G169FJC	Crosville Cymru	G283UMJ	The Shires
FKM863V	Maidstone & Dist	G102TND	North Western	G169YRE	Midland Red	G284UMJ	The Shires
FKM864V	Maidstone & Dist	G103TND	North Western	G170FJC	Crosville Cymru	G285UMJ	The Shires
FKM866V	The Shires	G104TND	North Western	G170YRE	Midland Red	G286UMJ	The Shires
FKM867V	Maidstone & Dist	G105TND	North Western	G171FJC	Crosville Cymru	G287UMJ	The Shires
FKM868V	Maidstone & Dist	G106TND	North Western	G171YRE	Midland Red	G288UMJ	The Shires
FKM869V	Maidstone & Dist	G107TND	North Western	G172FJC	Crosville Cymru	G289UMJ	The Shires
FKM873V	Maidstone & Dist	G108OUG	Yorkshire Bus	G172YRE	Midland Red	G290UMJ	The Shires
FKM874V	The Shires	G108TND	North Western	G173FJC	Crosville Cymru	G291UMJ	The Shires
FKM875V	Maidstone & Dist	G109OUG	Yorkshire Bus	G173YRE	Midland Red	G292UMJ	The Shires
FKM877V	Maidstone & Dist	G109TND	North Western	G174FJC	Crosville Cymru	G293UMJ	The Shires
FKM878V	Maidstone & Dist	G109YRE	Midland Red	G174YRE	Northumbria	G294UMJ	The Shires
FKM879V	Maidstone & Dist	G110OUG	Yorkshire Bus	G175DRF	Northumbria	G295UMJ	The Shires
FKM880V	Maidstone & Dist	G110TND	North Western	G175FJC	Crosville Cymru	G301DPA	Midland Red
FKM881V	Maidstone & Dist	G111TND	Midland Red	G176FJC	Crosville Cymru	G301RJA	Midland Fox
FKM882V	Maidstone & Dist	G112TND	North Western	G177FJC	Crosville Cymru	G302DPA	London & Country
FSU661	Midland Red	G113PGT	North Western	G183DRF	Midland Red	G303DPA	London & Country

G304DPA	London & Country	G524WJF	Midland Fox	G635BPH	Kentish Bus	G900TJA	Midland Red
G305DPA	London & Country	G525VBB	Leaside	G636BPH	Kentish Bus	G901MNS	Midland Red
G306DPA	Midland Red	G525WJF	Midland Fox	G637BPH	Kentish Bus	G901SKP	Maidstone & Dist
G307DPA	Midland Red	G526VBB	Leaside	G638BPH	Kentish Bus	G902MNS	Clydeside
G308DPA	Midland Red	G527VBB	Leaside	G639BPH	Kentish Bus	G902SKP	Maidstone & Dist
G309DPA	Midland Red	G528VBB	Leaside	G640BPH	Kentish Bus	G903SKP	Maidstone & Dist
G310DPA	Midland Red	G529VBB	Leaside	G640CHF	London & Country	G904SKP	Maidstone & Dist
G311DPA	London & Country	G530VBB	Leaside	G641BPH	Kentish Bus	G905SKP	Maidstone & Dist
G312DPA	London & Country	G531VBB	Leaside	G641CHF	Kentish Bus	G905TYR	Grey-Green
G313DPA	London & Country	G532VBB	Leaside	G642BPH	Kentish Bus	G906TYR	Grey-Green
G314DPA	London & Country	G533VBB	Leaside	G642CHF	Kentish Bus	G907TYR	Grey-Green
G315DPA	London & Country	G534VBB	Leaside	G643BPH	Kentish Bus	G908TYR	Grey-Green
G316DPA	London & Country	G535VBB	Leaside	G643CHF	London & Country	G909TYR	Grey-Green
G317NNW	Yorkshire Bus	G536VBB	Leaside	G644BPH	Midland Red	G910TYR	Grey-Green
G319NNW	Yorkshire Bus	G537VBB	Leaside	G644EVN	North Western	G916LHA	Midland Red
G321NNW	Yorkshire Bus	G538VBB	Leaside	G645BPH	Midland Red	G917LHA	Midland Red
G322NNW	Yorkshire Bus	G539VBB	Leaside	G645UPP	The Shires	G918LHA	Midland Red
G324NNW	Yorkshire Bus	G540VBB	Leaside	G646BPH	Midland Red	G918UPP	County
G324NUM	Yorkshire Bus	G541VBB	Leaside	G646UPP	The Shires	G919LHA	Midland Red
G326NUM	Yorkshire Bus	G542GAC	Yorkshire Bus	G647BPH	Midland Red	G919UPP	County
G327NUM	Yorkshire Bus	G542VBB	Leaside	G647EKA	London & Country	G924WGS	County
G327PHA	Midland Red	G543VBB	Leaside	G647UPP	The Shires	G925WGS	County
G328PHA	Midland Red	G544VBB	Leaside	G648EKA	Kentish Bus	G926WGS	County
G329NUM	Yorkshire Bus	G545JOG	County	G648UPP	The Shires	G927WGS	County
G330NUM	Yorkshire Bus	G545VBB	Leaside	G649EKA	Kentish Bus	G928WGS	County
G331NUM	Yorkshire Bus	G546NKJ	Maidstone & Dist	G649UPP	The Shires	G929WGS	County
G332NUM	Yorkshire Bus	G546VBB	Leaside	G650EKA	North Western	G930WGS	County
G360FOP	The Shires	G547VBB	Leaside	G650UPP	The Shires	G931WGS	County
G381EKA	North Western	G548VBB	Leaside	G651EKA	North Western	G932WGS	County
G382EKA	North Western	G549VBB	Leaside	G651UPP	The Shires	G974KJX	London & Country
G383EKA	North Western	G550VBB	Leaside	G652EKA	North Western	G998RKN	Maidstone & Dist
G384EKA	North Western	G551VBB	Leaside	G652UPP	The Shires	GBU1V	County
G385EKA	North Western	G552VBB	Leaside	G653EKA	North Western	GBU4V	County
G386EKA	North Western	G553VBB	Leaside	G653UPP	The Shires	GBU5V	County
G387EKA	North Western	G554VBB	Leaside	G654UPP	The Shires	GBU8V	County
G388EKA	North Western	G555VBB	Leaside	G655UPP	The Shires	GBU9V	County
G399FSF	Midland Red	G556VBB	Leaside	G656UPP	The Shires	GCS56V	Clydeside
G421MWY	Clydeside	G610BPH	London & Country	G657UPP	The Shires	GCS59V	Clydeside
G501SFT	London & Country	G610CFA	Midland Red	G659DTJ	Kentish Bus	GCS67V	Clydeside
G502SFT	London & Country	G611BPH	London & Country	G660DTJ	Kentish Bus	GDZ795	Midland Red
G503SFT	London & Country	G611CFA	Midland Red	G661DTJ	London & Country	GFM107X	Midland Red
G504SFT	London & Country	G612BPH	London & Country	G663FKA	London & Country	GFM110X	North Western
G505SFT	Midland Red	G612CFA	Midland Red	G664FKA	London & Country	GFR799W	London & Country
G506SFT	Midland Fox	G613BPH	London & Country	G665FKA	London & Country	GGE156T	London & Country
G507SFT	Midland Red	G614BPH	London & Country	G667FKA	North Western	GGE165T	London & Country
G508EAJ	United	G615BPH	London & Country	G689OHE	London & Country	GGE171T	Clydeside
G508SFT	Midland Fox	G616BPH	London & Country	G690OHE	London & Country	GGM69W	Maidstone & Dist
G509EAJ	United	G616WGS	Midland Red	G711LKW	North Western	GGR406N	North Western
G509SFT	Midland Red	G617BPH	London & Country	G714LKW	North Western	GHB84W	Maidstone & Dist
G510EAJ	United	G618BPH	London & Country	G715PGA	The Shires	GHB574V	The Shires
G510SFT	Midland Red	G619BPH	London & Country	G727RGA	Midland Red	GHU643N	North Western
G511EAJ	United	G620BPH	London & Country	G754UYT	United	GIL6253	The Shires
G511SFT	Midland Red	G621BPH	London & Country	G755UYT	United	GIL6949	The Shires
G512EAJ	United	G621YMG	County	G756UYT	United	GIL8487	Midland Red
G512SFT	Midland Fox	G622BPH	London & Country	G757UYT	United	GJG750D	County
G513SFT	Midland Fox	G623BPH	London & Country	G758UYT	United	GKE442Y	Clydeside
G514VBB	Leaside	G624BPH	London & Country	G759UYT	United	GLS289N	Crosville Cymru
G515VBB	Leaside	G625BPH	London & Country	G760UYT	United	GMA648T	Crosville Cymru
G516VBB	Leaside	G626BPH	London & Country	G761UYT	United	GMB372T	Midland Red
G517VBB	Leaside	G626EKA	London & Country	G762UYT	United	GMB373T	Midland Red
G518VBB	Leaside	G627BPH	London & Country	G785PWL	Midland Red	GMB374T	Midland Red
G519VBB	Leaside	G628BPH	London & Country	G801BPG	Maidstone & Dist	GMB375T	North Western
G520VBB	Leaside	G628EKA	London & Country	G801THA	Midland Red	GMB376T	Midland Red
G521VBB	Leaside	G629BPH	London & Country	G802BPG	Maidstone & Dist	GMB378T	Midland Red
G521WJF	Midland Fox	G629EKA	North Western	G802THA	Midland Red	GMB379T	North Western
G522VBB	Leaside	G630BPH	London & Country	G807FJX	Midland Red	GMB380T	North Western
G522WJF	Midland Fox	G631BPH	Kentish Bus	G866TCU	Kentish Bus	GMB383T	Midland Red
G523VBB	Leaside	G632BPH	Kentish Bus	G885SKE	Maidstone & Dist	GMB384T	North Western
G523WJF	Midland Fox	G633BPH	Kentish Bus	G896TGG	The Shires	GMB386T	North Western
G524VBB	Leaside	G634BPH	Kentish Bus	G897TGG	Midland Red	GMB390T	Midland Red

Reg	Operator	Reg	Operator	Reg	Operator	Reg	Operator
GMB392T	North Western	GYE511W	South London	H106RWT	Yorkshire Bus	H203GRO	The Shires
GMB657T	North Western	GYE515W	South London	H107GEV	Grey-Green	H204EKO	Maidstone & Dist
GMB663T	North Western	GYE517W	South London	H107JAR	London & Country	H231KBH	The Shires
GMB666T	North Western	GYE518W	South London	H108GEV	Grey-Green	H242MUK	The Shires
GNV656N	Midland Fox	GYE519W	South London	H108RWT	Yorkshire Bus	H243MUK	The Shires
GOG272W	Midland Red	GYE520W	South London	H109GEV	Grey-Green	H244MUK	The Shires
GSU347	Northumbria	GYE521W	South London	H110GEV	Grey-Green	H245MOE	Midland Fox
GSU854T	Midland Red	GYE522W	South London	H112DDS	Midland Red	H245MUK	The Shires
GSX865T	United	GYE525W	South London	H112GEV	Grey-Green	H251GEV	County
GTO48V	Midland Fox	GYE528W	South London	H113GEV	Grey-Green	H252GEV	County
GTO49V	Midland Fox	GYE529W	Leaside	H114GEV	Grey-Green	H253GEV	County
GTO299V	Midland Fox	GYE530W	Leaside	H115GEV	Grey-Green	H253PAJ	United
GTO301V	Midland Fox	GYE531W	Leaside	H120THE	South London	H254GEV	County
GTO302V	Midland Fox	GYE533W	Leaside	H122THE	South London	H254PAJ	United
GTO304V	Midland Fox	GYE534W	South London	H123THE	South London	H255GEV	County
GTO305V	Midland Fox	GYE535W	Leaside	H123WFM	Colchester	H256GEV	County
GTO306V	Midland Fox	GYE536W	Leaside	H124THE	South London	H256YLG	Maidstone & Dist
GTO307V	Midland Fox	GYE537W	County	H125THE	South London	H257GEV	County
GUW441W	The Shires	GYE538W	Leaside	H126THE	South London	H258GEV	County
GUW447W	The Shires	GYE540W	Leaside	H127THE	South London	H259CFT	Northumbria
GUW456W	The Shires	GYE541W	South London	H128THE	South London	H261CFT	Northumbria
GUW457W	The Shires	GYE543W	Leaside	H129CDB	North Western	H262CFT	Northumbria
GUW461W	The Shires	GYE544W	Leaside	H129THE	South London	H262GEV	Southend
GUW462W	The Shires	GYE547W	Leaside	H130CDB	North Western	H263CFT	Northumbria
GUW465W	The Shires	GYE548W	Leaside	H130LPU	Crosville Cymru	H263GEV	Southend
GUW475W	The Shires	GYE549W	Leaside	H130THE	South London	H264CFT	Northumbria
GUW494W	The Shires	GYE551W	Leaside	H131CDB	Midland Red	H264GEV	Southend
GVD47	Clydeside	GYE552W	South London	H131THE	South London	H265GEV	Southend
GYE346W	South London	GYE555W	South London	H132CDB	Midland Red	H266CFT	Northumbria
GYE353W	Leaside	GYE557W	Leaside	H132MOB	South London	H267CFT	Northumbria
GYE365W	South London	GYE559W	Leaside	H133CDB	Midland Red	H278LEF	United
GYE372W	South London	GYE562W	Leaside	H134CDB	Midland Red	H279LEF	United
GYE378W	South London	GYE567W	Leaside	H135CDB	Midland Red	H301FKL	Maidstone & Dist
GYE382W	Leaside	GYE568W	South London	H136CDB	Midland Red	H313WUA	Midland Red
GYE384W	South London	GYE569W	Leaside	H143MOB	South London	H314WUA	Midland Red
GYE386W	Leaside	GYE573W	County	H149NOJ	Kentish Bus	H329DHA	Midland Red
GYE388W	South London	GYE575W	Leaside	H155XYU	Grey-Green	H330DHA	Midland Red
GYE389W	Leaside	GYE577W	South London	H156XYU	Grey-Green	H331DHA	Midland Red
GYE395W	South London	GYE580W	South London	H157XYU	Grey-Green	H332DHA	Midland Red
GYE396W	South London	GYE581W	Leaside	H158XYU	Grey-Green	H334DHA	Midland Red
GYE399W	South London	GYE582W	Leaside	H166MFA	Midland Red	H334TYG	Yorkshire Bus
GYE400W	South London	GYE584W	Crosville Cymru	H176JVT	Midland Red	H335DHA	Midland Red
GYE402W	South London	GYE585W	Leaside	H177JVT	Midland Red	H335TYG	Yorkshire Bus
GYE410W	South London	GYE586W	Leaside	H181DHA	Midland Red	H336DHA	Midland Red
GYE417W	South London	GYE587W	Leaside	H182DHA	Midland Red	H336TYG	Yorkshire Bus
GYE419W	Leaside	GYE590W	Leaside	H183CNS	Clydeside	H337DHA	Midland Red
GYE422W	Leaside	GYE591W	Leaside	H183DHA	Midland Red	H337TYG	Yorkshire Bus
GYE426W	Leaside	GYE593W	Leaside	H184DHA	Midland Red	H338DHA	Midland Red
GYE439W	South London	GYE596W	Leaside	H185CNS	Clydeside	H338TYG	Yorkshire Bus
GYE441W	Leaside	GYE600W	Leaside	H185DHA	Midland Red	H338UWT	Yorkshire Bus
GYE445W	Leaside	GYE601W	South London	H186EHA	Midland Red	H339UWT	Yorkshire Bus
GYE450W	Leaside	GYE602W	Leaside	H187EHA	Midland Red	H341UWT	Yorkshire Bus
GYE454W	South London	GYE603W	Leaside	H188EHA	Midland Red	H342UWT	Yorkshire Bus
GYE456W	South London	GYE604W	Leaside	H189EHA	Midland Red	H343UWT	Yorkshire Bus
GYE458W	South London	GYE605W	Leaside	H191EHA	Midland Red	H343UWX	Yorkshire Bus
GYE464W	South London	H28MJN	Crosville Cymru	H192JNF	Midland Red	H344UWX	Yorkshire Bus
GYE469W	Leaside	H29MJN	Crosville Cymru	H196GRO	The Shires	H345UWX	Yorkshire Bus
GYE474W	South London	H31PAJ	United	H196JVT	Midland Red	H346UWX	Yorkshire Bus
GYE478W	Leaside	H32PAJ	United	H197GRO	The Shires	H347UWX	Yorkshire Bus
GYE485W	Leaside	H34PAJ	United	H197JVT	Midland Red	H350PNO	County
GYE491W	Leaside	H35DGD	The Shires	H198AOD	The Shires	H355WWX	Yorkshire Bus
GYE492W	South London	H47MJN	Colchester	H198GRO	The Shires	H356WWX	Yorkshire Bus
GYE493W	Leaside	H48MJN	Colchester	H198JVT	Midland Red	H357WWX	Yorkshire Bus
GYE496W	South London	H49MJN	Colchester	H199AOD	The Shires	H358WWY	Yorkshire Bus
GYE500W	South London	H101GEV	Grey-Green	H199GRO	The Shires	H359WWY	Yorkshire Bus
GYE503W	South London	H102GEV	Grey-Green	H199KEH	Midland Red	H372PHK	Southend
GYE507W	South London	H103GEV	Grey-Green	H201GRO	The Shires	H393WWY	Yorkshire Bus
GYE508W	South London	H104GEV	Grey-Green	H201LRF	Midland Red	H404BVR	North Western
GYE509W	Leaside	H105GEV	Grey-Green	H202GRO	The Shires	H406FGS	The Shires
GYE510W	Leaside	H106GEV	Grey-Green	H202LRF	Midland Red	H407BVR	North Western

Reg	Operator	Reg	Operator	Reg	Operator	Reg	Operator
H407ERO	The Shires	H681GPF	South London	H921XYT	Grey-Green	J36GCX	Maidstone & Dist
H407FGS	The Shires	H682GPF	South London	H922LOX	The Shires	J36SRF	Midland Red
H408BVR	The Shires	H683GPF	South London	H922XYT	Grey-Green	J56GCX	County
H408ERO	The Shires	H684GPF	South London	H923LOX	The Shires	J60MPS	Maidstone & Dist
H408FGS	The Shires	H695KKV	Midland Fox	H923XYT	Grey-Green	J64BJN	County
H408YMA	Midland Red	H697KKV	Midland Fox	H925LOX	The Shires	J65BJN	County
H409BVR	The Shires	H701UNW	Clydeside	H925XYT	Grey-Green	J65UNA	The Shires
H409ERO	The Shires	H702UNW	Clydeside	H926LOX	The Shires	J78MHF	North Western
H410ERO	The Shires	H703UNW	Clydeside	HBH426Y	London & Country	J143SRF	Midland Red
H433DHA	Midland Red	H704UNW	Clydeside	HDZ8354	County	J151WEH	Midland Fox
H458UGO	Leaside	H705UNW	Yorkshire Bus	HED204V	United	J154NKN	Kentish Bus
H459UGO	Leaside	H706UNW	Clydeside	HED205V	United	J162REH	Midland Red
H460UGO	Leaside	H707UNW	Yorkshire Bus	HFM186N	North Western	J169REH	Midland Red
H460WWY	Yorkshire Bus	H708LOL	Midland Red	HFM581D	Crosville Cymru	J171GGG	The Shires
H461UGO	Leaside	H708UNW	Yorkshire Bus	HHA212L	United	J203REH	Midland Red
H462UGO	Leaside	H709LOL	Midland Red	HIL2279	Maidstone & Dist	J204REH	Midland Red
H463UGO	Leaside	H709UNW	Yorkshire Bus	HIL2358	The Shires	J205REH	Midland Red
H464UGO	Leaside	H710LOL	Midland Red	HIL3652	Midland Red	J206REH	Midland Red
H465UGO	South London	H710UNW	Clydeside	HIL7467	The Shires	J207REH	Midland Red
H466UGO	South London	H711UNW	Yorkshire Bus	HIL7592	Crosville Cymru	J208SRF	Midland Red
H467UGO	South London	H712UNW	Clydeside	HIL7593	Crosville Cymru	J209SRF	Midland Red
H468UGO	South London	H713UNW	Clydeside	HIL7594	The Shires	J218HDS	Clydeside
H469UGO	South London	H729LOL	Midland Red	HIL7595	The Shires	J220HGY	Maidstone & Dist
H470UGO	South London	H731LOL	Midland Red	HIL7596	Midland Red	J221HGY	Maidstone & Dist
H501GHA	Midland Red	H733HWK	Crosville Cymru	HIL7597	The Shires	J246MFP	Midland Fox
H523SWE	The Shires	H755WWW	Yorkshire Bus	HIL8438	The Shires	J247MFP	Midland Fox
H566MPD	Southend	H756WWW	Yorkshire Bus	HIL8439	The Shires	J248SHP	Midland Fox
H567MPD	Southend	H757WWW	Yorkshire Bus	HKM883V	Maidstone & Dist	J249SHP	Midland Fox
H598CNL	Northumbria	H765EKJ	Kentish Bus	HKM884V	Maidstone & Dist	J255TJW	Midland Fox
H614CGG	The Shires	H766EKJ	Kentish Bus	HKM885V	Maidstone & Dist	J291NNB	North Western
H616UWR	Maidstone & Dist	H767EKJ	Kentish Bus	HKM886V	Maidstone & Dist	J292NNB	North Western
H618UWR	Maidstone & Dist	H768EKJ	Kentish Bus	HMA559T	North Western	J293NNB	North Western
H621TKU	South London	H769EKJ	Kentish Bus	HPK504N	London & Country	J296NNB	North Western
H637UWR	Maidstone & Dist	H770EKJ	Kentish Bus	HSB948Y	Clydeside	J297NNB	North Western
H641UWE	The Shires	H801SKY	Northumbria	HSB949Y	Clydeside	J298NNB	North Western
H642UWE	The Shires	H803RWJ	North Western	HUP757T	Northumbria	J299NNB	North Western
H643GRO	County	H803SKY	Northumbria	HUP758T	Northumbria	J301WHJ	County
H648GPF	South London	H804AHA	Midland Red	HUP759T	Northumbria	J302WHJ	County
H649GPF	South London	H804RWJ	North Western	HXI3006	Midland Red	J303WHJ	County
H650GPF	South London	H805AHA	Midland Red	HXI3007	Midland Red	J304WHJ	County
H651GPF	South London	H805RWJ	North Western	HXI3008	Midland Red	J305WHJ	County
H652GPF	South London	H806AHA	Midland Red	HXI3009	Midland Red	J306WHJ	County
H653GPF	South London	H813EKJ	Kentish Bus	HXI3010	Midland Red	J307WHJ	County
H654GPF	South London	H814EKJ	Maidstone & Dist	HXI3011	Midland Red	J308WHJ	County
H655GPF	South London	H815EKJ	Kentish Bus	HXI3012	Midland Red	J309WHJ	County
H656GPF	South London	H816EKJ	Maidstone & Dist	IAZ2314	The Shires	J310WHJ	County
H657GPF	South London	H840UUA	Northumbria	IAZ3457	The Shires	J311WHJ	County
H658GPF	South London	H845AHS	Southend	IAZ3977	The Shires	J312WHJ	County
H659GPF	South London	H846AHS	Maidstone & Dist	IAZ4037	The Shires	J313WHJ	County
H660GPF	South London	H847AHS	Maidstone & Dist	IDZ8561	Midland Red	J314XVX	County
H661GPF	South London	H848AUS	The Shires	IIL4821	The Shires	J315BSH	Leaside
H662GPF	South London	H851NOC	Midland Red	IIL4822	The Shires	J315XVX	County
H663GPF	South London	H880NFS	Midland Red	IIL4823	The Shires	J316BSH	Leaside
H664GPF	South London	H886CCU	Kentish Bus	IIL4824	The Shires	J316XVX	County
H665GPF	South London	H887CCU	Kentish Bus	IIL9168	Maidstone & Dist	J317BSH	Leaside
H667GPF	South London	H889CCU	Kentish Bus	IIL9169	Maidstone & Dist	J317XVX	County
H668GPF	South London	H890CCU	Kentish Bus	J3SLT	North Western	J318BSH	Leaside
H669GPF	South London	H901GNC	Clydeside	J4SLT	North Western	J319BSH	Leaside
H670GPF	South London	H903AHS	County	J6SLT	North Western	J320BSH	Leaside
H671GPF	South London	H912KUD	Midland Fox	J7SLT	North Western	J321BSH	Leaside
H672GPF	South London	H912XYT	Grey-Green	J9SLT	North Western	J322BSH	Leaside
H673GPF	South London	H913XYT	Grey-Green	J10SLT	North Western	J323BSH	Leaside
H674GPF	South London	H914XYT	Grey-Green	J16AMB	London & Country	J324BSH	Leaside
H675AGD	Clydeside	H915XYT	Grey-Green	J20NMS	Northumbria	J325BSH	Leaside
H675GPF	South London	H916XYT	Grey-Green	J25UNY	Maidstone & Dist	J326BSH	Leaside
H676GPF	South London	H917XYT	Grey-Green	J26UNY	Maidstone & Dist	J327BSH	Leaside
H677GPF	South London	H918XYT	Grey-Green	J27UNY	Maidstone & Dist	J328BSH	Leaside
H678GPF	South London	H919XYT	Grey-Green	J31SFA	Midland Red	J329BSH	Leaside
H679GPF	South London	H920XYT	Grey-Green	J32SFA	Midland Red	J330BSH	Leaside
H680GPF	South London			J34SRF	Midland Red	J331BSH	Leaside

Reg	Operator	Reg	Operator	Reg	Operator	Reg	Operator
J332BSH	Leaside	J608WHJ	County	JHE145W	Midland Fox	JJD526D	Leaside
J334BSH	Leaside	J609WHJ	County	JHE153W	Midland Fox	JJD527D	Leaside
J335BSH	Leaside	J610WHJ	County	JHE160W	Midland Fox	JJD531D	South London
J336BSH	Leaside	J611WHJ	County	JHE167W	Midland Fox	JJD533D	South London
J337BSH	Leaside	J612WHJ	County	JHE177W	Midland Fox	JJD534D	Leaside
J338BSH	Leaside	J620UHN	United	JHE179W	Midland Fox	JJD536D	South London
J339BSH	Leaside	J649OWK	Midland Fox	JHE189W	Midland Fox	JJD544D	Leaside
J340BSH	Leaside	J650OWK	Midland Fox	JHE192W	Midland Fox	JJD545D	South London
J341BSH	Leaside	J651OWK	Midland Fox	JHE193W	Midland Fox	JJD546D	Leaside
J342BSH	Leaside	J651UHN	United	JHK495N	Colchester	JJD548D	South London
J343BSH	Leaside	J652UHN	United	JIL2156	Midland Fox	JJD549D	South London
J344BSH	Leaside	J653UHN	United	JIL2157	Midland Fox	JJD552D	Leaside
J345BSH	Leaside	J654UHN	United	JIL2158	Midland Fox	JJD562D	Leaside
J346BSH	Leaside	J655OWK	Midland Fox	JIL2159	Midland Fox	JJD567D	Leaside
J347BSH	Leaside	J655UHN	United	JIL2160	Midland Fox	JJD571D	Leaside
J348BSH	Leaside	J656OWK	Midland Fox	JIL2161	Midland Fox	JJD572D	South London
J349BSH	Leaside	J656UHN	United	JIL2162	Midland Fox	JJD573D	South London
J350BSH	Leaside	J657OWK	Midland Fox	JIL2163	Midland Fox	JJD574D	South London
J351BSH	Leaside	J657UHN	United	JIL2164	Midland Fox	JJD577D	South London
J352BSH	Leaside	J658UDU	Midland Fox	JIL2165	Midland Fox	JJD586D	South London
J353BSH	Leaside	J658UHN	United	JIL2190	London & Country	JJD588D	Leaside
J362YWX	Yorkshire Bus	J659UDU	Midland Fox	JIL2193	London & Country	JJD589D	Leaside
J363BNW	Northumbria	J661UHN	United	JIL2194	Colchester	JJD591D	South London
J363YWX	Yorkshire Bus	J701NHA	Midland Red	JIL2195	Colchester	JJD595D	Leaside
J364YWX	Yorkshire Bus	J714CUM	Yorkshire Bus	JIL2196	London & Country	JJD597D	Leaside
J365YWX	Yorkshire Bus	J715CUM	Yorkshire Bus	JIL2197	London & Country	JOX480P	Midland Red
J366BNW	Northumbria	J716CUM	Yorkshire Bus	JIL2198	London & Country	JOX500P	United
J366YWX	Yorkshire Bus	J717CUM	Yorkshire Bus	JIL2199	London & Country	JOX515P	North Western
J367YWX	Yorkshire Bus	J718CUM	Yorkshire Bus	JIL5367	London & Country	JOX522P	North Western
J368YWX	Yorkshire Bus	J719CUM	Yorkshire Bus	JIW3696	County	JOX528P	London & Country
J369YWX	Yorkshire Bus	J720CUM	Yorkshire Bus	JJD370D	Leaside	JOX717P	Midland Red
J370YWX	Yorkshire Bus	J721CUM	Yorkshire Bus	JJD372D	Leaside	JPA121K	London & Country
J371AWT	Yorkshire Bus	J722CUM	Yorkshire Bus	JJD373D	Leaside	JPE233V	The Shires
J371YWX	Yorkshire Bus	J734MFY	North Western	JJD375D	South London	JPE236V	The Shires
J372AWT	Yorkshire Bus	J735MFY	North Western	JJD380D	Leaside	JPE237V	The Shires
J373AWT	Yorkshire Bus	J766SOC	Midland Fox	JJD382D	South London	JSK994	Crosville Cymru
J374AWT	Yorkshire Bus	J866UPY	United	JJD383D	South London	JTD390P	Crosville Cymru
J375AWT	Yorkshire Bus	J867UPY	United	JJD386D	Leaside	JTD392P	Southend
J376AWT	Yorkshire Bus	J8SLT	North Western	JJD387D	South London	JTD395P	Crosville Cymru
J377AWT	Yorkshire Bus	J917HGD	The Shires	JJD391D	Leaside	JTD396P	Southend
J379BWU	Yorkshire Bus	J917VHP	Midland Fox	JJD394D	Leaside	JTH757P	United
J380BWU	Yorkshire Bus	J918VHP	Midland Fox	JJD401D	Leaside	JTH763P	Northumbria
J381BWU	Yorkshire Bus	J926CYL	County	JJD406D	Leaside	JTL804V	Crosville Cymru
J382BWU	Yorkshire Bus	J927CYL	County	JJD407D	South London	JTU574T	Crosville Cymru
J401FNS	Midland Fox	J928CYL	County	JJD408D	Leaside	JUP115T	Northumbria
J401XVX	County	J929CYL	South London	JJD409D	Leaside	JUR818V	Maidstone & Dist
J402XVX	County	J930CYL	South London	JJD410D	South London	JWF493W	Midland Fox
J403XVX	County	J931CYL	South London	JJD416D	Leaside	JWF494W	Midland Fox
J404XVX	County	J933WHJ	County	JJD418D	Leaside	JYG429V	United
J413NCP	South London	J934WHJ	County	JJD424D	Leaside	K1SLT	North Western
J414NCP	South London	J935WHJ	County	JJD452D	South London	K2SLT	North Western
J433BSH	Leaside	J936WHJ	County	JJD457D	Leaside	K3SLT	North Western
J463MKL	Maidstone & Dist	J937WHJ	County	JJD460D	Leaside	K8BUS	The Shires
J464MKL	Maidstone & Dist	J938WHJ	County	JJD468D	Leaside	K25WND	The Shires
J465MKL	Maidstone & Dist	J961JNL	Kentish Bus	JJD477D	South London	K26WND	The Shires
J465UFS	The Shires	J961TOF	Midland Fox	JJD483D	Leaside	K27EWC	Crosville Cymru
J466OKP	Maidstone & Dist	J962JNL	Kentish Bus	JJD491D	South London	K27WND	The Shires
J467OKP	Maidstone & Dist	J963TOF	Midland Fox	JJD492D	Leaside	K28WND	The Shires
J468OKP	Maidstone & Dist	J964NLL	The Shires	JJD494D	Leaside	K29WND	The Shires
J473RDU	Midland Fox	J969JNL	London & Country	JJD503D	Leaside	K31WND	The Shires
J474RDU	Midland Fox	J970JNL	Kentish Bus	JJD504D	Leaside	K32WND	The Shires
J480XHL	London & Country	J973JNL	Kentish Bus	JJD505D	South London	K36XNE	London & Country
J556GTP	Midland Red	J974JNL	Kentish Bus	JJD510D	Leaside	K37XNE	London & Country
J601WHJ	County	J975JNL	Kentish Bus	JJD512D	South London	K38XNE	London & Country
J602WHJ	County	JBO75W	County	JJD514D	South London	K73SRG	North Western
J603WHJ	County	JBO80W	County	JJD518D	Leaside	K74SRG	North Western
J604WHJ	County	JCK851W	North Western	JJD521D	South London	K75SRG	North Western
J605WHJ	County	JCK852W	London & Country	JJD523D	South London	K91RGA	Clydeside
J606WHJ	County	JDE972X	Midland Fox	JJD524D	South London	K92RGA	Clydeside
J607WHJ	County	JDJ350N	Midland Fox	JJD525D	Leaside	K100SLT	North Western

K124TCP	County	K448XPA	The Shires	K852RBB	Northumbria	KPJ283W	London & Country
K131FKW	Northumbria	K457EVC	North Western	K853RBB	Northumbria	KPJ284W	London & Country
K131XRE	Midland Fox	K469SKO	Maidstone & Dist	K854RBB	Northumbria	KPJ285W	London & Country
K132FKW	Northumbria	K470SKO	Maidstone & Dist	K876UDB	North Western	KPJ286W	London & Country
K132XRE	London & Country	K471SKO	Maidstone & Dist	K877UDB	North Western	KPJ288W	London & Country
K136ARE	Midland Red	K503BHN	United	K878UDB	North Western	KRP560V	The Shires
K137ARE	Midland Red	K504BHN	United	K879UDB	North Western	KRS536V	Clydeside
K138BRF	Midland Red	K505BHN	United	K880UDB	North Western	KUB671V	Midland Red
K139BRF	Midland Red	K506BHN	United	K882UDB	North Western	KYO609V	Leaside
K140BFA	Midland Red	K507BHN	United	K884UDB	North Western	KYO610X	Leaside
K140RYS	Midland Red	K508BHN	United	K887UDB	North Western	KYO611X	Leaside
K141BFA	Midland Red	K509BHN	United	K890UDB	North Western	KYO612X	Leaside
K142BFA	Midland Red	K510BHN	United	K906SKR	Maidstone & Dist	KYO613X	Leaside
K148BRF	Midland Fox	K511BHN	United	K907SKR	Maidstone & Dist	KYO614X	Leaside
K150BRF	Midland Red	K512BHN	United	K908SKR	Maidstone & Dist	KYO615X	Leaside
K154BRF	London & Country	K513BHN	United	K909SKR	Maidstone & Dist	KYO617X	Leaside
K155CRE	London & Country	K514BHN	United	K910SKR	Maidstone & Dist	KYO619X	Leaside
K156BRF	London & Country	K515BHN	United	K932VCP	Grey-Green	KYO622X	County
K157BRF	London & Country	K516BHN	United	K933VCP	Grey-Green	KYO624X	Leaside
K158HRF	Midland Fox	K517BHN	United	K945SGG	Clydeside	KYO625X	Leaside
K184GDU	The Shires	K518BHN	United	K946SGG	Clydeside	KYO626X	Leaside
K200SLT	North Western	K523RJX	North Western	K947BRE	Midland Red	KYO627X	Leaside
K202FEH	The Shires	K538ORH	South London	K947SGG	Clydeside	KYO628X	Leaside
K203FEH	The Shires	K539ORH	South London	K981KGY	Kentish Bus	KYO629X	South London
K211UHA	Midland Red	K540ORH	South London	K982KGY	Kentish Bus	KYO630X	Leaside
K212UHA	Midland Red	K541ORH	South London	K983KGY	Kentish Bus	KYO631X	Leaside
K213UHA	Midland Red	K542ORH	South London	KDW362P	London & Country	KYV408X	Clydeside
K214UHA	Midland Red	K543OGA	The Shires	KGH858A	Leaside	KYV632X	Leaside
K215UHA	Midland Red	K543ORH	South London	KGH975A	Leaside	KYV633X	South London
K216UHA	Midland Red	K544ORH	South London	KGJ118A	South London	KYV634X	South London
K217UHA	Midland Red	K545ORH	County	KGJ142A	Leaside	KYV635X	Leaside
K218UHA	Midland Red	K546ORH	County	KGJ614D	London & Country	KYV636X	Leaside
K219UHA	Midland Red	K546RJX	North Western	KHT118P	United	KYV637X	Leaside
K318CVX	County	K547ORH	South London	KHT121P	North Western	KYV638X	Leaside
K319CVX	County	K548ORH	South London	KJW296W	Midland Red	KYV641X	Leaside
K320CVX	County	K549ORH	Leaside	KJW301W	Midland Red	KYV642X	Leaside
K321CVX	County	K550ORH	Leaside	KJW305W	Midland Red	KYV643X	Leaside
K322CVX	County	K551ORH	Leaside	KJW306W	Midland Red	KYV644X	Leaside
K323CVX	County	K552ORH	Leaside	KJW310W	Midland Red	KYV645X	Leaside
K390NGG	Midland Fox	K578YOJ	The Shires	KJW318W	Midland Red	KYV646X	Leaside
K401HWW	Yorkshire Bus	K579YOJ	The Shires	KJW320W	Midland Red	KYV647X	Leaside
K402HWW	Yorkshire Bus	K580YOJ	The Shires	KJW322W	Midland Red	KYV648X	Leaside
K402VPK	London & Country	K657KNL	The Shires	KKE739N	Crosville Cymru	KYV649X	County
K403HWW	Yorkshire Bus	K707FNO	County	KKG109W	Clydeside	KYV650X	Leaside
K403VPK	London & Country	K708FNO	County	KMA395T	North Western	KYV651X	Leaside
K404HWW	Yorkshire Bus	K709FNO	County	KMA396T	North Western	KYV652X	Leaside
K404VPK	London & Country	K710FNO	County	KMA397T	North Western	KYV653X	Leaside
K405FHJ	County	K711FNO	County	KMA400T	North Western	KYV654X	South London
K405HWX	Yorkshire Bus	K712FNO	County	KMA401T	Midland Red	KYV657X	Leaside
K405VPK	London & Country	K723HUG	Yorkshire Bus	KMA402T	Midland Red	KYV658X	Leaside
K406FHJ	County	K724HUG	Yorkshire Bus	KMA403T	North Western	KYV659X	Leaside
K407FHJ	County	K725HUG	Yorkshire Bus	KNV513P	The Shires	KYV660X	Leaside
K408BHN	United	K726HUG	Yorkshire Bus	KNV514P	North Western	KYV661X	Leaside
K408FHJ	County	K727HUG	Yorkshire Bus	KPA367P	London & Country	KYV663X	Leaside
K409BHN	United	K728HUG	Yorkshire Bus	KPA372P	London & Country	KYV664X	Leaside
K409FHJ	County	K729HUG	Yorkshire Bus	KPJ241W	The Shires	KYV665X	Leaside
K410BHN	United	K741CWK	Midland Fox	KPJ242W	The Shires	KYV666X	Leaside
K410FHJ	County	K742CWK	Midland Fox	KPJ243W	The Shires	KYV669X	Leaside
K411BHN	United	K745CWK	Midland Fox	KPJ248W	County	KYV671X	South London
K411FHJ	County	K746CWK	Midland Fox	KPJ258W	London & Country	KYV672X	Leaside
K412BHN	United	K760JVX	County	KPJ259W	London & Country	KYV673X	Leaside
K412FHJ	County	K761JVX	County	KPJ262W	London & Country	KYV675X	Leaside
K413BHN	United	K762JVX	County	KPJ267W	London & Country	KYV676X	Leaside
K413FHJ	County	K787VNR	North Western	KPJ270W	Kentish Bus	KYV679X	Leaside
K414BHN	United	K801HWW	Yorkshire Bus	KPJ271W	Kentish Bus	KYV680X	South London
K414FHJ	County	K802HWW	Yorkshire Bus	KPJ274W	Kentish Bus	KYV681X	Leaside
K415BHN	United	K803HWW	Yorkshire Bus	KPJ276W	Kentish Bus	KYV682X	South London
K416BHN	United	K804HWW	Yorkshire Bus	KPJ277W	Kentish Bus	KYV684X	Leaside
K417BHN	United	K805HWX	Yorkshire Bus	KPJ281W	London & Country	KYV686X	Leaside
K447XPA	The Shires	K851RBB	Northumbria	KPJ282W	Kentish Bus	KYV688X	Leaside

Reg	Operator	Reg	Operator	Reg	Operator	Reg	Operator
KYV689X	Leaside	KYV765X	Leaside	L114YVK	Kentish Bus	L154YVK	Kentish Bus
KYV691X	South London	KYV766X	Leaside	L115YVK	Leaside	L155UEM	North Western
KYV692X	Leaside	KYV767X	Leaside	L116YVK	Leaside	L155UKB	North Western
KYV694X	Leaside	KYV768X	Leaside	L117YVK	Leaside	L155WAG	South London
KYV698X	Leaside	KYV770X	Leaside	L118YVK	Leaside	L155YVK	Kentish Bus
KYV699X	Leaside	KYV771X	Leaside	L119YVK	Leaside	L156UEM	North Western
KYV700X	Leaside	KYV772X	Leaside	L120YVK	London & Country	L156UKB	North Western
KYV701X	Leaside	KYV773X	Leaside	L121YVK	London & Country	L156WAG	South London
KYV702X	Leaside	KYV774X	Leaside	L122YVK	London & Country	L156YVK	Maidstone & Dist
KYV703X	Leaside	KYV775X	Leaside	L123YVK	London & Country	L157WAG	South London
KYV704X	Leaside	KYV776X	Leaside	L124YVK	London & Country	L157YVK	Kentish Bus
KYV705X	Leaside	KYV777X	Leaside	L125YVK	London & Country	L158BFT	Kentish Bus
KYV707X	Leaside	KYV778X	Leaside	L126YVK	London & Country	L158WAG	South London
KYV708X	Leaside	KYV780X	Leaside	L127YVK	Kentish Bus	L159BFT	Kentish Bus
KYV709X	Leaside	KYV781X	Leaside	L128YVK	Kentish Bus	L159GYL	Grey-Green
KYV710X	Leaside	KYV782X	County	L129YVK	Kentish Bus	L160GYL	Grey-Green
KYV711X	Leaside	KYV783X	Leaside	L130YVK	Kentish Bus	L161GYL	Grey-Green
KYV712X	Leaside	KYV784X	Leaside	L131YVK	Kentish Bus	L193DBC	North Western
KYV713X	Leaside	KYV785X	Leaside	L132NHP	Midland Fox	L200BUS	The Shires
KYV714X	Leaside	KYV786X	Leaside	L132YVK	Kentish Bus	L201YCU	London & Country
KYV715X	Leaside	KYV787X	Leaside	L133HVS	The Shires	L202YCU	London & Country
KYV716X	Leaside	KYV788X	Leaside	L133NHP	Midland Fox	L203YCU	London & Country
KYV717X	Leaside	KYV789X	Leaside	L133YVK	Kentish Bus	L204YCU	London & Country
KYV718X	Leaside	KYV790X	Leaside	L134YVK	Kentish Bus	L205YCU	London & Country
KYV719X	Leaside	KYV791X	Leaside	L135YVK	Kentish Bus	L206YCU	London & Country
KYV720X	Leaside	KYV792X	Leaside	L136YVK	Kentish Bus	L207YCU	London & Country
KYV721X	Leaside	KYV793X	Leaside	L137YVK	Kentish Bus	L208YCU	London & Country
KYV722X	South London	KYV795X	Leaside	L138YVK	Kentish Bus	L209YCU	London & Country
KYV723X	Leaside	KYV796X	Leaside	L139YVK	Kentish Bus	L210YCU	London & Country
KYV724X	South London	KYV798X	Leaside	L140YVK	Kentish Bus	L211YCU	London & Country
KYV726X	Leaside	KYV799X	South London	L141YVK	Kentish Bus	L212YCU	London & Country
KYV727X	Leaside	KYV803X	South London	L142YVK	Kentish Bus	L226JFA	Midland Fox
KYV728X	Leaside	KYV805X	South London	L143NHP	Midland Fox	L227HRF	Midland Fox
KYV729X	Leaside	L1SLT	North Western	L143YVK	Kentish Bus	L228HRF	Midland Red
KYV730X	Leaside	L2SLT	North Western	L144YVK	Kentish Bus	L229HRF	Midland Red
KYV731X	Leaside	L3SLT	North Western	L145NHP	Midland Fox	L230HRF	Midland Red
KYV732X	Leaside	L11SLT	North Western	L145YVK	Kentish Bus	L231HRF	Midland Red
KYV733X	Leaside	L25LSX	Clydeside	L146NHP	Midland Fox	L232HRF	Midland Red
KYV734X	Leaside	L33NMS	Northumbria	L146YVK	Kentish Bus	L233HRF	Midland Red
KYV736X	Leaside	L34PNN	Midland Fox	L147WAG	South London	L253NFA	Midland Red
KYV737X	Leaside	L35OKV	Crosville Cymru	L148NHP	Midland Fox	L254NFA	Midland Red
KYV738X	Leaside	L35PNN	Midland Fox	L148WAG	South London	L255NFA	Midland Red
KYV740X	Leaside	L36OKV	Crosville Cymru	L148YVK	Kentish Bus	L263VSU	Clydeside
KYV741X	South London	L36PNN	Midland Fox	L149NHP	Midland Fox	L271FVN	United
KYV742X	Leaside	L37OKV	Crosville Cymru	L149WAG	South London	L272FVN	United
KYV743X	Leaside	L37PNN	Midland Fox	L149YVK	Kentish Bus	L273FVN	United
KYV744X	Leaside	L38OKV	Crosville Cymru	L150SBG	North Western	L274FVN	United
KYV745X	Leaside	L38PNN	Midland Fox	L150WAG	South London	L275FVN	United
KYV746X	Leaside	L43MEH	The Shires	L150YVK	Kentish Bus	L287EKK	Maidstone & Dist
KYV747X	Leaside	L51LSG	Clydeside	L151SBG	North Western	L300BUS	The Shires
KYV748X	Leaside	L52LSG	Clydeside	L151WAG	South London	L300SBS	Midland Red
KYV749X	Leaside	L53LSG	Clydeside	L151YVK	London & Country	L301NFA	Midland Red
KYV750X	Leaside	L54LSG	Clydeside	L152SBG	North Western	L302NFA	Midland Red
KYV751X	Leaside	L70MPS	Maidstone & Dist	L152WAG	South London	L303AUT	Midland Fox
KYV752X	Leaside	L80MPS	Maidstone & Dist	L152YVK	Kentish Bus	L303NFA	Midland Red
KYV753X	Leaside	L94HRF	Midland Red	L153UEM	North Western	L304AUT	Midland Fox
KYV754X	Leaside	L95HRF	Midland Red	L153UKB	North Western	L304NFA	Midland Red
KYV756X	Leaside	L100BUS	The Shires	L153WAG	South London	L305AUT	Midland Fox
KYV757X	Leaside	L100SBS	Midland Red	L153YVK	Kentish Bus	L305HPP	The Shires
KYV758X	Leaside	L102MEH	Midland Red	L154UEM	North Western	L305NFA	Midland Red
KYV761X	Leaside	L112YVK	Kentish Bus	L154UKB	North Western	L306AUT	Midland Fox
KYV762X	Leaside	L113YVK	Kentish Bus	L154WAG	South London	L306HPP	The Shires

Opposite:- **Concluding the colour section for the 1998 Cowie Bus Handbook are two buses from midlands operations. The upper picture shows City Rider 29, a Scania with East Lancashire European bodywork while the lower picture shows Midland Red/Stevensons 2151 in Burtonbus colours. The East Lancashire European has now been succeeded by the Flyte while the low floor version has become the Spryte. Though this was originally conceived for the Dennis Dart it is now being produced on many low floor buses.**

Reg	Operator	Reg	Operator	Reg	Operator	Reg	Operator
L307AUT	Midland Fox	L505CPJ	London & Country	L563YCU	Kentish Bus	L801KNO	County
L307HPP	The Shires	L506BNX	Midland Red	L564YCU	Kentish Bus	L802KNO	County
L308AUT	Midland Fox	L506CPJ	London & Country	L565YCU	Kentish Bus	L803KNO	County
L308HPP	The Shires	L507BNX	Midland Red	L588JSG	Clydeside	L804KNO	County
L309AUT	Midland Fox	L507CPJ	London & Country	L600BUS	The Shires	L805OVX	County
L309HPP	The Shires	L508BNX	Midland Red	L601EKM	Maidstone & Dist	L806NNW	Yorkshire Bus
L310AUT	Midland Fox	L508CPJ	London & Country	L601FHN	United	L807NNW	Yorkshire Bus
L310HPP	The Shires	L509BNX	Midland Red	L602EKM	Maidstone & Dist	L808NNW	Yorkshire Bus
L311AUT	Midland Fox	L509CPJ	London & Country	L602FHN	United	L809NNW	Yorkshire Bus
L311HPP	The Shires	L510BNX	Midland Red	L603EKM	Maidstone & Dist	L810NNW	Yorkshire Bus
L312AUT	Midland Fox	L510CPJ	London & Country	L603FHN	United	L811NNW	Yorkshire Bus
L312HPP	The Shires	L511BNX	Midland Red	L604EKM	Maidstone & Dist	L812NNW	Yorkshire Bus
L313AUT	Midland Fox	L511CPJ	London & Country	L604FHN	United	L813NNW	Yorkshire Bus
L313HPP	The Shires	L512BNX	Midland Red	L605BNX	Midland Red	L814NNW	Yorkshire Bus
L314AUT	Midland Fox	L512CPJ	London & Country	L605EKM	Maidstone & Dist	L815NNW	Yorkshire Bus
L314HPP	The Shires	L513BNX	Midland Red	L605FHN	United	L816NWY	Yorkshire Bus
L315AUT	Midland Fox	L513CPJ	London & Country	L606EKM	Maidstone & Dist	L817NWY	Yorkshire Bus
L315HPP	The Shires	L514BNX	Midland Red	L607EKM	Maidstone & Dist	L818NWY	Yorkshire Bus
L316AUT	Midland Fox	L514CPJ	London & Country	L608EKM	Maidstone & Dist	L819NWY	Yorkshire Bus
L316HPP	The Shires	L515BNX	Midland Red	L609EKM	Maidstone & Dist	L820NWY	Yorkshire Bus
L317AUT	Midland Fox	L515CPJ	London & Country	L610EKM	Maidstone & Dist	L821NWY	Yorkshire Bus
L318AUT	Midland Fox	L516BNX	Midland Red	L613LVX	County	L822NWY	Yorkshire Bus
L319AUT	Midland Fox	L516CPJ	London & Country	L614LVX	County	L823NWY	Yorkshire Bus
L320AUT	Midland Fox	L517BNX	Midland Red	L618BNX	Midland Red	L824NWY	Yorkshire Bus
L321AUT	Midland Fox	L519BNX	Midland Red	L620BNX	Midland Red	L825NWY	Yorkshire Bus
L322AUT	Midland Fox	L519FHN	United	L638DNA	Crosville Cymru	L826NYG	Yorkshire Bus
L323AUT	Midland Fox	L520FHN	United	L641DNA	North Western	L827NYG	Yorkshire Bus
L324AUT	Midland Fox	L521BNX	Midland Red	L642DNA	North Western	L828NYG	Yorkshire Bus
L325AUT	Midland Fox	L521FHN	United	L643DNA	North Western	L829NYG	Yorkshire Bus
L326AUT	The Shires	L522BNX	Midland Red	L646DNA	North Western	L830NYG	Yorkshire Bus
L327AUT	The Shires	L522FHN	United	L647DNA	North Western	L837MWT	Kentish Bus
L328AUT	The Shires	L523BNX	Midland Red	L648DNA	North Western	L838MWT	Kentish Bus
L400BUS	The Shires	L523FHN	United	L649DNA	North Western	L855WRG	Northumbria
L406NUA	Yorkshire Bus	L524FHN	United	L700BUS	The Shires	L856WRG	Northumbria
L407NUA	Yorkshire Bus	L525FHN	United	L705AGA	Clydeside	L857WRG	Northumbria
L408NUA	Yorkshire Bus	L526FHN	United	L713OVX	County	L858WRG	Northumbria
L409NUA	Yorkshire Bus	L527FHN	United	L714EKO	Maidstone & Dist	L860LFS	Clydeside
L415NHJ	County	L528FHN	United	L714OVX	County	L861LFS	Clydeside
L418FHN	United	L529FHN	United	L715OVX	County	L862LFS	Clydeside
L419FHN	United	L529XNR	North Western	L715WCC	Crosville Cymru	L863BEA	The Shires
L420FHN	United	L530FHN	United	L716OVX	County	L863LFS	Clydeside
L421CPB	London & Country	L531FHN	United	L716WCC	Crosville Cymru	L864BEA	The Shires
L421FHN	United	L532EHD	Northumbria	L717OVX	County	L864LFS	Clydeside
L422CPB	London & Country	L532FHN	United	L717WCC	Crosville Cymru	L865LFS	Clydeside
L422FHN	United	L533EHD	Northumbria	L718OVX	County	L866LFS	Clydeside
L423CPB	London & Country	L533FHN	United	L722OVX	County	L867LFS	Clydeside
L424CPB	London & Country	L534FHN	United	L723PHK	County	L868LFS	Clydeside
L425CPB	London & Country	L535FHN	United	L724PHK	County	L869LFS	Clydeside
L426CPB	London & Country	L536FHN	United	L730MWW	Yorkshire Bus	L870LFS	Clydeside
L427CPB	London & Country	L537FHN	United	L731MWW	Yorkshire Bus	L922LJO	The Shires
L428CPC	London & Country	L538FHN	United	L732MWW	Yorkshire Bus	L923LJO	The Shires
L429CPC	London & Country	L539FHN	United	L733MWW	Yorkshire Bus	L934GYL	Grey-Green
L430CPJ	London & Country	L540FHN	United	L734MWW	Yorkshire Bus	L935GYL	Grey-Green
L431CPJ	London & Country	L541FHN	United	L735PUA	Yorkshire Bus	L936GYL	Grey-Green
L433CPJ	London & Country	L542FHN	United	L736PUA	Yorkshire Bus	L937GYL	Grey-Green
L434CPJ	London & Country	L543FHN	United	L737PUA	Yorkshire Bus	L938GYL	Grey-Green
L435CPJ	London & Country	L544EHD	North Western	L738PUA	Yorkshire Bus	L939GYL	Grey-Green
L436CPJ	London & Country	L544GHN	United	L739PUA	Yorkshire Bus	L940GYL	Grey-Green
L437CPJ	London & Country	L545GHN	United	L740PUA	Yorkshire Bus	L941GYL	Grey-Green
L438FPA	London & Country	L546GHN	United	L741PUA	Yorkshire Bus	L970VGE	Clydeside
L439FPA	London & Country	L547GHN	United	L766DPE	Maidstone & Dist	LAZ5765	The Shires
L500BUS	The Shires	L548GHN	United	L771RWW	Yorkshire Bus	LAZ5785	The Shires
L500DKT	Maidstone & Dist	L549GHN	United	L772RWW	Yorkshire Bus	LAZ5847	Clydeside
L501MOO	County	L550GHN	United	L773RWW	Yorkshire Bus	LAZ5929	The Shires
L502BNX	Midland Red	L551GHN	United	L774RWW	Yorkshire Bus	LAZ5962	The Shires
L503BNX	Midland Red	L557YCU	Kentish Bus	L775RWW	Yorkshire Bus	LAZ5964	The Shires
L503CPB	London & Country	L558YCU	Kentish Bus	L776RWW	Yorkshire Bus	LAZ6771	The Shires
L503HKM	Maidstone & Dist	L559YCU	Kentish Bus	L778RWW	Yorkshire Bus	LBD837P	The Shires
L504BNX	Midland Red	L561YCU	Kentish Bus	L779RWW	Yorkshire Bus	LFR854X	North Western
L504CPB	London & Country	L562YCU	Kentish Bus	L800BUS	The Shires	LFR867X	North Western

Reg	Operator	Reg	Operator	Reg	Operator	Reg	Operator
LFR869X	North Western	M110RMS	Clydeside	M173GRY	Midland Fox	M236KNR	London & Country
LFR875X	Midland Red	M112RMS	Clydeside	M173YKA	North Western	M239XLV	North Western
LHO992Y	United	M113RMS	Clydeside	M174GRY	Midland Fox	M240XLV	North Western
LIL2168	London & Country	M114RMS	Clydeside	M174YKA	North Western	M247SPP	The Shires
LIL2180	London & Country	M115RMS	Clydeside	M175GRY	Midland Fox	M247WWX	Yorkshire Bus
LIL2288	The Shires	M116RMS	Clydeside	M175YKA	North Western	M248SPP	The Shires
LJI5631	Midland Fox	M117RMS	Clydeside	M176GRY	Midland Fox	M249SPP	The Shires
LJI5632	Midland Fox	M118RMS	Clydeside	M176YKA	North Western	M250SPP	The Shires
LJI8156	Midland Fox	M119RMS	Clydeside	M177GRY	Midland Fox	M251SPP	The Shires
LJI8157	Midland Fox	M120RMS	Clydeside	M177YKA	North Western	M266VPU	County
LMA412T	North Western	M120YCM	North Western	M178GRY	Midland Fox	M267VPU	County
LMS154W	Clydeside	M121RMS	Clydeside	M178LYP	Grey-Green	M268VPU	County
LOA839X	Midland Fox	M121YCM	North Western	M178YKA	North Western	M269VPU	County
LPB218P	London & Country	M122UUB	Northumbria	M179LYP	Grey-Green	M276FNS	Clydeside
LPB219P	North Western	M122YCM	North Western	M179YKA	North Western	M277FNS	Clydeside
LPF600P	London & Country	M123YCM	North Western	M180LYP	Grey-Green	M278FNS	Clydeside
LPT701T	Northumbria	M124YCM	North Western	M180YKA	North Western	M290AJC	Crosville Cymru
LPT703T	United	M125YCM	North Western	M181YKA	North Western	M291AJC	Crosville Cymru
LPT707T	Northumbria	M126YCM	North Western	M182YKA	North Western	M301SAJ	United
LRB201W	North Western	M127YCM	North Western	M183YKA	North Western	M302SAJ	United
LRB202W	North Western	M128YCM	North Western	M184YKA	North Western	M303SAJ	United
LRB206W	Crosville Cymru	M129YCM	North Western	M185YKA	North Western	M304SAJ	United
LRN664N	North Western	M150RBH	The Shires	M186YKA	North Western	M305SAJ	United
LSK641	Maidstone & Dist	M151RBH	The Shires	M187YKA	North Western	M322AKB	North Western
LSK643	Maidstone & Dist	M152RBH	The Shires	M188YKA	North Western	M331MRW	Midland Fox
LUP900T	United	M153RBH	The Shires	M189YKA	North Western	M332MRW	Midland Fox
LUP904T	United	M154RBH	The Shires	M190YKA	North Western	M363KVR	North Western
LUY742	Midland Red	M156RBH	The Shires	M191YKA	North Western	M364KVR	North Western
M2SLT	North Western	M157RBH	The Shires	M192YKA	North Western	M365KVR	North Western
M5SLT	North Western	M157WKA	North Western	M193YKA	North Western	M366KVR	North Western
M20MPS	Maidstone & Dist	M157WWM	North Western	M194YKA	North Western	M367KVR	North Western
M30MPS	Maidstone & Dist	M158RBH	The Shires	M195YKA	North Western	M368KVR	North Western
M38WUR	The Shires	M158WKA	North Western	M196YKA	North Western	M369KVR	North Western
M39WUR	The Shires	M158WWM	North Western	M197YKA	North Western	M370FTY	Northumbria
M40MPS	Maidstone & Dist	M159GRY	Midland Fox	M198YKA	North Western	M370KVR	North Western
M41WUR	The Shires	M159RBH	The Shires	M199YKA	North Western	M371EFD	Midland Red
M42WUR	The Shires	M159WKA	North Western	M200CBB	Maidstone & Dist	M371FTY	Northumbria
M43WUR	The Shires	M160GRY	Midland Fox	M201YKA	North Western	M371KVR	North Western
M45WUR	The Shires	M160RBH	The Shires	M202YKA	North Western	M372EFD	Midland Red
M46WUR	The Shires	M160SKR	London & Country	M203YKA	North Western	M372FTY	Northumbria
M47WUR	The Shires	M160WKA	North Western	M204YKA	North Western	M372KVR	North Western
M51AWW	Yorkshire Bus	M161GRY	Midland Fox	M205SKE	Maidstone & Dist	M373EFD	Midland Red
M52AWW	Yorkshire Bus	M161SKR	London & Country	M205YKA	North Western	M373FTY	Northumbria
M53AWW	Yorkshire Bus	M161WKA	North Western	M206SKE	Maidstone & Dist	M374EFD	Midland Red
M54AWW	Yorkshire Bus	M162GRY	Midland Fox	M206YKA	North Western	M374FTY	Northumbria
M55AWW	Yorkshire Bus	M162SKR	London & Country	M207YKA	North Western	M375EFD	Midland Red
M56AWW	Yorkshire Bus	M162WKA	North Western	M208YKA	North Western	M375FTY	Northumbria
M59WKA	North Western	M163GRY	Midland Fox	M209YKA	North Western	M376EFD	Midland Red
M61WKA	North Western	M163SKR	London & Country	M210YKA	North Western	M376FTY	Northumbria
M62WKA	North Western	M163WKA	North Western	M211YKD	North Western	M377EFD	Midland Red
M63WKA	North Western	M164GRY	Midland Fox	M212YKD	North Western	M377FTY	Northumbria
M64WKA	North Western	M164WKA	North Western	M213YKD	North Western	M378EFD	Midland Red
M65FDS	Clydeside	M165GRY	Midland Fox	M214YKD	North Western	M379EFD	Midland Red
M65WKA	North Western	M165WKA	North Western	M215YKD	North Western	M380EFD	Midland Red
M67FDS	Clydeside	M166GRY	Midland Fox	M216YKD	North Western	M381EFD	Midland Red
M67WKA	North Western	M166WKA	North Western	M217AKB	North Western	M385KVR	Crosville Cymru
M100CBB	Maidstone & Dist	M166WTJ	North Western	M218AKB	North Western	M394KVR	Crosville Cymru
M101WKA	North Western	M167GRY	Midland Fox	M219AKB	North Western	M401EFD	Midland Red
M102RMS	Clydeside	M167WKA	North Western	M220AKB	North Western	M402EFD	Midland Red
M102WKA	North Western	M168GRY	Midland Fox	M221AKB	North Western	M403EFD	Midland Red
M103RMS	Clydeside	M168WKA	North Western	M223AKB	North Western	M404EFD	Midland Red
M103WKA	North Western	M169GRY	Midland Fox	M224AKB	North Western	M410UNW	Yorkshire Bus
M104RMS	Clydeside	M169WKA	North Western	M225AKB	North Western	M411BEY	Crosville Cymru
M104WKA	North Western	M170GRY	Midland Fox	M226AKB	North Western	M411UNW	Yorkshire Bus
M105RMS	Clydeside	M170WKA	North Western	M227AKB	North Western	M412BEY	Crosville Cymru
M105WKA	North Western	M171GRY	Midland Fox	M228AKB	North Western	M412UNW	Yorkshire Bus
M106RMS	Clydeside	M171YKA	North Western	M229AKB	North Western	M413BEY	Crosville Cymru
M107RMS	Clydeside	M172GRY	Midland Fox	M230AKB	North Western	M413UNW	Yorkshire Bus
M108RMS	Clydeside	M172YKA	North Western	M231AKB	North Western	M414UNW	Yorkshire Bus
M109RMS	Clydeside			M232AKB	North Western	M415UNW	Yorkshire Bus

Reg	Operator	Reg	Operator	Reg	Operator	Reg	Operator
M416UNW	Yorkshire Bus	M521MPF	London & Country	M729UTW	County	M880DDS	Clydeside
M417UNW	Yorkshire Bus	M522MPF	London & Country	M730AOO	County	M883DDS	Clydeside
M418UNW	Yorkshire Bus	M523MPF	London & Country	M731AOO	County	M890DHP	Midland Fox
M419UNW	Yorkshire Bus	M524MPF	London & Country	M732AOO	County	M901DHP	Midland Fox
M420UNW	Yorkshire Bus	M525MPM	London & Country	M733AOO	County	M903DHP	Midland Fox
M421UNW	Yorkshire Bus	M526MPM	London & Country	M734AOO	County	M904DHP	Midland Fox
M422GUS	Clydeside	M611PKP	Maidstone & Dist	M735AOO	County	M905DHP	Midland Fox
M422UNW	Yorkshire Bus	M612PKP	Maidstone & Dist	M736AOO	County	M906DHP	Midland Fox
M423GUS	Clydeside	M613PKP	Maidstone & Dist	M737AOO	County	M907DHP	Midland Fox
M423UNW	Yorkshire Bus	M614PKP	Maidstone & Dist	M738AOO	County	M908DHP	Midland Fox
M424UNW	Yorkshire Bus	M615PKP	Maidstone & Dist	M742UUA	Yorkshire Bus	M909DHP	Midland Fox
M425UNW	Yorkshire Bus	M615XLG	North Western	M743UUA	Yorkshire Bus	M910DHP	Midland Fox
M426UNW	Yorkshire Bus	M616PKP	Maidstone & Dist	M744UUA	Yorkshire Bus	M911DHP	Midland Fox
M427UNW	Yorkshire Bus	M617PKP	Maidstone & Dist	M745UUA	Yorkshire Bus	M911MKM	Maidstone & Dist
M428UNW	Yorkshire Bus	M618PKP	Maidstone & Dist	M746WWX	Yorkshire Bus	M912DHP	Midland Fox
M429UNW	Yorkshire Bus	M619PKP	Maidstone & Dist	M748WWX	Yorkshire Bus	M912MKM	Maidstone & Dist
M430UNW	Yorkshire Bus	M651ERW	Midland Fox	M749WWR	Yorkshire Bus	M913DHP	Midland Fox
M431UNW	Yorkshire Bus	M652ERW	Midland Fox	M750WWR	Yorkshire Bus	M913MKM	Maidstone & Dist
M432UNW	Yorkshire Bus	M685HPF	London & Country	M751WWR	Yorkshire Bus	M914DHP	Midland Fox
M433UNW	Yorkshire Bus	M686HPF	London & Country	M752WWR	Yorkshire Bus	M914MKM	Maidstone & Dist
M440HPF	London & Country	M687HPF	London & Country	M753WWR	Yorkshire Bus	M915DHP	Midland Fox
M441HPF	London & Country	M688HPF	London & Country	M761JPA	Southend	M915MKM	Maidstone & Dist
M442HPF	London & Country	M689FJF	North Western	M762JPA	Southend	M916DHP	Midland Fox
M443HPF	London & Country	M689HPF	London & Country	M763JPA	Southend	M916MKM	Maidstone & Dist
M444HPF	Kentish Bus	M690HPF	London & Country	M764JPA	Southend	M917DHP	Midland Fox
M445HPF	Kentish Bus	M691HPF	London & Country	M791EUS	Clydeside	M917MKM	Maidstone & Dist
M446HPF	Kentish Bus	M692HPF	London & Country	M792EUS	Clydeside	M918DHP	Midland Fox
M447HPF	Kentish Bus	M693HPF	London & Country	M793EUS	Clydeside	M918MKM	Maidstone & Dist
M448HPF	Kentish Bus	M694HPF	London & Country	M794EUS	Clydeside	M919DHP	Midland Fox
M449HPF	Kentish Bus	M695HPF	London & Country	M799EUS	Clydeside	M919MKM	Maidstone & Dist
M450HPF	Kentish Bus	M696HPF	London & Country	M802MOJ	Midland Red	M920DHP	Midland Fox
M451EDH	Midland Red	M697HPF	London & Country	M803MOJ	Midland Red	M920MKM	Maidstone & Dist
M451HPF	Kentish Bus	M698HPF	London & Country	M804MOJ	Midland Red	M921PKN	Maidstone & Dist
M452EDH	Midland Red	M699HPF	London & Country	M805MOJ	Midland Red	M922PKN	Maidstone & Dist
M452HPG	Kentish Bus	M700HPF	London & Country	M831SDA	Midland Red	M923PKN	Maidstone & Dist
M453EDH	Midland Red	M701HPF	London & Country	M832SDA	Midland Red	M924PKN	Maidstone & Dist
M453HPG	Kentish Bus	M702HPF	London & Country	M833SDA	Midland Red	M925PKN	Maidstone & Dist
M454EDH	Midland Red	M703HPF	London & Country	M834SDA	Midland Red	M927EYS	North Western
M454HPG	London & Country	M704HPF	London & Country	M835SDA	Midland Red	M928EYS	North Western
M455EDH	Midland Red	M710OMJ	The Shires	M841DDS	Clydeside	M929EYS	North Western
M455HPG	London & Country	M711OMJ	The Shires	M841RCP	North Western	M930EYS	North Western
M456EDH	Midland Red	M711YJC	Crosville Cymru	M842DDS	Clydeside	M931EYS	North Western
M456HPG	London & Country	M712OMJ	The Shires	M842RCP	North Western	M932EYS	North Western
M457EDH	Midland Red	M712YJC	Crosville Cymru	M843DDS	Clydeside	M933EYS	North Western
M457HPG	London & Country	M713OMJ	The Shires	M843RCP	North Western	M934EYS	North Western
M458EDH	Midland Red	M713YJC	Crosville Cymru	M844DDS	Clydeside	M935EYS	North Western
M458JPA	London & Country	M714OMJ	The Shires	M845DDS	Clydeside	M936EYS	North Western
M459EDH	Midland Red	M714YJC	Crosville Cymru	M846DDS	Clydeside	M942LYR	Grey-Green
M459JPA	London & Country	M715OMJ	The Shires	M847DDS	Clydeside	M943LYR	Grey-Green
M460EDH	Midland Red	M716OMJ	The Shires	M847RCP	Crosville Cymru	M943UDT	Crosville Cymru
M460JPA	London & Country	M717OMJ	The Shires	M849RCP	Crosville Cymru	M944LYR	Grey-Green
M461EDH	Midland Red	M718OMJ	The Shires	M859KCU	Northumbria	M945LYR	Grey-Green
M461JPA	London & Country	M719OMJ	The Shires	M860KCU	Northumbria	M946LYR	Grey-Green
M462EDH	Midland Red	M719UTW	County	M861KCU	Northumbria	M947LYR	Grey-Green
M462JPA	London & Country	M720OMJ	The Shires	M862KCU	Northumbria	M948LYR	Grey-Green
M463JPA	London & Country	M720UTW	County	M863KCU	Northumbria	M949LYR	Grey-Green
M464JPA	London & Country	M721OMJ	The Shires	M864KCU	Northumbria	M950LYR	Grey-Green
M465LPG	London & Country	M721UTW	County	M865KCU	Northumbria	M951LYR	County
M466MPM	London & Country	M722OMJ	The Shires	M866KCU	Northumbria	M95EGE	Clydeside
M467MPM	London & Country	M723OMJ	The Shires	M867KCU	Northumbria	M998XRF	North Western
M501AJC	Crosville Cymru	M724OMJ	The Shires	M868KCU	Northumbria	MAR781P	North Western
M501PKJ	Maidstone & Dist	M725OMJ	The Shires	M869KCU	Northumbria	MBZ6454	The Shires
M502AJC	Crosville Cymru	M725UTW	County	M870KCU	Northumbria	MBZ6455	The Shires
M502RKO	Maidstone & Dist	M726OMJ	The Shires	M871KCU	Northumbria	MEF822W	United
M503AJC	Crosville Cymru	M726UTW	County	M872LBB	Northumbria	MEF823W	United
M504AJC	Crosville Cymru	M727OMJ	The Shires	M873LBB	Northumbria	MEF824W	United
M517KPA	London & Country	M727UTW	County	M874LBB	Northumbria	MEL553P	London & Country
M518KPA	London & Country	M728OMJ	The Shires	M875LBB	Northumbria	MEV83V	Colchester
M519KPA	London & Country	M728UTW	County	M876LBB	Northumbria	MEV84V	Colchester
M520KPA	London & Country	M729OMJ	The Shires	M878DDS	Clydeside	MEV85V	Colchester

MEV86V	Colchester	MUH290X	The Shires	N174PUT	Midland Fox	N242VPH	London & Country
MEV87V	Colchester	MUP712T	Northumbria	N175DWM	North Western	N243CKA	North Western
MGR659P	Clydeside	MUP713T	Crosville Cymru	N175PUT	Midland Fox	N243VPH	London & Country
MHJ722V	Crosville Cymru	MUP714T	Northumbria	N176DWM	North Western	N244CKA	North Western
MHJ727V	Crosville Cymru	MXX313	London & Country	N176PUT	Midland Fox	N244VPH	London & Country
MHN128W	United	N26KYS	Clydeside	N177DWM	North Western	N245CKA	North Western
MHN129W	United	N27KYS	Clydeside	N177PUT	Midland Fox	N245VPH	London & Country
MHN130W	United	N28KGS	The Shires	N178DWM	North Western	N246CKA	North Western
MIL2350	The Shires	N29KGS	The Shires	N178PUT	Midland Fox	N246VPH	London & Country
MIL5573	North Western	N31KGS	The Shires	N179DWM	North Western	N247CKA	North Western
MIL5574	North Western	N32KGS	The Shires	N179PUT	Midland Fox	N247VPH	London & Country
MIL5575	North Western	N35JPP	The Shires	N181OYH	Grey-Green	N248CKA	North Western
MIL5580	North Western	N36JPP	The Shires	N182OYH	Grey-Green	N248VPH	London & Country
MIL5581	North Western	N37JPP	The Shires	N183OYH	Grey-Green	N249CKA	North Western
MIL5582	North Western	N38JPP	The Shires	N186EMJ	The Shires	N249VPH	London & Country
MIL6676	North Western	N39JPP	The Shires	N187EMJ	The Shires	N24FWU	Crosville Cymru
MIL6677	North Western	N41JPP	The Shires	N188EMJ	The Shires	N250BKK	Kentish Bus
MIL6678	North Western	N42JPP	The Shires	N189EMJ	The Shires	N250CKA	North Western
MIL6679	North Western	N43JPP	The Shires	N190EMJ	The Shires	N251BKK	Kentish Bus
MIL6680	North Western	N45JPP	The Shires	N191EMJ	The Shires	N251CKA	North Western
MIL6681	North Western	N46JPP	The Shires	N192EMJ	The Shires	N252BKK	Kentish Bus
MIL7612	North Western	N81PUS	Clydeside	N192RVK	Northumbria	N252CKA	North Western
MIL7613	North Western	N82PUS	Clydeside	N193EMJ	The Shires	N253BKK	Kentish Bus
MIL7614	North Western	N101YVU	North Western	N194EMJ	The Shires	N253CKA	North Western
MIL7615	North Western	N103YVU	North Western	N195EMJ	The Shires	N253PGD	Clydeside
MIL7616	North Western	N104YVU	North Western	N196EMJ	The Shires	N254BKK	Kentish Bus
MIL7617	North Western	N105YVU	North Western	N201NHS	Clydeside	N254CKA	North Western
MIL7618	North Western	N106DWM	North Western	N202NHS	Clydeside	N254PGD	Clydeside
MIL7619	North Western	N107DWM	North Western	N203NHS	Clydeside	N255BKK	Kentish Bus
MIL7620	North Western	N108DWM	North Western	N204NHS	Clydeside	N255CKA	North Western
MIL7621	North Western	N109DWM	North Western	N205NHS	Clydeside	N256BKK	Kentish Bus
MIL7622	North Western	N110DWM	North Western	N206NHS	Clydeside	N256CKA	North Western
MIL7623	North Western	N112DWM	North Western	N207CKP	Maidstone & Dist	N256PGD	Clydeside
MIL7624	North Western	N113DWM	North Western	N207NHS	Clydeside	N257BKK	Kentish Bus
MIL9320	Clydeside	N114DWM	North Western	N208CKP	Maidstone & Dist	N257CKA	North Western
MNH569V	The Shires	N115DWM	North Western	N208NHS	Clydeside	N257PGD	Clydeside
MNH577V	The Shires	N116DWM	North Western	N209CKP	Maidstone & Dist	N258BKK	Kentish Bus
MNW131V	United	N117DWM	North Western	N210TPK	London & Country	N258CKA	North Western
MPJ210L	Southend	N118DWM	North Western	N211DWM	North Western	N258PGD	Clydeside
MRJ231W	Southend	N119DWM	North Western	N211TBC	Midland Fox	N259BKK	Kentish Bus
MRJ232W	Southend	N120DWM	North Western	N211TPK	London & Country	N259CKA	North Western
MRJ233W	Southend	N121DWM	North Western	N212TBC	Midland Fox	N25FWU	Crosville Cymru
MRJ234W	Southend	N122DWM	North Western	N212TPK	London & Country	N260CKA	North Western
MRJ235W	Southend	N123DWM	North Western	N213TPK	London & Country	N261CKA	North Western
MRJ236W	Southend	N124DWM	North Western	N214TPK	London & Country	N262CKA	North Western
MRJ237W	Southend	N125DWM	North Western	N215TPK	London & Country	N263CKA	North Western
MRJ238W	Southend	N126DWM	North Western	N216TPK	London & Country	N264CKA	North Western
MRJ239W	Southend	N127DWM	North Western	N217TPK	London & Country	N281NCN	Northumbria
MRJ240W	Southend	N128DWM	North Western	N218TPK	London & Country	N282NCN	Northumbria
MRJ241W	Southend	N129DWM	North Western	N219TPK	London & Country	N283NCN	Northumbria
MRJ242W	Southend	N130DWM	North Western	N220TPK	London & Country	N284NCN	Northumbria
MRO993P	Midland Red	N131DWM	North Western	N221TPK	London & Country	N285NCN	Northumbria
MTU116Y	Midland Fox	N132DWM	North Western	N223TPK	London & Country	N286NCN	Northumbria
MTU117Y	Midland Fox	N133DWM	North Western	N224TPK	London & Country	N287NCN	Northumbria
MTU118Y	Midland Fox	N134DWM	North Western	N228MUS	Clydeside	N288NCN	Northumbria
MTU119Y	Midland Fox	N160VVO	Midland Fox	N233CKA	North Western	N289NCN	Northumbria
MTU121Y	Midland Fox	N161VVO	Midland Fox	N234CKA	North Western	N290NCN	Northumbria
MTV309W	Midland Fox	N162VVO	Midland Fox	N235CKA	North Western	N301ENX	Midland Red
MTV310W	Midland Fox	N163VVO	Midland Fox	N236CKA	North Western	N302ENX	Midland Red
MTV311W	Midland Fox	N164VVO	Midland Fox	N237CKA	North Western	N303ENX	Midland Red
MTV312W	Midland Fox	N165XVO	Midland Fox	N237VPH	London & Country	N304ENX	Midland Red
MTV313W	Midland Fox	N166PUT	Midland Fox	N238CKA	North Western	N305ENX	Midland Red
MTV314W	Midland Fox	N166XVO	Midland Fox	N238VPH	London & Country	N322TPK	London & Country
MTV315W	Midland Fox	N167PUT	Midland Fox	N239CKA	North Western	N331OFP	Midland Fox
MUH281X	Southend	N168PUT	Midland Fox	N239VPH	London & Country	N344OBC	Midland Fox
MUH283X	Southend	N169PUT	Midland Fox	N240CKA	North Western	N345OBC	Midland Fox
MUH284X	The Shires	N170PUT	Midland Fox	N240VPH	London & Country	N346OBC	Midland Fox
MUH285X	Southend	N171PUT	Midland Fox	N241CKA	North Western	N347OBC	Midland Fox
MUH286X	Southend	N172PUT	Midland Fox	N241VPH	London & Country	N348OBC	Midland Fox
MUH287X	The Shires	N173PUT	Midland Fox	N242CKA	North Western	N349OBC	Midland Fox

Reg	Operator	Reg	Operator	Reg	Operator	Reg	Operator
N350OBC	Midland Fox	N474XRC	Midland Fox	N688GUM	Leaside	N801PDS	Clydeside
N351OBC	Midland Fox	N475XRC	Midland Fox	N689GUM	Leaside	N801TPK	London & Country
N351YKE	Maidstone & Dist	N476XRC	Midland Fox	N691GUM	Leaside	N802BKN	Kentish Bus
N352BKK	Maidstone & Dist	N477XRC	Midland Fox	N693EUR	The Shires	N802PDS	Clydeside
N352OBC	Midland Fox	N478XRC	Midland Fox	N694EUR	The Shires	N802TPK	London & Country
N353OBC	Midland Fox	N479XRC	Midland Fox	N695EUR	The Shires	N803BKN	Kentish Bus
N354OBC	Midland Fox	N480XRC	Midland Fox	N696EUR	The Shires	N803PDS	Clydeside
N355OBC	Midland Fox	N481XRC	Midland Fox	N697EUR	The Shires	N803TPK	London & Country
N356OBC	Midland Fox	N511XVN	United	N698EUR	The Shires	N804BKN	Kentish Bus
N357OBC	Midland Fox	N512XVN	United	N699EUR	The Shires	N804PDS	Clydeside
N358OBC	Midland Fox	N513XVN	United	N701EUR	The Shires	N804TPK	London & Country
N366JGS	The Shires	N514XVN	United	N701GUM	London & Country	N805BKN	Kentish Bus
N367JGS	The Shires	N515XVN	United	N702EUR	The Shires	N805PDS	Clydeside
N368JGS	The Shires	N516XVN	United	N702GUM	London & Country	N805TPK	London & Country
N369JGS	The Shires	N517XVN	United	N703EUR	The Shires	N806BKN	Kentish Bus
N370JGS	The Shires	N518XVN	United	N703GUM	London & Country	N806EHA	Midland Red
N371JGS	The Shires	N519XVN	United	N704EUR	The Shires	N806PDS	Clydeside
N372JGS	The Shires	N520XVN	United	N704GUM	London & Country	N806TPK	London & Country
N373JGS	The Shires	N521XVN	United	N705EUR	The Shires	N806XHN	United
N374JGS	The Shires	N522XVN	United	N705GUM	London & Country	N807BKN	Kentish Bus
N375JGS	The Shires	N523XVN	United	N705TPK	Southend	N807EHA	Midland Red
N376JGS	The Shires	N524XVN	United	N706EUR	The Shires	N807PDS	Clydeside
N377JGS	The Shires	N525XVN	United	N706GUM	London & Country	N807TPK	London & Country
N378JGS	The Shires	N527SPA	London & Country	N706TPK	Southend	N807XHN	United
N379JGS	The Shires	N528SPA	London & Country	N707EUR	The Shires	N808BKN	Kentish Bus
N380JGS	The Shires	N529SPA	London & Country	N707GUM	London & Country	N808EHA	Midland Red
N381JGS	The Shires	N530SPA	London & Country	N707TPK	Southend	N808PDS	Clydeside
N381OTY	Northumbria	N539TPF	London & Country	N708EUR	The Shires	N808TPK	London & Country
N382JGS	The Shires	N540TPF	London & Country	N708GUM	London & Country	N808XHN	United
N382OTY	Northumbria	N541TPF	London & Country	N708TPK	Southend	N809PDS	Clydeside
N383JGS	The Shires	N542TPK	London & Country	N709EUR	The Shires	N809TPK	London & Country
N383OTY	Northumbria	N543TPK	London & Country	N709GUM	London & Country	N809XHN	United
N384JGS	The Shires	N544TPK	London & Country	N709TPK	Southend	N810TPK	London & Country
N384OTY	Northumbria	N551LUA	County	N710EUR	The Shires	N810XHN	United
N385JGS	The Shires	N552LUA	County	N710GUM	South London	N852YKE	Kentish Bus
N385OTY	Northumbria	N601DWY	Leaside	N711EUR	The Shires	N877RTN	Northumbria
N386JGS	The Shires	N602DWY	Leaside	N711GUM	South London	N878RTN	Northumbria
N386OTY	Northumbria	N603DWY	Leaside	N712EUR	The Shires	N879RTN	Northumbria
N387JGS	The Shires	N604DWY	Leaside	N712GUM	South London	N880RTN	Northumbria
N387OTY	Northumbria	N605DWY	Leaside	N713EUR	The Shires	N881RTN	Northumbria
N388OTY	Northumbria	N606DWY	Leaside	N713TPK	London & Country	N882RTN	Northumbria
N389OTY	Northumbria	N607DWY	Leaside	N714EUR	The Shires	N883RTN	Northumbria
N390OTY	Northumbria	N608DWY	Leaside	N714TPK	London & Country	N884RTN	Northumbria
N391OTY	Northumbria	N609DWY	Leaside	N715EUR	The Shires	N885RTN	Northumbria
N392OTY	Northumbria	N610DWY	Leaside	N715TPK	London & Country	N886RTN	Northumbria
N393OTY	Northumbria	N611DWY	Leaside	N716EUR	The Shires	N887RTN	Northumbria
N429XRC	Midland Fox	N612DWY	Leaside	N716TPK	London & Country	N889RTN	Northumbria
N430XRC	Midland Fox	N613DWY	Leaside	N718DJC	Crosville Cymru	N890RTN	Northumbria
N431XRC	Midland Fox	N621KUA	Yorkshire Bus	N719DJC	Crosville Cymru	N891RTN	Northumbria
N432XRC	Midland Fox	N622KUA	Yorkshire Bus	N739AVW	County	N906ETM	The Shires
N433XRC	Midland Fox	N623KUA	Yorkshire Bus	N740AVW	County	N907ETM	The Shires
N439GHG	Clydeside	N671GUM	Leaside	N741AVW	County	N908ETM	The Shires
N440GHG	Clydeside	N671TPF	London & Country	N742AVW	County	N909ETM	The Shires
N463EHA	Midland Red	N672GUM	Leaside	N743ANW	County	N910ETM	The Shires
N464EHA	Midland Red	N673GUM	Leaside	N744ANW	County	N911ETM	The Shires
N465EHA	Midland Red	N674GUM	Leaside	N750LUS	Clydeside	N912ETM	The Shires
N466EHA	Midland Red	N675GUM	Leaside	N752LUS	Clydeside	N913ETM	The Shires
N467EHA	Midland Red	N676GUM	Leaside	N753LUS	Clydeside	N914ETM	The Shires
N468EHA	Midland Red	N677GUM	Leaside	N754LUS	Clydeside	N915ETM	The Shires
N468SPA	London & Country	N678GUM	Leaside	N754LWW	Yorkshire Bus	N916ETM	The Shires
N469EHA	Midland Red	N679GUM	Leaside	N755LWW	Yorkshire Bus	N917ETM	The Shires
N469SPA	London & Country	N680GUM	Leaside	N756LWW	Yorkshire Bus	N918ETM	The Shires
N470EHA	Midland Red	N680GUM	Leaside	N757LWW	Yorkshire Bus	N919ETM	The Shires
N470SPA	London & Country	N681GUM	Leaside	N779EUA	Yorkshire Bus	N935ETU	Crosville Cymru
N471EHA	Midland Red	N682GUM	Leaside	N780EUA	Yorkshire Bus	N936ETU	Crosville Cymru
N472EHA	Midland Red	N683GUM	Leaside	N781EUA	Yorkshire Bus	N941MGG	Clydeside
N472XRC	Midland Fox	N684GUM	Leaside	N782EUA	Yorkshire Bus	N942MGG	Clydeside
N473MUS	Clydeside	N685GUM	Leaside	N783EUA	Yorkshire Bus	N991KUS	Clydeside
N473XRC	Midland Fox	N686GUM	Leaside	N784EUA	Yorkshire Bus	N993CCC	Crosville Cymru
N474MUS	Clydeside	N687GUM	Leaside	N801BKN	Kentish Bus	N994CCC	Crosville Cymru

N995CCC	Crosville Cymru	OJD809Y	South London	P96MOX	Midland Fox	P183SRO	The Shires
N996CCC	Crosville Cymru	OJD825Y	South London	P100LOW	The Shires	P183VUA	Yorkshire Bus
N996KUS	Crosville Cymru	OJD827Y	South London	P101HCH	Midland Fox	P184GND	North Western
N997CCC	Crosville Cymru	OJD850Y	South London	P102HCH	Midland Fox	P184LKL	Kentish Bus
NAT198V	United	OJD858Y	South London	P103HCH	Midland Fox	P184SRO	The Shires
NAT199V	United	OJD863Y	South London	P104HCH	Midland Fox	P184VUA	Yorkshire Bus
NDC238W	Northumbria	OJD865Y	South London	P105HCH	Midland Fox	P185LKL	Kentish Bus
NDC501W	Northumbria	OJD869Y	South London	P106HCH	Midland Fox	P185SRO	The Shires
NDC502W	Northumbria	OJD891Y	Leaside	P107HCH	Midland Fox	P185VUA	Yorkshire Bus
NDC503W	Northumbria	OJN357P	County	P108HCH	Midland Fox	P186LKJ	Kentish Bus
NDC504W	Northumbria	OKY822X	Midland Red	P109HCH	Midland Fox	P186SRO	The Shires
NGR681P	Midland Red	OLS540P	London & Country	P110HCH	Midland Fox	P186VUA	Yorkshire Bus
NGR685P	Northumbria	ONH925V	The Shires	P111MML	Midland Fox	P187LKJ	Kentish Bus
NIB8459	The Shires	ONH928V	The Shires	P112HCH	Midland Fox	P187SRO	The Shires
NIW6507	Colchester	ONH929V	The Shires	P113HCH	Midland Fox	P187VUA	Yorkshire Bus
NIW6508	Colchester	OOV761X	Midland Red	P114HCH	Midland Fox	P188LKJ	Kentish Bus
NIW6509	Colchester	OOX801R	North Western	P115HCH	Midland Fox	P188SRO	The Shires
NIW6510	Colchester	OOX802R	North Western	P116HCH	Midland Fox	P188VUA	Yorkshire Bus
NIW6511	Colchester	OOX803R	North Western	P117HCH	Midland Fox	P189LKJ	Kentish Bus
NIW6512	Colchester	OOX805R	North Western	P118HCH	Midland Fox	P189SRO	The Shires
NJF204W	The Shires	OOX807R	North Western	P119HCH	Midland Fox	P189VUA	Yorkshire Bus
NKN650	Maidstone & Dist	OOX809R	North Western	P120HCH	Midland Fox	P190LKJ	Kentish Bus
NLE882	London & Country	OOX810R	North Western	P121HCH	Midland Fox	P190SRO	The Shires
NLG35Y	United	OOX811R	North Western	P122HCH	Midland Fox	P190VUA	Yorkshire Bus
NML608E	South London	OOX813R	North Western	P123HCH	Midland Fox	P191LKJ	Kentish Bus
NML611E	Leaside	OOX818R	North Western	P124HCH	Midland Fox	P191VUA	Yorkshire Bus
NML617E	Leaside	OOX826R	United	P125HCH	Midland Fox	P192LKJ	Maidstone & Dist
NML619E	South London	OSK774	Northumbria	P126HCH	Midland Fox	P192VUA	Yorkshire Bus
NML625E	Leaside	OVV851R	The Shires	P135GND	North Western	P193LKJ	Maidstone & Dist
NML628E	Leaside	OVV852R	The Shires	P136GND	North Western	P193VUA	Yorkshire Bus
NML632E	Leaside	OVV853R	The Shires	P137GND	North Western	P194LKJ	Maidstone & Dist
NML635E	Leaside	OVV855R	The Shires	P138GND	North Western	P194VUA	Yorkshire Bus
NML636E	South London	OYD693	London & Country	P139GND	North Western	P195LKJ	Maidstone & Dist
NML638E	Leaside	P3SLT	North Western	P140GND	North Western	P195VUA	Yorkshire Bus
NML643E	Leaside	P28LOE	Midland Red	P167BTV	Midland Fox	P196LKJ	Maidstone & Dist
NML653E	South London	P29LOE	Midland Fox	P168BTV	Midland Fox	P196VUA	Yorkshire Bus
NML655E	Leaside	P31XUG	Yorkshire Bus	P169BTV	Midland Fox	P197LKJ	Maidstone & Dist
NMS700	Northumbria	P36LOE	Midland Fox	P170VUA	Yorkshire Bus	P197VUA	Yorkshire Bus
NOE536R	London & Country	P37LOE	Midland Fox	P171VUA	Yorkshire Bus	P198LKJ	Maidstone & Dist
NOE600R	London & Country	P41MVU	North Western	P172VUA	Yorkshire Bus	P198VUA	Yorkshire Bus
NPJ478R	London & Country	P42MVU	North Western	P173VUA	Yorkshire Bus	P199LKJ	Maidstone & Dist
NPJ479R	London & Country	P43MVU	North Western	P174VUA	Yorkshire Bus	P199VUA	Yorkshire Bus
NPK242P	North Western	P45MVU	North Western	P175SRO	The Shires	P201HRY	Midland Fox
NPK245P	North Western	P46MVU	North Western	P175VUA	Yorkshire Bus	P201LKJ	Maidstone & Dist
NPK250R	North Western	P49MVU	North Western	P176LKL	Maidstone & Dist	P202HRY	Midland Fox
NPK259R	North Western	P51HOJ	Midland Red	P176SRO	The Shires	P202LKJ	Maidstone & Dist
NPK263R	North Western	P52HOJ	Midland Red	P176VUA	Yorkshire Bus	P203HRY	Midland Fox
NRP581V	The Shires	P52MVU	North Western	P177LKL	Maidstone & Dist	P203LKJ	Maidstone & Dist
NTC627M	United	P53HOJ	Midland Red	P177SRO	The Shires	P204HRY	Midland Fox
NTC640M	United	P53MVU	North Western	P177VUA	Yorkshire Bus	P204LKJ	Maidstone & Dist
NTK611	Maidstone & Dist	P54HOJ	Midland Red	P178LKL	Maidstone & Dist	P205HRY	Midland Fox
NTU11Y	North Western	P56HOJ	Midland Red	P178SRO	The Shires	P205LKJ	Maidstone & Dist
NTU12Y	North Western	P56MVU	North Western	P178VUA	Yorkshire Bus	P206HRY	Midland Fox
NTU13Y	North Western	P56XTN	Northumbria	P179LKL	Maidstone & Dist	P206LKJ	Maidstone & Dist
NTU15Y	North Western	P57HOJ	Midland Red	P179SRO	The Shires	P207LKJ	Maidstone & Dist
OAH552M	North Western	P57LOE	Midland Fox	P179VUA	Yorkshire Bus	P208LKJ	Maidstone & Dist
OBN505R	Northumbria	P57XTN	Northumbria	P180GND	North Western	P209LKJ	Maidstone & Dist
OBR769T	Northumbria	P58HOJ	Midland Red	P180LKL	Maidstone & Dist	P210JKK	Maidstone & Dist
OCU809R	Northumbria	P58LOE	Midland Fox	P180SRO	The Shires	P210LKJ	Maidstone & Dist
OCU810R	Northumbria	P58MVU	North Western	P180VUA	Yorkshire Bus	P211JKL	Maidstone & Dist
OCU812R	Northumbria	P58XTN	Northumbria	P181GND	North Western	P211LKJ	Maidstone & Dist
OCY916R	The Shires	P59HOJ	Midland Red	P181LKL	Maidstone & Dist	P212JKL	Maidstone & Dist
ODC470W	Maidstone & Dist	P59XTN	Northumbria	P181SRO	The Shires	P212LKJ	Maidstone & Dist
OGL518	Midland Red	P61HOJ	Midland Red	P181VUA	Yorkshire Bus	P213JKL	Maidstone & Dist
OHE274X	Colchester	P61MVU	North Western	P182GND	North Western	P213LKJ	Maidstone & Dist
OHE280X	Colchester	P61XTN	Northumbria	P182LKL	Maidstone & Dist	P214JKL	Maidstone & Dist
OIB3520	County	P94MOX	Midland Fox	P182SRO	The Shires	P214LKJ	Maidstone & Dist
OIB3521	County	P95HOF	Midland Fox	P182VUA	Yorkshire Bus	P215JKL	Maidstone & Dist
OIB3522	County	P95MOX	Midland Fox	P183GND	North Western	P215LKJ	Maidstone & Dist
OIB3523	County	P96HOF	Midland Fox	P183LKL	Maidstone & Dist	P216JKL	Maidstone & Dist

Reg	Operator	Reg	Operator	Reg	Operator	Reg	Operator
P216LKJ	Maidstone & Dist	P260NBA	North Western	P327HVX	County	P486CAL	Midland Fox
P217JKL	Maidstone & Dist	P261FPK	Southend	P328HVX	County	P487CAL	Midland Fox
P217MKL	Maidstone & Dist	P262FPK	Southend	P329HVX	County	P488CAL	Midland Fox
P217SGB	Clydeside	P263FPK	Southend	P330HVX	County	P489CAL	Midland Fox
P218LKK	Maidstone & Dist	P264FPK	Southend	P331HVX	County	P490CAL	Midland Fox
P218MKL	Maidstone & Dist	P265FPK	Southend	P332HVX	County	P490TGA	Clydeside
P218SGB	Clydeside	P266FPK	Southend	P334HVX	County	P491CAL	Midland Fox
P219LKK	Maidstone & Dist	P267FPK	Southend	P380FPK	London & Country	P491TGA	Clydeside
P219MKL	Maidstone & Dist	P268FPK	London & Country	P382FEA	Midland Red	P492CAL	Midland Fox
P219SGB	Clydeside	P269FPK	London & Country	P383FEA	Midland Red	P492TGA	Clydeside
P220LKK	Maidstone & Dist	P270FPK	London & Country	P384FEA	Midland Red	P526UGA	Clydeside
P220MKL	Maidstone & Dist	P271FPK	London & Country	P385FEA	Midland Red	P527UGA	Clydeside
P220SGB	Clydeside	P271VRG	Northumbria	P386FEA	Midland Red	P528UGA	Clydeside
P221LKK	Maidstone & Dist	P272FPK	London & Country	P387FEA	Midland Red	P529UGA	Clydeside
P221MKL	Maidstone & Dist	P272VRG	Northumbria	P388FEA	Midland Red	P601CAY	Midland Fox
P221SGB	Clydeside	P273FPK	London & Country	P389FEA	Midland Red	P602CAY	Midland Fox
P222MML	Midland Fox	P273VRG	Northumbria	P390FEA	Midland Red	P603CAY	Midland Fox
P223LKK	Maidstone & Dist	P274FPK	London & Country	P391FEA	Midland Red	P604CAY	Midland Fox
P223MKL	Maidstone & Dist	P274VRG	Northumbria	P392FEA	Midland Red	P605CAY	Midland Fox
P223SGB	Clydeside	P275FPK	London & Country	P393FEA	Midland Red	P606CAY	Midland Fox
P224LKK	Maidstone & Dist	P275VRG	Northumbria	P394FEA	Midland Red	P606FHN	United
P224MKL	Maidstone & Dist	P276FPK	London & Country	P395FEA	Midland Red	P607CAY	Midland Fox
P224SGB	Clydeside	P276VRG	Northumbria	P396FEA	Midland Red	P607FHN	United
P225LKK	Maidstone & Dist	P277FPK	London & Country	P397FEA	Midland Red	P608CAY	Midland Fox
P225MKL	Maidstone & Dist	P277VRG	Northumbria	P398FEA	Midland Red	P608FHN	United
P225SGB	Clydeside	P278FPK	London & Country	P399FEA	Midland Red	P609CAY	Midland Fox
P226LKK	Maidstone & Dist	P278VRG	Northumbria	P401FEA	Midland Red	P609FHN	United
P226MKL	Maidstone & Dist	P279FPK	London & Country	P410CCU	Northumbria	P610CAY	Midland Fox
P226SGB	Clydeside	P279VRG	Northumbria	P411CCU	Northumbria	P610FHN	United
P227LKK	Maidstone & Dist	P281FPK	London & Country	P412CCU	Northumbria	P611CAY	Midland Fox
P227MKL	Maidstone & Dist	P282FPK	London & Country	P413CCU	Northumbria	P611FHN	United
P227SGB	Clydeside	P283FPK	London & Country	P414CCU	Northumbria	P612CAY	Midland Fox
P228LKK	Maidstone & Dist	P284FPK	London & Country	P415CCU	Northumbria	P612FHN	United
P228MKL	Maidstone & Dist	P285FPK	London & Country	P416CCU	Northumbria	P613CAY	Midland Fox
P229LKK	Maidstone & Dist	P286FPK	London & Country	P416HVX	County	P613FHN	United
P229MKL	Maidstone & Dist	P287FPK	London & Country	P417CCU	Northumbria	P614FHN	United
P230LKK	Maidstone & Dist	P288FPK	London & Country	P417HVX	County	P615FHN	United
P230MKL	Maidstone & Dist	P289FPK	London & Country	P418CCU	Northumbria	P616FHN	United
P231MKL	Maidstone & Dist	P290FPK	London & Country	P418HVX	County	P617FHN	United
P232MKL	Maidstone & Dist	P291FPK	London & Country	P419CCU	Northumbria	P618FHN	United
P233MKN	Maidstone & Dist	P292FPK	London & Country	P419HVX	County	P619FHN	United
P234MKN	Maidstone & Dist	P293FPK	London & Country	P420CCU	Northumbria	P620FHN	United
P235MKN	Maidstone & Dist	P294FPK	London & Country	P420HVX	County	P621FHN	United
P236MKN	Maidstone & Dist	P295FPK	London & Country	P421HVX	County	P622FHN	United
P237MKN	Maidstone & Dist	P296FPK	London & Country	P422HVX	County	P623FHN	United
P238MKN	Maidstone & Dist	P306FEA	Midland Red	P423HVX	County	P624FHN	United
P239MKN	Maidstone & Dist	P307FEA	Midland Red	P424HVX	County	P625FHN	United
P240MKN	Maidstone & Dist	P308FEA	Midland Red	P425HVX	County	P626FHN	United
P241MKN	Maidstone & Dist	P309FEA	Midland Red	P426HVX	County	P627FHN	United
P242MKN	Maidstone & Dist	P310FEA	Midland Red	P427HVX	County	P628FHN	United
P243MKN	Maidstone & Dist	P311FEA	Midland Red	P428HVX	County	P629FHN	United
P244MKN	Maidstone & Dist	P312FEA	Midland Red	P429HVX	County	P630FHN	United
P244NBA	North Western	P313FEA	Midland Red	P430HVX	County	P631FHN	United
P245MKN	Maidstone & Dist	P314FEA	Midland Red	P431HVX	County	P632FHN	United
P246MKN	Maidstone & Dist	P315FEA	Midland Red	P438HKN	London & Country	P633FHN	United
P247MKN	Maidstone & Dist	P316FEA	Midland Red	P472APJ	London & Country	P634FHN	United
P250APM	London & Country	P317FEA	Midland Red	P473APJ	London & Country	P635FHN	United
P250NBA	North Western	P318FEA	Midland Red	P474APJ	London & Country	P636FHN	United
P251APM	London & Country	P319HOJ	Midland Red	P475DPE	London & Country	P637FHN	United
P252APM	London & Country	P320HOJ	Midland Red	P476DPE	London & Country	P638FHN	United
P253APM	London & Country	P321HOJ	Midland Red	P477DPE	London & Country	P639FHN	United
P254APM	London & Country	P322HOJ	Midland Red	P478DPE	Southend	P640FHN	United
P255APM	London & Country	P323HOJ	Midland Red	P479DPE	London & Country	P641FHN	United
P255HOJ	Midland Red	P324HOJ	Midland Red	P480DPE	London & Country	P642FHN	United
P256FPK	Southend	P324HVX	County	P481DPE	Southend	P643FHN	United
P257FPK	Southend	P325HOJ	Midland Red	P482CAL	Midland Fox	P644FHN	United
P258FPK	Southend	P325HVX	County	P482DPE	Southend	P645FHN	United
P259FPK	Southend	P326HOJ	Midland Red	P483CAL	Midland Fox	P658KEY	Crosville Cymru
P260FPK	Southend	P326HVX	County	P484CAL	Midland Fox	P669PNM	The Shires
P260HOJ	Midland Red	P327HOJ	Midland Red	P485CAL	Midland Fox	P670PNM	The Shires

The 1998 Cowie Bus Handbook

Reg	Operator	Reg	Operator	Reg	Operator	Reg	Operator
P671OPP	The Shires	P830RWU	South London	P913PWW	South London	PAJ827X	Northumbria
P671PNM	The Shires	P831KES	Clydeside	P914PWW	South London	PAJ829X	Northumbria
P672OPP	The Shires	P831RWU	South London	P915PWW	South London	PCA423V	North Western
P673OPP	The Shires	P832KES	Clydeside	P916PWW	South London	PCA424V	North Western
P674OPP	The Shires	P832RWU	South London	P917PWW	South London	PCA425V	North Western
P688KCC	Crosville Cymru	P833HVX	County	P918PWW	South London	PCW946	Midland Red
P753RWU	County	P833KES	Clydeside	P926MKL	Maidstone & Dist	PDZ6261	Kentish Bus
P754RWU	County	P833RWU	South London	P927MKL	Maidstone & Dist	PDZ6262	Kentish Bus
P801RWU	Clydeside	P834KES	Clydeside	P928MKL	Maidstone & Dist	PDZ6263	London & Country
P802RWU	Clydeside	P834RWU	South London	P929MKL	Maidstone & Dist	PDZ6264	London & Country
P803RWU	Clydeside	P835KES	Clydeside	P930MKL	Maidstone & Dist	PDZ6265	London & Country
P804RWU	Clydeside	P835RWU	South London	P930YSB	Clydeside	PDZ6273	London & Country
P805RWU	Clydeside	P836KES	Clydeside	P931MKL	Maidstone & Dist	PDZ6274	London & Country
P806DBS	Clydeside	P836RWU	South London	P931YSB	Clydeside	PDZ6275	London & Country
P807DBS	Clydeside	P837KES	Clydeside	P932MKL	Maidstone & Dist	PDZ6276	London & Country
P808DBS	Clydeside	P837RWU	South London	P932YSB	Clydeside	PDZ6277	London & Country
P809DBS	Clydeside	P838KES	Clydeside	P933MKL	Maidstone & Dist	PFA50W	Crosville Cymru
P810DBS	Clydeside	P838RWU	South London	P934MKL	Maidstone & Dist	PFM126Y	North Western
P811DBS	Clydeside	P839KES	Clydeside	P935MKL	Maidstone & Dist	PFM128Y	North Western
P812DBS	Clydeside	P839RWU	South London	P936MKL	Maidstone & Dist	PFM129Y	North Western
P813DBS	Clydeside	P840KES	Clydeside	P936YSB	Clydeside	PFM130Y	Midland Red
P814DBS	Clydeside	P840PWW	Leaside	P937MKL	Maidstone & Dist	PJI3745	Southend
P814YTY	Northumbria	P841PWW	Leaside	P937YSB	Clydeside	PKM111R	Maidstone & Dist
P815DBS	Clydeside	P842PWW	Leaside	P938MKL	Maidstone & Dist	PKM112R	Maidstone & Dist
P816GMS	Clydeside	P843PWW	Leaside	P939HVX	County	PKM116R	Maidstone & Dist
P817GMS	Clydeside	P844PWW	Leaside	P939MKL	Maidstone & Dist	PKP546R	London & Country
P818GMS	Clydeside	P845PWW	Leaside	P940MKL	Maidstone & Dist	PPM892R	London & Country
P819GMS	Clydeside	P846PWW	Leaside	P941MKL	Maidstone & Dist	PPT823T	Northumbria
P820GMS	Clydeside	P847PWW	Leaside	P942MKL	Maidstone & Dist	PRJ486R	Northumbria
P821GMS	Clydeside	P848PWW	Leaside	P943MKL	Maidstone & Dist	PRJ488R	Northumbria
P822GMS	Clydeside	P849PWW	Leaside	P952RUL	Grey-Green	PRJ489R	Northumbria
P822RWU	South London	P850PWW	Leaside	P953RUL	Grey-Green	PRJ490R	Northumbria
P823GMS	Clydeside	P851PWW	Leaside	P954RUL	Grey-Green	PRJ492R	Northumbria
P823RWU	South London	P852PWW	Leaside	P955RUL	Grey-Green	PRJ494R	Northumbria
P824GMS	Clydeside	P853PWW	Leaside	P956RUL	Grey-Green	PRP802M	The Shires
P824RWU	South London	P854PWW	Leaside	P957RUL	Grey-Green	PSV323	Midland Red
P825KES	Clydeside	P855PWW	Leaside	P958RUL	Grey-Green	PTD639S	Northumbria
P825RWU	South London	P861PWW	North Western	P959RUL	Grey-Green	PUK630R	United
P826KES	Clydeside	P865VTJ	County	P960RUL	Grey-Green	PUK636R	United
P826RWU	South London	P892XCU	Northumbria	P961RUL	Grey-Green	PUK637R	Midland Red
P827KES	Clydeside	P893XCU	Northumbria	P962RUL	Grey-Green	PUK639R	Midland Red
P827RWU	South London	P894XCU	Northumbria	P963RUL	Grey-Green	PUK647R	Midland Red
P828KES	Clydeside	P895XCU	Northumbria	P964RUL	Grey-Green	PUK652R	Midland Red
P828RWU	South London	P896XCU	Northumbria	P965RUL	Grey-Green	PUP505T	North Western
P829KES	Clydeside	P902DRG	Northumbria	P966RUL	Grey-Green	PUP506T	United
P829RWU	South London	P903DRG	Northumbria	P967RUL	Grey-Green	PUS226P	Clydeside
P830KES	Clydeside	P904DRG	Northumbria	P968RUL	Grey-Green	PWE534R	Midland Fox

Cowie are looking at the opportunities which alternative fuels offer. A DAF low-floor LPG-powered bus was produced for demonstration during 1997. The vehicle is seen on a run near the Hughes-DAF premises in Yorkshire. Visible are the roof-mounted tanks which hold the gas.
Bill Potter

235

PWR442W	United	R301CMV	London & Country	R603MHN	United	RAU811R	United
Q124VOE	Midland Red	R302CMV	London & Country	R604MHN	United	RBC500W	Midland Fox
Q125VOE	Midland Red	R303CMV	London & Country	R606MHN	United	RDC734X	United
Q126VOE	Midland Red	R304CMV	London & Country	R607MHN	United	RDC736X	Northumbria
Q475MEV	Southend	R305CMV	London & Country	R608MHN	United	RDC737X	United
Q476MEV	Southend	R307CMV	London & Country	R609MHN	United	RDC739X	United
Q552MEV	Southend	R308CMV	London & Country	R685MHN	United	RDS83W	The Shires
Q553MEV	Southend	R310CMV	London & Country	R701KCU	Northumbria	RDS84W	The Shires
Q554MEV	Southend	R329TJW	Midland Red	R701MHN	United	RDZ1701	Leaside
R47XVM	North Western	R330TJW	Midland Red	R702MHN	United	RDZ1702	Leaside
R48XVM	North Western	R331TJW	Midland Red	R703MHN	United	RDZ1703	Leaside
R51XVM	North Western	R332TJW	Midland Red	R704MHN	United	RDZ1704	Leaside
R54XVM	North Western	R332TJW	Midland Red	R705MHN	United	RDZ1705	Leaside
R57XVM	North Western	R333TJW	Midland Red	R706MHN	United	RDZ1706	Leaside
R59XVM	North Western	R334TJW	Midland Red	R707MHN	United	RDZ1707	Leaside
R165GNW	County	R334TJW	Midland Red	R708MHN	United	RDZ1708	Leaside
R169GNW	County	R335TJW	Midland Red	R709MHN	United	RDZ1709	Leaside
R170GNW	County	R336TJW	Midland Red	R710MHN	United	RDZ1710	Leaside
R171VBM	The Shires	R337TJW	Midland Red	R711MHN	United	RDZ1711	Leaside
R172VBM	The Shires	R338TJW	Midland Red	R712MHN	United	RDZ1712	Leaside
R173VBM	The Shires	R339TJW	Midland Red	R713MHN	United	RDZ1713	Leaside
R174VBM	The Shires	R340TJW	Midland Red	R714MHN	United	RDZ1714	Leaside
R175VBM	The Shires	R341TJW	Midland Red	R715MHN	United	RDZ4278	London & Country
R176VBM	The Shires	R415TJW	Midland Red	R716MHN	United	RDZ4279	London & Country
R177VBM	The Shires	R416COO	County	R717MHN	United	REP328Y	United
R178VBM	The Shires	R416TJW	Midland Red	R718MHN	United	REU323S	Crosville Cymru
R179VBM	The Shires	R417COO	County	R719MHN	United	RHG882X	United
R180VBM	The Shires	R417TJW	Midland Red	R720MHN	United	RHG885X	United
R181VBM	The Shires	R418COO	County	R721MHN	United	RHG887X	United
R182VBM	The Shires	R418TJW	Midland Red	R722MHN	United	RJI5344	United
R183VBM	The Shires	R419COO	County	R723MHN	United	RJI5755	United
R184VBM	The Shires	R419TJW	Midland Red	R724MHN	United	RJI6861	The Shires
R191RBM	The Shires	R420COO	County	R725MHN	United	RJI6862	The Shires
R192RBM	The Shires	R420TJW	Midland Red	R758DUB	Yorkshire Bus	RLG427V	Midland Fox
R193RBM	The Shires	R421COO	County	R758DUB	Yorkshire Bus	RLG429V	Crosville Cymru
R194RBM	The Shires	R421TJW	Midland Red	R760DUB	Yorkshire Bus	RMO201Y	United
R195RBM	The Shires	R422COO	County	R761DUB	Yorkshire Bus	RMO202Y	United
R196RBM	The Shires	R422TJW	Midland Red	R762DUB	Yorkshire Bus	RMO204Y	United
R197RBM	The Shires	R423COO	County	R763DUB	Yorkshire Bus	ROK467M	United
R198RBM	The Shires	R423TJW	Midland Red	R764DUB	Yorkshire Bus	ROP835R	Midland Red
R199RBM	The Shires	R424COO	County	R765DUB	Yorkshire Bus	RRA219X	United
R201RBM	The Shires	R424TJW	Midland Red	R766DUB	Yorkshire Bus	RUF42R	Kentish Bus
R202RBM	The Shires	R425COO	County	R767DUB	Yorkshire Bus	RUJ351R	Midland Red
R203RBM	The Shires	R425TJW	Midland Red	R768DUB	Yorkshire Bus	RUP307V	United
R204RBM	The Shires	R426COO	County	R769DUB	Yorkshire Bus	RUP309V	United
R205RBM	The Shires	R426TJW	Midland Red	R770DUB	Yorkshire Bus	RVW88W	Colchester
R206GMJ	The Shires	R427COO	County	R785DUB	Yorkshire Bus	RVW89W	Colchester
R207GMJ	The Shires	R427TJW	Midland Red	R787DUB	Yorkshire Bus	RVW90W	Colchester
R208GMJ	The Shires	R428COO	County	R788DUB	Yorkshire Bus	SBD524R	The Shires
R209GMJ	The Shires	R428TJW	Midland Red	R789DUB	Yorkshire Bus	SBF233	Midland Red
R210GMJ	The Shires	R429COO	County	R790DUB	Yorkshire Bus	SCK688P	North Western
R211GMJ	The Shires	R429TJW	Midland Red	R791DUB	Yorkshire Bus	SCK692P	North Western
R212GMJ	The Shires	R430COO	County	R792DUB	Yorkshire Bus	SCK693P	North Western
R213GMJ	The Shires	R431COO	County	R793DUB	Yorkshire Bus	SCK698P	North Western
R214GMJ	The Shires	R447SKX	The Shires	R794DUB	Yorkshire Bus	SFJ132R	London & Country
R215GMJ	The Shires	R448SKX	The Shires	R795DUB	Yorkshire Bus	SGR777V	Northumbria
R251JNL	Northumbria	R449SKX	The Shires	R796DUB	Yorkshire Bus	SGR783V	Northumbria
R255WRJ	North Western	R450SKX	The Shires	R797DUB	Yorkshire Bus	SGR784V	Northumbria
R278VOK	Midland Fox	R451SKX	The Shires	R798DUB	Yorkshire Bus	SGR786V	Northumbria
R279VOK	Midland Fox	R452SKX	The Shires	R799DUB	Yorkshire Bus	SGR788V	United
R288VOK	Midland Fox	R453SKX	The Shires	R905JNL	Northumbria	SGR789V	Northumbria
R289VOK	Midland Fox	R454SKX	The Shires	R906JNL	Northumbria	SGR795V	Northumbria
R291KRG	Northumbria	R455SKX	The Shires	R907JNL	Northumbria	SGR797V	Northumbria
R292KRG	Northumbria	R456SKX	The Shires	R908JNL	Northumbria	SGS497W	County
R293KRG	Northumbria	R486UCC	Crosville Cymru	R909JNL	Northumbria	SHE559S	Midland Fox
R294KRG	Northumbria	R487UCC	Crosville Cymru	R910JNL	Northumbria	SHE560S	Midland Fox
R296CMV	London & Country	R521UCC	Crosville Cymru	R912JNL	Northumbria	SIB1278	London & Country
R297CMV	London & Country	R522UCC	Crosville Cymru	R913JNL	Northumbria	SIB1279	Kentish Bus
R298CMV	London & Country	R601MHN	United	R914JNL	Northumbria	SIB1280	Kentish Bus
R299CMV	London & Country	R602MHN	United	RAU597R	North Western	SIB1281	Kentish Bus

Reg	Operator	Reg	Operator	Reg	Operator	Reg	Operator
SIB1282	Kentish Bus	SPY205X	Northumbria	TPD104X	County	UGE388W	Clydeside
SIB1283	Kentish Bus	SPY206X	United	TPD105X	County	UGE389W	Clydeside
SIB1284	Kentish Bus	SPY207X	United	TPD106X	Clydeside	UGR698R	United
SIB1285	Kentish Bus	SPY208X	United	TPD107X	County	UHG724R	North Western
SIB1286	Kentish Bus	SPY209X	United	TPD108X	London & Country	UHG741R	North Western
SIB1287	Kentish Bus	SPY210X	Northumbria	TPD109X	County	UJI2337	Maidstone & Dist
SIB1288	Kentish Bus	SRC109X	Midland Fox	TPD110X	County	UJI2338	Maidstone & Dist
SIB4846	The Shires	SRC110X	Midland Fox	TPD111X	County	UJI2339	Maidstone & Dist
SIB6705	Kentish Bus	SRC111X	Midland Fox	TPD112X	Crosville Cymru	UJN430Y	Midland Red
SIB6706	Kentish Bus	SRC112X	Midland Fox	TPD113X	London & Country	ULS615X	Midland Fox
SIB6707	Kentish Bus	SRC113X	Midland Fox	TPD114X	London & Country	UNW930R	United
SIB6708	Kentish Bus	SRC114X	Midland Fox	TPD115X	County	UOI772	Midland Red
SIB6709	London & Country	SRC115X	Midland Fox	TPD116X	Clydeside	UPB331S	London & Country
SIB6710	Maidstone & Dist	STV122X	Midland Fox	TPD117X	County	UPB335S	North Western
SIB6711	London & Country	STV123X	Midland Fox	TPD118X	London & Country	UPB348S	London & Country
SIB6712	Maidstone & Dist	STW18W	Midland Fox	TPD119X	Crosville Cymru	UPB349S	London & Country
SIB6713	London & Country	SVL830R	Midland Fox	TPD120X	Crosville Cymru	UPK135S	London & Country
SIB6714	London & Country	SVS617	South London	TPD121X	London & Country	UPK146S	London & Country
SIB6715	Kentish Bus	SVV588W	The Shires	TPD122X	Crosville Cymru	UPK147S	London & Country
SIB6716	Kentish Bus	TCH116X	Midland Fox	TPD123X	County	URA605S	North Western
SIB7480	The Shires	TCH117X	Midland Fox	TPD124X	London & Country	URB822S	United
SIB7481	The Shires	TCH118X	Midland Fox	TPD125X	Crosville Cymru	URH657	Midland Fox
SIB7689	Midland Red	TCH119X	Midland Fox	TPD126X	Crosville Cymru	URP946W	The Shires
SIB8529	The Shires	TCH120X	Midland Fox	TPD127X	London & Country	URP947W	The Shires
SIB8583	Crosville Cymru	TCH121X	Midland Fox	TPD128X	London & Country	UVT49X	Crosville Cymru
SIB9492	Crosville Cymru	TDC854X	Midland Red	TPD129X	London & Country	UWW13X	United
SJI5066	London & Country	TDC857X	United	TPD130X	Clydeside	UWW14X	United
SJI5569	London & Country	THX180S	London & Country	TPE159S	Midland Red	UWW512X	Midland Red
SJI5570	London & Country	THX202S	Kentish Bus	TPE163S	Midland Red	UWW513X	Midland Red
SJI5571	London & Country	THX291S	Maidstone & Dist	TPE166S	Midland Red	UWW515X	Midland Red
SJI5572	London & Country	TIB4873	The Shires	TPU67R	Colchester	UWW517X	Midland Red
SLT59	London & Country	TIB4886	The Shires	TPU68R	Colchester	VAY879	Northumbria
SLU261	The Shires	TIB5901	Maidstone & Dist	TPU69R	Colchester	VBG84X	Crosville Cymru
SMK658F	Leaside	TIB5903	Kentish Bus	TPU71R	Colchester	VBG89V	North Western
SMK660F	Leaside	TIB5904	Kentish Bus	TPU74R	Colchester	VBG91X	Crosville Cymru
SMK666F	Leaside	TIB5905	Kentish Bus	TPU75R	Colchester	VBG92X	Crosville Cymru
SMK675F	Leaside	TIB5906	The Shires	TPU86R	Colchester	VBG93V	United
SMK678F	Leaside	TIB7835	The Shires	TR6147	Midland Red	VBG94X	Crosville Cymru
SMK682F	Leaside	TNH865R	The Shires	TRN470V	The Shires	VCA453W	North Western
SMK684F	Leaside	TOE480N	United	TRN477V	The Shires	VCA454W	North Western
SMK685F	Leaside	TOE482N	United	TSJ35S	Clydeside	VCA458W	Midland Red
SMK688F	Leaside	TOE521N	United	TSJ36S	Clydeside	VCA459W	Crosville Cymru
SMK692F	South London	TOE525N	United	TSJ38S	Clydeside	VCA460W	Midland Red
SMK708F	Leaside	TOF684S	Midland Red	TSJ47S	Clydeside	VCA461W	Maidstone & Dist
SMK715F	South London	TOF685S	Midland Red	TSJ52S	Clydeside	VCA462W	Crosville Cymru
SMK716F	Leaside	TOF687S	Midland Red	TSJ54S	Clydeside	VCA463W	North Western
SMK718F	South London	TOF693S	Midland Red	TSJ59S	Clydeside	VDB916	North Western
SMK726F	South London	TOF698S	Midland Red	TSJ64S	London & Country	VDV125S	Northumbria
SMK730F	South London	TOF699S	Midland Red	TSJ83S	London & Country	VKE566S	North Western
SMK741F	South London	TOF701S	Midland Red	TSU636	Northumbria	VLT5	Leaside
SMK742F	Leaside	TOF702S	Midland Red	TSU642W	Clydeside	VLT6	South London
SMK746F	Leaside	TOF703S	Midland Red	TSU644	Maidstone & Dist	VLT12	County
SMK747F	Leaside	TOF704S	Midland Red	TSU645	Maidstone & Dist	VLT13	South London
SMK750F	Leaside	TOF705S	Midland Red	TSU646	North Western	VLT25	South London
SMK753F	South London	TOF713S	London & Country	TVC402W	Midland Fox	VLT27	South London
SMK754F	Leaside	TOF714S	United	TVP836S	United	VLT32	Leaside
SMK758F	Leaside	TOF718S	Midland Red	TVP837S	North Western	VLT47	South London
SMK759F	South London	TOF719S	Midland Red	TVP863S	United	VLT88	County
SND296X	Northumbria	TOJ592S	Midland Red	TWY7	Yorkshire Bus	VLT166	Midland Red
SNS824W	Crosville Cymru	TOS799X	North Western	UBR110V	Northumbria	VLT173	South London
SNU384R	Northumbria	TOU962	Midland Red	UBR111V	United	VLT244	South London
SNV932W	The Shires	TPC101X	Midland Red	UBR112V	United	VLT275	South London
SNV933W	The Shires	TPC102X	Midland Red	UBR113V	Northumbria	VLT295	Leaside
SNV934W	The Shires	TPC103X	Midland Red	UBR114V	United	VOD601S	United
SNV938W	The Shires	TPC104X	Midland Red	UDM446V	Crosville Cymru	VOI6874	Midland Red
SPC279R	North Western	TPC107X	Midland Red	UDM447V	Crosville Cymru	VOV926S	Midland Red
SPY201X	Northumbria	TPC114X	Midland Red	UDM448V	The Shires	VPA152S	London & Country
SPY202X	Northumbria	TPD101X	County	UDM449V	Crosville Cymru	VPA153S	London & Country
SPY203X	Northumbria	TPD102X	County	UFG58S	London & Country	VPK148S	London & Country
SPY204X	Northumbria	TPD103X	County	UFG60S	London & Country	VPK149S	London & Country

Reg	Operator	Reg	Operator	Reg	Operator	Reg	Operator
VPK151S	London & Country	WLT924	Clydeside	WYW69T	South London	YMB501W	Crosville Cymru
VRP531S	The Shires	WLT956	Clydeside	WYW74T	South London	YMB502W	Crosville Cymru
VVV951W	The Shires	WLT970	South London	XAF759	Midland Red	YMB503W	Crosville Cymru
VVV955W	The Shires	WLT997	South London	XOR841	Midland Red	YMB504W	Crosville Cymru
VVV956W	The Shires	WPH118Y	Midland Red	XOV748T	United	YMB510W	Crosville Cymru
VVV957W	The Shires	WPH121Y	Midland Red	XOV759T	United	YMB512W	Crosville Cymru
VVV960W	The Shires	WPH122Y	Midland Red	XPA110	Midland Fox	YMB513W	Crosville Cymru
VYJ806	South London	WPH123Y	Midland Red	XPG172T	Kentish Bus	YMB514W	Crosville Cymru
VYJ808	South London	WPH125Y	Midland Red	XPG175T	London & Country	YMB516W	Crosville Cymru
WAE192T	United	WPH126Y	Midland Red	XPG182T	London & Country	YMB517W	Crosville Cymru
WAO395Y	United	WPH130Y	County	XPG184T	London & Country	YMB518W	Crosville Cymru
WAO399Y	United	WPH139Y	Midland Red	XPG186T	Kentish Bus	YMB519W	Crosville Cymru
WBD877S	The Shires	WPT718R	United	XPG187T	London & Country	YMB938T	The Shires
WDC211Y	Northumbria	WPT720R	United	XPG201T	London & Country	YNO77S	Colchester
WDC212Y	Northumbria	WPT723R	United	XPT686R	Midland Red	YNO78S	Colchester
WDC213Y	Northumbria	WPT724R	United	XPT801V	United	YNO80S	Colchester
WDC214Y	United	WRA224Y	United	XPT802V	Northumbria	YNO81S	Colchester
WDC215Y	United	WRA225Y	United	XPT803V	Northumbria	YNO82S	Colchester
WDC216Y	United	WRC833S	Maidstone & Dist	XPT804V	United	YNW401S	Maidstone & Dist
WDC217Y	United	WSU441S	North Western	XRR50S	Clydeside	YOT607	Northumbria
WDC218Y	United	WSU442S	North Western	XSV689	Northumbria	YPB820T	London & Country
WDC219Y	Kentish Bus	WSU450S	North Western	XSV691	Maidstone & Dist	YPH407T	London & Country
WDC220Y	Crosville Cymru	WSU475	Clydeside	XTE221V	Southend	YPJ207Y	Midland Red
WDS199V	Clydeside	WSU476	Clydeside	XTE222V	Southend	YPL376T	London & Country
WDS199V	Clydeside	WSV565	Northumbria	XTE223V	Southend	YPL377T	London & Country
WDS220V	Clydeside	WSV566	Northumbria	XTE224V	Southend	YPL378T	London & Country
WDS234V	Clydeside	WSV567	Northumbria	XTE225V	Southend	YPL380T	London & Country
WHN594M	Clydeside	WSV568	Northumbria	XTE226V	Southend	YPL381T	London & Country
WIB1113	The Shires	WSV570	Northumbria	XTE227V	Southend	YPL382T	London & Country
WIB1114	The Shires	WSV571	Northumbria	XTE228V	Southend	YPL385T	London & Country
WIB1115	The Shires	WSV572	Northumbria	XTE229V	Southend	YPL393T	London & Country
WIB1118	The Shires	WTL954	South London	XTE230V	Southend	YPL394T	London & Country
WKO125S	Maidstone & Dist	WTU467W	Crosville Cymru	XUA76X	Crosville Cymru	YPL420T	London & Country
WKO133S	Maidstone & Dist	WTU468W	Crosville Cymru	XVS997	South London	YPL427T	London & Country
WKO137S	Maidstone & Dist	WTU470W	Midland Red	XVV537S	The Shires	YPL440T	London & Country
WKO138S	Maidstone & Dist	WTU473W	Southend	XVV538S	The Shires	YPL443T	Crosville Cymru
WKO139S	Maidstone & Dist	WTU475W	Crosville Cymru	XWA72X	United	YSU870	Maidstone & Dist
WLT348	South London	WTU476W	Crosville Cymru	XWA73X	United	YSU871	Maidstone & Dist
WLT372	South London	WTU477W	Crosville Cymru	XWA74X	United	YSU872	Maidstone & Dist
WLT385	South London	WTU478W	Crosville Cymru	XWA75X	United	YSU873	Maidstone & Dist
WLT531	South London	WTU479W	North Western	XWY477X	United	YSU895	Maidstone & Dist
WLT554	South London	WTU480W	North Western	XWY478X	United	YSU896	Maidstone & Dist
WLT664	South London	WTU496W	North Western	XWY479X	United	YSU897	Maidstone & Dist
WLT676	South London	WTU497W	North Western	XYJ418	Leaside	YSU953	Maidstone & Dist
WLT719	South London	WYR562	Midland Red	XYS596S	Clydeside	YSU954	Midland Red
WLT751	South London	WYV60T	Clydeside	YAU126Y	Midland Fox	YTU986S	North Western
WLT807	South London	WYW6T	Leaside	YAU127Y	Midland Fox	YUM515S	Maidstone & Dist
WLT859	Northumbria	WYW7T	South London	YAU128Y	Midland Fox	YVV893S	The Shires
WLT882	Leaside	WYW10T	South London	YBF686S	Southend	YVV894S	The Shires
WLT884	Leaside	WYW14T	Leaside	YCF826	Midland Fox	YVV895S	The Shires
WLT888	Leaside	WYW38T	South London	YCS91T	Clydeside	YWX401X	Crosville Cymru
WLT892	South London	WYW40T	South London	YCU961T	Crosville Cymru	YWX402X	Crosville Cymru
WLT895	South London	WYW49T	South London	YEL98Y	Northumbria	YXI3751	United
WLT896	Leaside	WYW51T	Leaside	YIB2396	The Shires	YYE290T	Kentish Bus
WLT897	Leaside	WYW63T	South London	YIB2397	The Shires	YYJ955	Midland Red
WLT901	Leaside	WYW64T	South London	YLX281	United		
WLT916	South London	WYW66T	South London	YMB500W	Crosville Cymru		

ISBN 1 897990 71 5

Published by British Bus Publishing Ltd
The Vyne, 16 St Margarets Drive, Wellington, Telford, TF1 3PH
Fax orderline - (+44) (0) 1952 255669